GCSE

ALS?   ✓ ALD

GCSE CLASSBOOK

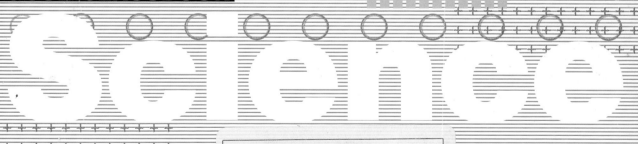

Science

David Baylis • Graham Booth • Bob McDuell

First published 1996
Reprinted 1996
Second edition 2001

Letts Educational
Aldine House
Aldine Place
London W12 8AW
Tel 020 8740 2266
Fax 020 8743 8451

Text: © David Baylis, Graham Booth, Bob McDuell

Design and illustrations © Letts Educational Ltd

Design, page layout and illustrations: Ken Vail Graphic Design

Cover design: Santamaria

British Library Cataloguing-in-Publication Data

A CIP record for this book is available from the British Library

ISBN 1 84085 562 2

Printed and bound in the United Kingdom

Letts Educational Limited, a division of Granada Learning Limited.
Part of the Granada Media Group.

Acknowledgements

The authors and publishers are grateful to the following for permission to reproduce photographs:

Action Plus 19.1; 19.4; 21.3; 127.3; 156.4; The Ancient Art & Architecture Collection 78.6; Art Directors & TRIP Photo Library 50.1; 50.2; 82.1; Biophoto Associates 1.1; 1.4; 1.10; 3.2; 16.2; 22.3a; 22.3b; 27.1b; 27.2a; 39.1a; 39.1b; 43.1; 46.3; 51.2; Graham Booth 113.1; 114.2; 114.3; 124.4b; 150.4; BT Corporate Pictures 140.2; 140.3; Camping Gaz (GB)Limited 124.4a; Aron Carr 1.3; Bruce Coleman Limited 1.2; 1.5; 1.7; 19.3; 27.1a; 27.2b; 44.2; 44.3; 47.1; 48.1; 48.2; 48.3; 51.1; 62.4; 75.2; 77.2(conglomerate); 78.2; 79.3; 91.4; 103.1;123.3; Wayne Davies 133.2; John Dixon 20.3; 113.3; 155.1; Dorling Kindersley Limited 1.9; 36.2; Electricity Association 115.1; 122.3; The Environmental Picture Library Limited 54.1; Ford Motor Company Limited 97.2; Mark Gadd 20.1; Geoscience Features Picture Library 77.2 (limestone & sandstone); 77.3; 77.5; 79.1; 142.1; Health Education Authority 31.1; Heinz Foods 35.2e; High Peak Borough Council 78.3; Holt Studios International 36.1; 37.1; 37.3; 40.2; 52.1; 106.3; Hutchison Photo Library 80.2; ICI Plc. 106.1; The Image Bank 35.2c; 35.2d; 45.2; Image Select 88.2; The Kobal Collection 23.4; Frank Lane Picture Agency Limited 19.2; 47.2; 54.2; Levington Horticulture Limited 37.2; Bob McDuell 72.2; Michelin Tyre Plc. 123.5; Milepost 921/2 Picture Library 73.2; 119.5; NASA 130.4; Natural History Photographic Agency 1.6; 54.3; Oxford Scientific Films Limited 17.4; 103.2; 122.1; Philips Electronics UK Limited 139.4; Quadrant Picture Library 35.2b; 126.3; 128.2; Rex Features Limited 91.5; 109.4; 117.1; Royal Albert Hall 132.1; Science & Society Picture Library 9; Science Photo Library 1.8; 5.3; 12.1; 12.2; 16.1a; 16.1b; 18.3a; 18.3b; 20.2; 23.3; 23.5; 26.1; 26.2; 28.3; 30.2a; 30.2b; 30.3; 34.2; 35.2a; 38.3a; 38.3b; 45.1; 46.1; 49.2; 49.3; 53.1; 57.1; 62.1; 68.1; 76.4; 77.1; 78.4; 80.9; 82.2; 88.1; 90.1; 91.1; 91.2; 91.3; 100.1; 101.2; 102.1; 121.3; 129.1; 129.5; 132.4; 139.2; 141.2; 142.3; 144.1; 144.3; 145.3; 146.1; 146.2; 147.1; 147.2; 147.4; 147.5; 150.1; 155.2; 159.1; 159.2; 159.3; Shout Picture Company 31.2; Tony Stone Images 20.4; 29.2; United Distillers 64; Wilson/Biss Lancaster Plc. 60.6.

CONTENTS

PHYSICAL PROCESSES 224

Ideas introduced in the unit

Ideas and evidence information box

130 Falling down

In this unit you will learn the answers to these questions:
- What forces are involved when two objects interact?
- What affects the size of the Earth's pull on an object?
- Why do heavy and light objects have the same free-fall acceleration?

In previous units you have studied the motion of objects with both balanced and unbalanced forces and seen how unbalanced forces cause a change in velocity. This unit is a study of the vertical motion caused by the Earth's gravitational pull.

The Earth's pull

Newton realised that gravitational forces act between all masses, but the effects are only noticeable when one of them is very massive. As a result we notice the effects of the gravitational forces due to planets, but not those due to ourselves!

Another of Newton's important discoveries was that objects exert forces on each other, so if one object pulls or pushes a second, then the second object pulls or pushes the first with an equal-sized force in the opposite direction. You came across this idea in Unit 127 when considering the force that propels a bicycle.

Fig 1 The forces between you and the Earth are equal in size but opposite in direction

It may be comforting to know that although the Earth is pulling you towards it, you are pulling the Earth towards you with an equal-sized force. However this won't help you if you fall. The effect of your pull on the Earth's mass is negligible so rather than you move towards you, you move towards the Earth.

The size of the Earth's pull is called its gravitational field strength, or g for short. Close to the surface of the Earth this has a value of 10 N/kg, so each kg of your body mass is pulled towards the centre of the Earth with a force of 10 N. This downward pull is the force called weight, which can be calculated using the formula:

$$\text{weight} = \text{mass} \times \text{gravitational field strength} \quad \text{or} \quad W = mg$$

Q1 Why is it incorrect to say that 'a bag of sugar weighs 1 kg'?

Q2 Potatoes can be bought in 50 kg sacks.
  a) How much does a sack of potatoes weigh on the Earth?
  b) The Moon's gravitational field strength is 1.5 N/kg. How much would a sack of potatoes weigh on the Moon?

Free-fall acceleration

If you hold a 1p coin in one hand and a 10p coin in the other, and then let them go at the same time from the same height, you find that they reach the ground together. Releasing a coin and a sheet of paper together may not give the same result, unless you do it in a vacuum. In the absence of air resistance, all objects have the same free-fall acceleration, regardless of their mass.

Fig 2 Free-fall acceleration

Fig 3 Galileo's famous experiment – did he ever do it?

This came as a revelation at the time of Galileo in the sixteenth century. In fact his proclamation that heavy objects do not fall faster than light objects cost him his job as professor of mathematics at the University of Pisa. However, Newton's work around 100 years later revealed a simple explanation: a 2 kg mass is twice as heavy as a 1 kg mass, so there is twice the pulling force acting on it from the Earth. But there is also twice as much mass to be accelerated, so as force = mass × acceleration the two masses should accelerate at the same rate.

Comparing the equations

$$\text{force} = \text{mass} \times \text{acceleration}$$
and
$$\text{weight} = \text{mass} \times \text{gravitational field strength}$$

for an object falling freely with no resistive forces acting, you can see that they are equivalent. Consequently 'gravitational field strength' and 'free-fall acceleration' are the same physical quantity, having the same value of 10 N/kg or 10 m/s².

Ideas and evidence

Galileo Galilei
As an old man, Galileo told the story of how, having failed to convince people by argument, he had dropped a large ball and a small ball from the top of the leaning tower of Pisa. Experimental proof was very rare in the sixteenth century, when scientific ideas were debated but not tested. Galileo reports that, due to the effects of air resistance, the large ball reached the ground fractionally ahead of the smaller one. Despite this demonstration, many people clung to the view that a heavy object falls at ten times the speed of one with only one tenth of the weight.

ICT Extra!
Use data logging to measure free-fall acceleration.

Q3 a) Use the equation $W = mg$ to calculate the weight of a 5 kg mass and a 10 kg mass.
  b) Now use $F = ma$ to calculate the acceleration of each mass due to the Earth's pull.
  c) Explain why a feather does not have the same acceleration as a 50p coin when they are dropped together.
  d) You may have seen the famous film where an astronaut on the Moon releases a hammer and a feather at the same time. Explain why they reach the ground together.

Fig 4 An astronaut releasing a hammer and a feather on the Moon

Questions for you to answer

ICT activity box

INTRODUCTION

This new edition of Letts successful GCSE Science Classbook has been written to meet the requirements of new GCSE courses being introduced in September 2001 for first examination in June 2003. It is suitable for both Foundation and Higher tiers.

It is closely liked to the new National Curriculum. New GCSE specifications directly examine only Key Stage 4 content, however, success at GCSE will rely on mastery of Key Stage 3 content. For this reason this book contains some Key stage 3 material.

The material is identified as follows:

KS3 Key Stage 3 content. Most able students may miss this out.

KS4 This is content that bridges Key Stage 3 and Key Stage 4.

KS4 This material is all Key Stage 4 content.

The book is suitable for all Double Science specifications. If your are doing Single Science, you teacher will be able to tell you which parts of the book you should study.

This classbook has been written in three co-ordinated sections:

1 Life processes and living things
2 Materials and their properties
3 Physical processes

It has also been split into 160 topics called 'units'. Each unit covers two pages and begins with a list of questions which will introduce you to the ideas in that unit. Each is clearly written and illustrated, and there are questions for you to think about which will help you to understand the ideas involved.

It is very important to do regular homework in support of your work at school. We have therefore produced a homework book to accompany this classbook which contains a wide variety of questions, very closely linked to the content of this book. It also has topic summaries to remind you of the key points from the classbook, and a glossary so that you can find out the meaning of any important scientific terms. The homework book will provide a valuable way to practise and reinforce what you learn in class.

In the introductory section there is help with **Key Skills, Ideas and Evidence** and **ICT**. Then throughout this book you will find **Ideas and Evidence boxes** and **ICT** boxes. This is all intended to help you to address these new requirements.

We hope that this classbook and the homework book will help you to progress in GCSE Science, as both have been written by experienced examiners and teachers, very much with exam success in mind. But as well as helping you to achieve your desired grade, we hope that these books will give you an insight into and enjoyment of Science, which is vital to an understanding of the modern world.

KEY SKILLS

You may have the opportunities to complete a Key Skills Qualification. This is an on-going qualification that you will continue when you move on to AS or A2 examinations.

You will have to collect evidence from all subjects to produce a portfolio of evidence. An Examination Group then moderates this portfolio. For Key Skills 1–3 you will also have to take a written test. Work you will do in Science will be useful in your portfolio.

There are six Key Skills.

■ Three Key Skills that lead to a qualification:

1 Application of Number

2 Communication

3 Information Technology

■ Three wider key Skills that are desirable but do not form apart of a qualification:

4 Improving own Learning and Performance.

5 Working with others

6 Problem-solving

If you want to find out more about Key Skills contact the QCA website, http://www.qca.org.uk/keyskills.

The following tables give the criteria you must satisfy for each Key Skill at levels 1 and 2. There is also an example of where you might find evidence for Key Skills 1–3. There are many other possible places and your teacher will advise you when there are opportunities.

Application of number

Level 1	You should be able to:	Example
N.1.1	Interpret information from different sources	Use textbook and databook to gather information about structures and physical properties of hydrocarbons
N.1.2	Carry out straightforward calculations using amounts and sizes, or scales and proportion, or handling statistics	Recognise that different organisms are restricted to certain habitats and are not distributed at random in a habitat
N.1.3	Interpret results and present findings using one chart or diagram	As part of your Sc1 Coursework
Level 2		
N.2.1	Interpret information from different sources including material containing a graph	Consider braking distances and factors that affect them, including reference to the Highway Code
N.2.2	Carry out calculations using amounts and sizes, or scales and proportion, or handling statistics, or using formulae	Be able to calculate the half life of a radioactive isotope using an activity–time graph.
N.2.3	Interpret results and present findings using at least one graph, chart or diagram	As part of your Sc1 Coursework

Communication

Level 1	You should be able to:	Example
C.1.1	Take part in one-to-one discussion or group discussion about straightforward subjects	Evaluate the oil industry in terms of usefulness of products, impact on the environment and the work of different scientists
C.1.2	Read and obtain information from two different documents including one image	Explain how organisms such as camel and polar bear are adapted to living in a particular environment
C.1.3	Write two different types of document, including one image	Your Sc1 Coursework report will involve an extended piece of writing and an image. A second document could be a report
Level 2		
C.2.1a	Contribute to discussion	Take part in a discussion about the siting of a limestone mine
C.2.1b	Give a short talk using an image	Talk on the greenhouse effect with a diagram as illustration
C.2.2	Read and summarise information from two extended documents, including one image	Discuss the social and environmental issues associated with different methods of generating electricity
C.2.3	Write two different types of document. One piece of writing should include an image	Your Sc1 Coursework report will involve an extended piece of writing and an image. A second document could be a report

Information Technology

Level 1	You should be able to:	Example
IT.1.1	Find, explore and develop information for two different purposes	Obtain information about elements from databook and Internet/CD ROM and look for patterns in physical properties
IT.1.2	Present information for two different purposes including text, image and numbers	Word process your Sc1 investigation, with a chart or line graph and some numerical calculations
Level 2		
IT.2.1	Search for and select information for two different purposes	Describe how hormones can be used to control and promote fertility and, illegally, to enhance sporting performances
IT.2.2	Explore and develop information, and derive information, for two different purposes	Describe examples of selective breeding of dogs for appearance and behaviour
IT.2.3	Present combined information for two different purposes. Must include text, image and numbers	Interpret information about developments in ideas of plate tectonics

Improving own Learning and Performance

Level 1	You should be able to:
LP1.1	Confirm understanding of your short-term targets and plan how these will be met
LP1.2	Follow your plan, using support, to meet targets
LP1.3	Review your progress and achievements in meeting targets
Level 2	
LP2.1	Set short-term targets and plan how these will be met
LP2.2	Take responsibility for some decisions about your learning, using your plan and support from others to meet targets
LP2.3	Review progress with an appropriate person and provide evidence of achievements, including how you have used learning from one task to meet the demands of a new task. Include an image

Working with others

Level 1	You should be able to:
WO1.1	Confirm what needs to be done to achieve given objectives, including your responsibilities and working arrangements
WO1.2	Work with others towards achieving given objectives
WO1.3	Identify progress and suggest ways of improving work with others
Level 2	
WO2.1	Plan straightforward work with others, identifying objectives and clarifying responsibilities
WO2.2	Work cooperatively with others towards achieving identified objectives
WO2.3	Exchange information on progress and agree ways of improving work

Problem solving

Level 1	You should be able to:
PS1.1	Confirm your understanding of the given problem with an appropriate person and identify two options for solving it
PS1.2	Plan and try out at least one option for solving the problem, using advice and support given by others.
PS1.3	Check if the problem has been solved by following given methods, and describe the results, including ways to improve your approach to problem-solving
Level 2	
PS2.1	Identify a problem and come up with two options for solving it
PS2.2	Plan and try out at least one option for solving the problem, obtaining support and making changes to your plan when needed
PS2.3	Check if the problem has been solved by applying given methods, and describe results and explain your approach to problem-solving

IDEAS AND EVIDENCE

In all GCSE examinations 5% of the total marks must be allocated to questions testing the Ideas and Evidence section of Sc1 Scientific Enquiry.

There are places within Letts Classbook where topics relevant to aspects of Ideas and Evidence are considered. Questions testing Ideas and Evidence usually do not require a lot of recall of information. Instead you have to apply your experience of similar situations to ones you are given in the question.

You will be expected to deal with historical situations such as history of circulation of blood, development of the periodic table or the theories of plate tectonics. You will also be expected to deal with current scientific and technological issues such as genetic engineering, development of new polymers that conduct electricity, and safe disposal of radioactive materials.

The National Curriculum develops four strands for Ideas and Evidence.

1 How scientific ideas are presented, evaluated and disseminated

Scientists report their findings to other scientists in specialist journals, e.g. *Nature*. The reports are not published unless other scientists feel the work is of good quality and unless the results are repeatable. Today, with easier and faster ways to travel, and the Internet, telecommunications and postal systems, it has never been easier for scientists to communicate with each other. In the past there have been examples where scientists have carried out similar research independently.

The general public depends upon mass media (television, newspapers, radio etc) to keep informed about scientific and technological advances. Reporting in this way can be biased, not scientifically accurate or not sufficiently detailed. This can affect:

- the issues being discussed
- the opinions those members of the public have
- decisions about whether a project is to be funded and to what extent.

2 How scientific controversies can arise from different ways of interpreting empirical evidence

You may be aware from investigations you have carried out that the results can sometimes be interpreted in more than one way. Scientists need to have imagination in interpreting their results.

3 Ways in which scientific work may be affected by the contexts in which it takes place and how these contexts may affect whether or not ideas are accepted

Scientists are people and they have scientific, moral, religious and social views. These are influenced by the society in which they live. People are unwilling to give up explanations that they have been brought up with and are currently believed by others. New explanations, which run counter to existing ideas, are often ignored. A new explanation is more likely to be accepted if it can be used to make predictions that can be tested and can be seen to be correct.

4 Consider the power and limitations of science in addressing industrial, social and environmental questions, including the kinds of questions science can and cannot answer, uncertainties in scientific knowledge and ethical issues involved

New developments in science and technology can provide enormous improvements in peoples' lives. They can, however, also do harm to other people and to the environment.

There must always be a judgement of the value of the benefits against any social, economic and environmental costs. Even when there is agreement about the likely effects of some process, there may still be other moral issues about whether it should be allowed.

ICT

ICT should figure in work you are doing throughout your Science course. It is important that you attempt ICT which is sufficiently demanding.

Opportunities for ICT include:

- Gathering and using information from the Internet.
- Using CD-ROM to provide information.
- Word–processing or DTP in the production of reports, posters, case studies, and so on.
- Using spreadsheets to process experimental data or to model situations and compare theories.
- Monitoring experiments using sensors linked to data logger or directly to a computer.
- Using computer simulations to model experimental situations.

Throughout this Letts Classbook there are examples of where you can use ICT. These are shown in ICT boxes, e.g.

ICT Extra!

Find out all about the elements in the Periodic Table using the Interactive Periodic Table (http://www.shef.ac.uk/chemistry/webelements). You can plot physical properties such as melting point against atomic number.

Life processes and living things

This part of the book is divided into five sections and covers aspects of Biology and Environmental Science. You will already have come across many of the topics covered in this part of the book and you will also be introduced to topics which may be new to you, such as cell division, monohybrid inheritance, mutation and biotechnology (including genetic engineering). The five sections are intended to increase your knowledge and understanding of life processes and living things.

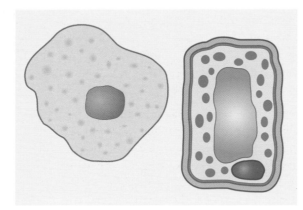

The first section is about **Life processes and cell activity**. After revising the life processes common to living things, this section looks at the way organisms are organised at cell, tissue, organ and organ system levels, and considers the relationship between the structure of living things and their functions. You will study the processes of diffusion, osmosis and active transport. The section considers the way that cell activity is controlled by the nucleic acid in the chromosomes, and how this genetic information is inherited. A brief study of the behaviour of chromosomes during mitosis and meiosis completes this section.

The second section looks at **Humans as organisms**. You may have studied most of the areas in this section before, but perhaps in less detail. The section concentrates on aspects of human nutrition, circulation, breathing and respiration. After studying these processes you will learn how the human body is coordinated through the activities of the nervous and hormonal systems. The coordination of organ systems and their activities to maintain a 'steady state' is considered in units on homeostasis. The section ends with an exploration of the body's defence mechanisms, and the dangers associated with solvent and drug abuse.

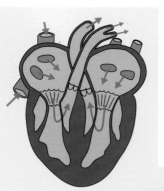

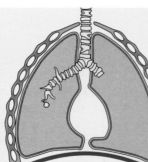

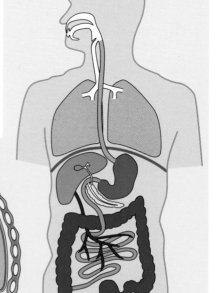

The third section, **Green plants as organisms**, considers the way plants make food, what they do with it and how we make use of plant products. One unit explores the concept of limiting factors, and how an understanding of this concept helps us to maintain more productive artificial environments for crop plants. You will learn how plant growth and development are coordinated by plant hormones and how they are used commercially as selective weedkillers and in the production of seedless fruits. Finally in this section, the role of water in the life of plants is studied. This includes a more detailed look at the tissues involved in the conduction of water and the translocation of sucrose.

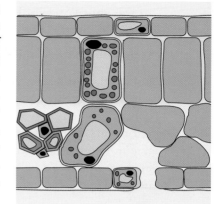

The fourth section of this part of the book discusses some of the basic information on **Variation, inheritance and evolution**, which will help you to gain some understanding of some of the applications and implications of biotechnology. Biotechnology is one branch of science which has produced very exciting advances in a relatively short time. The section considers the nature of variation, how differences arise and how some of these differences are inherited, including those which lead to genetic diseases. In studying this section you will learn about cloning, selective

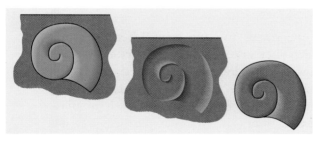

breeding, and have a brief look at genetic engineering and its possible significance for the future. The section ends with material which should give you an understanding of the way evolution may have occurred by natural selection, and the evidence which we have to support the theory.

The last section is entitled **Living things in their environment**. In it, you will learn about the way living things affect their environment, and the way they in turn are affected by their environment. Pollution and conservation issues are frequently reported in the media, and it is important that you have an informed view based on scientific facts and principles. Only then will you be able to make objective judgements about what you read, hear or see. The concepts of adaptation and competition are explored with respect to humans and other organisms. You will study information about energy and nutrient transfer in natural ecosystems and consider the way these principles can be applied to artificial ecosystems. An understanding of this area of science is essential if we are to develop more efficient crop management and land use, to provide for an increasing world population.

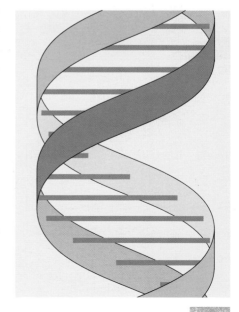

1 Life processes

In this unit you will learn the answer to this question:
■ **What are the life processes of plants and animals?**

Living things carry out **seven processes** to stay alive.

Look at Figs 1 and 2. An oak tree starts off its life as an acorn. The acorn contains an embryo and some food. Fifty years later it may look like the tree in Fig 2. It has made a permanent increase in size. You too will have got much bigger since your birth.

Fig 1   **Fig 2**

1 All living things **grow**.

Plants and animals need energy to stay alive. Food materials contain energy. Chemical reactions release this energy. Because they are going on inside the cell these reactions are difficult to observe. The process of releasing energy from food chemicals is called respiration.

2 All living things **respire**.

Q1 Suggest one way in which energy from respiration might be used **a)** by you and **b)** by an oak tree.

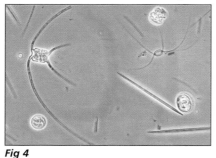

Fig 3

Fig 3 shows a crying baby. When do babies cry? They cry if they are hungry or perhaps upset by a loud noise. Potted plants left on a window sill may grow towards the light coming into the room. Each of these living things is aware of changes in and around them.

3 All living things show **sensitivity** or irritability.

Fig 4 shows unicellular plants. The long hair-like structures are used to move the plant through the water. Most of the plants we see around us, however, are usually firmly rooted to the ground. Even these move as they grow. The shoot tip of a climbing plant moves around its support as it grows. Movement shown by animals is much more obvious (Fig 5).

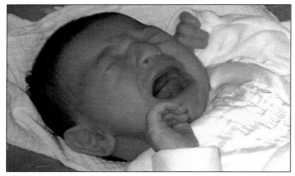

Fig 4

4 All living things **move**.

Q2 Why is movement in animals easier to see than movement in plants?

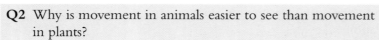

Fig 5

Biochemical processes such as respiration produce waste products. Some wastes are harmful and have to be got rid of. The hyena in Fig 6 is getting rid of a solution called urine. Urine contains a harmful substance called urea. Urea is made by mammalian liver cells from surplus amino acids. Some plants lose their leaves in autumn. Some of their waste by-products are lost at the same time. The process by which living things get rid of their biochemical wastes is called excretion.

5 All living things **excrete**.

Fig 6

Q3 Why do mammals have to excrete urea?

Figs 7 and 8 show animals feeding. Fig 7 shows a carnivore and Fig 8 shows a herbivore. The way in which green plants feed is not obvious. They take in simple materials from their environment, and use light energy to make complex foods. The process is called photosynthesis (see Units 32 and 33).

6 All living things feed and the process is called **nutrition**.

Fig 7

Fig 8

Q4 In what way do we indirectly rely on sunlight for our food?

Individual plants and animals must eventually die. However, before they die, most will have been involved in the production of replacements or offspring. Fig 9 shows a plant called *Kalanchoe*. This plant produces large numbers of plantlets. The horse in Fig 10 has produced only one 'replacement'. All plant and animal species must produce replacements. If they do not, their species may become extinct. Replacements are provided by the process of reproduction.

Fig 9

7 All living things **reproduce**.

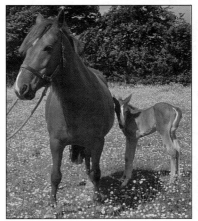

Fig 10

Q5 Many sexually reproducing organisms produce more than two offspring (replacements). Why do you think this is necessary?

2 Organ systems

In this unit you will learn the answers to these questions:
- What do the terms cells, tissues, organs and organ systems mean?
- What is division of labour?
- How is division of labour achieved by human organ systems?

The human body is made up of many **cells** (approximately 10^{14}). The cells are not all the same, however. Each has a special function to perform. A collection of cells of the same type, as a group, does a particular job. Such collections of cells are called **tissues**. In the same way, groups of tissues form **organs** and groups of organs form **organ systems**, each with a particular role to play in the body.

The work of the body is divided up amongst the organ systems. Humans have a greater efficiency at carrying out life processes than *Amoeba*, for example, due to division of labour.

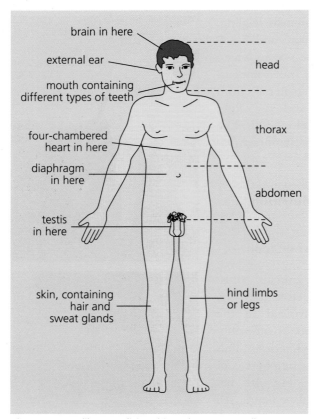

Fig 1 Humans, like most living things, have many cells to carry out their life processes. They are called **multicellular** organisms

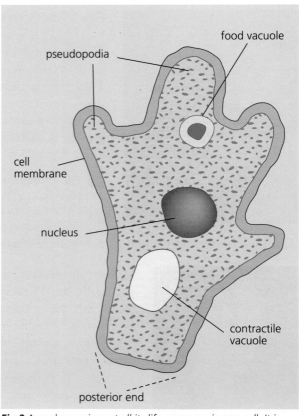

Fig 2 Amoeba carries out all its life processes in one cell. It is called a **unicellular** organism

Q1 What is a tissue?

Q2 What do you call a group of tissues together performing a specialised function?

Q3 What do you understand by the term 'division of labour'?

One group of organs performing a specialised function, i.e. an organ system, is the mammalian reproductive system (see Unit 41).

Reproductive system

The human male and female reproductive systems are shown in Fig 3a and Fig 3b.

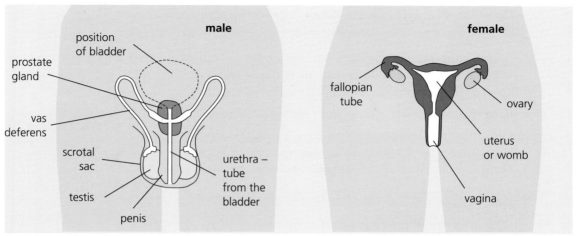

Fig 3a *Male reproductive organs, front view*

Fig 3b *Female reproductive organs, front view*

Other organ systems

Digestive system (see Units 10–12) This group of organs deals with the food we eat. One job is to store food. Some of the organs produce secretions which alter the food, others act as regions of absorption.

Circulatory system (see Units 13–16) The circulatory system provides a transport medium (blood and lymph), a pump (the heart) and a series of tubes (arteries, capillaries and veins) which are able to pick up, transport and release materials in the body. Sets of valves exist in some of these tubes to make sure blood flows in one direction only.

Gaseous exchange system (see Units 17 and 18) The lungs offer an efficient surface to exchange gases. Muscular contractions pump air to and from the lung surface through a series of air tubes. The lungs have a very good point of contact with the blood circulatory system.

Nervous system (see Units 21–23) The nervous system involves organs functioning as sensors (e.g. eyes), coordinators (e.g. brain) and communication links (nerves).

Endocrine system (see Units 24–26) Organs which secrete hormones, releasing them into the bloodstream for distribution, make up the endocrine system.

Excretory system (see Units 28 and 29) Organs which are involved with excretion in humans include the lungs, the kidneys and the skin.

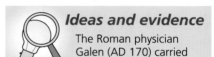

Ideas and evidence

The Roman physician Galen (AD 170) carried out experiments on live animals making many accurate observations. All Galen's ideas were accepted as correct until the fifteenth century when human dissection, illegal in most civilisations, was legalised.

How is the validity of a piece of research tested?

Q4 What functions do the organs of the circulatory system have to perform?

Q5 What do you understand by the term 'organ system'?

3 Plant and animal cells

In this unit you will learn the answers to these questions:
- What are the functions of the cell membrane, cytoplasm and nucleus in plant and animal cells?
- What do chloroplasts and cell walls do in plant cells?
- In what ways are plant and animal cells similar in structure?

A **cell** is the basic unit of life. It is made from **cytoplasm** together with some genetic material which is usually contained within a **nucleus**. The whole cell is surrounded by a surface **membrane** which keeps the cell together.

Some organisms exist as a single cell. These unicells are known as **acellular** organisms. However most of the living things which you see around you are composed of many cells. These are called **multicellular** organisms.

Q1 What do we call the basic unit of life?

Q2 How are all the contents of a cell kept together?

Ideas and evidence

Theodor Schwann (1810–1882) and others developed the Cell Theory. This proposed that all living things are made of cells.

Can you think of any exceptions?

Fig 1a shows the structure of a typical animal cell and Fig 1b shows a typical plant cell.

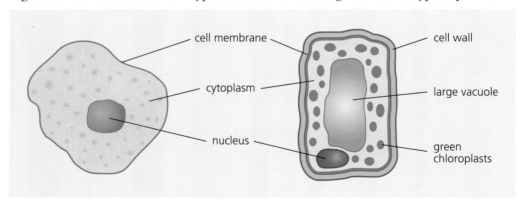

cell membrane

cytoplasm

nucleus

cell wall

large vacuole

green chloroplasts

Fig 1a *A typical animal cell*   **Fig 1b** *A typical plant cell*

The surface membrane of the cytoplasm controls the movement of materials into and out of the cell. The membrane is selective in that it only lets certain particles pass through it. For this reason it is said to be **partially** or **selectively permeable**.

The cytoplasm has within it a number of very small structures called **organelles**. These are not usually visible with an optical microscope, except for the nucleus. In order to see a more complete picture of the structure of a cell it is necessary to use an **electron microscope** to produce a picture called an **electron micrograph**. Fig 2 shows an electron micrograph of a plant cell.

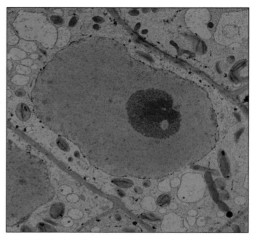

Fig 2 *An electron micrograph of a plant cell*

The nucleus is the control centre of the cell. Here nucleic acids and proteins form **chromosomes**. These carry the genetic information needed to organise the cell's chemical activities (see Units 5 and 45).

Chloroplasts are only found in plant cells. They contain the green pigment **chlorophyll**. This absorbs the light used in **photosynthesis** to manufacture food (see Unit 32).

The wall of a plant cell is composed of a carbohydrate called **cellulose**. Cellulose has very large molecules which form fibres. The plant cell wall is built up from these fibres. The wall is strong and supportive, but at the same time it is flexible and porous. The porous nature of the wall makes it permeable to water and dissolved particles, allowing them to pass through relatively easily.

Q3 What does the term 'partially permeable' mean?

Q4 Why is it important that the cell wall of a plant is porous?

Plant and animal cells are similar in the ways listed below. Both plant and animal cells:

1 have a cell membrane around the outside;

2 have a jelly-like substance called cytoplasm;

3 have microscopic structures in the cytoplasm called organelles, e.g. mitochondria;

4 usually have a large organelle called the nucleus.

There are also differences between plant and animal cells. These are summarised in the table.

Plant cells	Animal cells
cell walls made from cellulose	cell wall absent
mature cells have large, central vacuole	vacuoles, if present, are small and scattered
thin lining of cytoplasm against wall	cytoplasm throughout the cell
nucleus at the edge of the cell	nucleus anywhere but often in the centre of cell
chloroplasts present in many cells	chloroplasts never present
starch grains used for storage	glycogen granules or oil used for storage

Q5 Name two organelles which animal and plant cells have in common.

Q6 Name one organelle found only in plant cells.

Q7 How do the vacuoles of plant and animal cells differ?

Q8 Name the products commonly stored by animal cells.

Q9 How is the structure of a plant cell wall related to its function?

Q10 Why is it necessary to use an electron microscope to see some cell organelles but not others?

4 Movement of particles

In this unit you will learn the answers to these questions:
- ■ What happens during diffusion?
- ■ Where does diffusion occur in plants and animals?
- ■ How does osmosis differ from diffusion?
- ■ What is active transport?

Diffusion

Particles of matter are in constant motion. The particles of a solid substance vibrate. When the substance is liquid the particles move more easily. When the substance is a gas the particles move extremely easily. Their movement is **random**.

The changes shown in Fig 1 occur because of diffusion. Particles move from an area of high concentration to an area of low concentration, until the concentrations are equal. How quickly diffusion happens depends on the differences between the concentrations to begin with. The difference between two concentrations results in a concentration gradient from high to low. The bigger the difference the steeper the gradient.

Examples of diffusion in biological systems are shown in the table.

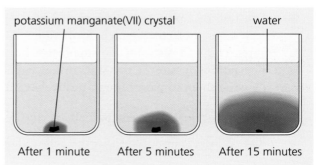

Fig 1 Potassium manganate(VII) crystal in water

Substance	Diffuses from (source)	Diffuses to (sink)
products of digestion	gut cavity	blood capillaries in villi
oxygen	air sacs of alveoli	alveolar blood capillaries
carbon dioxide	alveolar blood capillaries	air sacs of alveoli
urea	fetal bloodstream	maternal bloodstream
carbon dioxide (in plants)	leaf air spaces	leaf palisade mesophyll cells
oxygen (in plants)	chloroplasts	leaf air spaces

Osmosis

Osmosis is a special type of diffusion. It occurs across a permeable membrane which allows some particles to diffuse through it and not others. Most cell membranes are like that, being permeable to water and some solutes only. Osmosis is therefore the diffusion of water through a partially permeable membrane. The basic principles of diffusion apply here. However, the direction and rate of osmosis depends on the difference in water concentration between the two sides of the membrane. Water will continue to move into an area of lower water concentration until the two concentrations are equal (and equilibrium is reached) (see Figs 2 and 3).

Q1 How does the movement of particles in solids, liquids and gases differ?

Q2 What do you understand by the term 'diffusion'?

Q3 Write down two examples of diffusion in plants and two examples in animals.

Q4 What determines the steepness of a concentration gradient?

Q5 How does the gradient affect the direction and rate of diffusion?

Fig 2

Fig 3

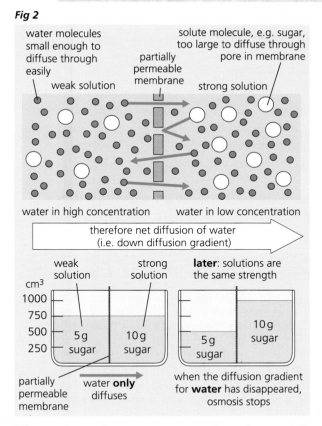

water molecules small enough to diffuse through easily

solute molecule, e.g. sugar, too large to diffuse through pore in membrane

partially permeable membrane

weak solution

strong solution

water in high concentration

water in low concentration

therefore net diffusion of water (i.e. down diffusion gradient)

weak solution

strong solution

later: solutions are the same strength

cm³
1000
750
500
250

5 g sugar

10 g sugar

5 g sugar

10 g sugar

partially permeable membrane

water **only** diffuses

when the diffusion gradient for **water** has disappeared, osmosis stops

Two cylinders of tissue were cut from the same potato. Cylinder A was placed in a beaker containing distilled water. Cylinder B was placed in a beaker containing a concentrated sugar solution. After 1 hour they were removed from the beakers. The following diagrams show what they looked like.

Cylinder A
1 The water concentration in the beaker was much higher than the concentration of water in the potato.
2 Water moved INTO the potato by osmosis.
3 The potato became hard, stiff and enlarged.

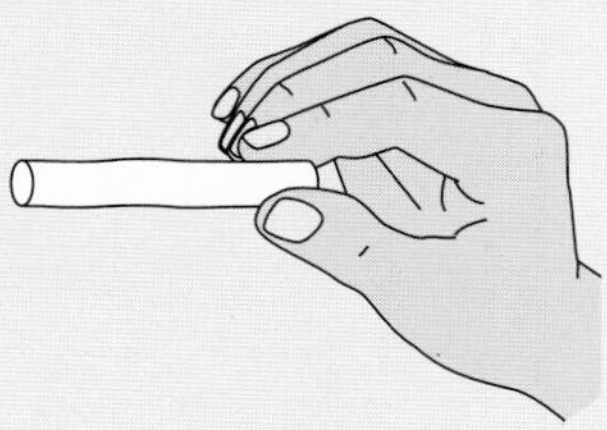

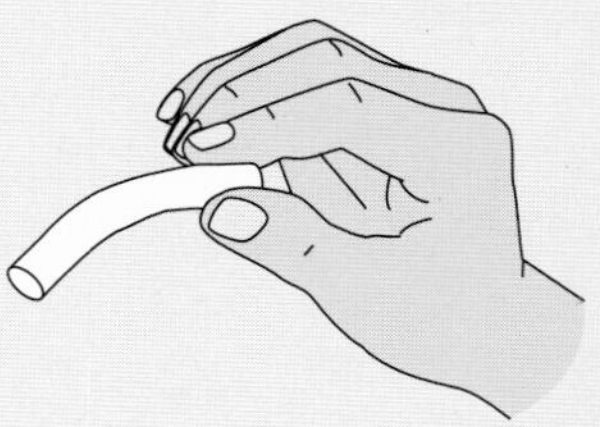

Cylinder B
1 The water concentration in the potato was greater than the concentration of water in the beaker.
2 Water moved OUT of the potato by osmosis.
3 The potato became soft, floppy and shrank.

The tendency for water to move through a partially permeable membrane is described as its **water potential** and is at a maximum in pure water. The addition of solutes to water lowers its water potential. The amount the potential is lowered is determined by how much solute is added. This means that more concentrated solutions have lower water potentials than more dilute solutions. Water will therefore have a greater tendency to move from pure water to any aqueous solution and from a more dilute solution to a more concentrated one.

Active transport

There are some examples of transfer or exchange in biological systems where the movement of particles cannot be explained in terms of simple diffusion alone. For example, root hair cells (see Unit 38) absorb ions from the soil even when the concentration of the ions is greater inside the cell than in the soil outside it.

Particles (e.g. ions) can be moved against a concentration gradient. Moving anything 'up hill' is expensive in terms of energy. Movement of ions or any particles against a concentration gradient uses up energy. This type of transport is called **active transport** and involves the use of energy from respiration (ATP) (see Unit 19). Cells capable of active transport tend to have more mitochondria than other cells. Mitochondria are involved in aerobic respiration and the production of ATP.

Q6 What part does a partially permeable membrane play in osmosis?

Q7 What will determine the direction and rate of water movement in osmosis?

ICT Extra!

Use spreadsheets to process experimental data obtained from investigations into mass or volumetric changes brought about by osmosis.

5 Chromosomes

In this unit you will learn the answers to these questions:
■ Where are chromosomes found?
■ What are chromosomes made from?
■ What are genes and what do they do?

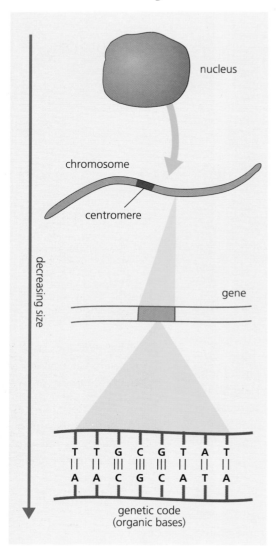

Fig 1

The nucleus is the largest and most obvious structure within a cell. When a cell is not dividing, the nucleus appears to be relatively uniform. However, when it divides it becomes obvious that there are separate, recognisable structures within it. These are the **chromosomes** (see Fig 1).

All organisms have a definite number of chromosomes within the nuclei of their cells. The **chromosome number** is a characteristic of a species. For example, human body cells (i.e. all types of cells except gametes (see Unit 41)) have nuclei containing 46 chromosomes (23 pairs).

A preparation of dividing cells can be made using a stain which makes the chromosomes visible under microscopic examination. Stained chromosomes stand out as long, thread-like structures of varying length and thickness. Each chromosome possesses a **centromere**, which plays an important part in nuclear division (see Units 6 and 7).

Chemical analysis of a nucleus shows it to contain protein and nucleic acid, in particular **deoxyribonucleic acid (DNA)**. During nuclear division the protein and DNA become more compact and form the chromosomes.

Q1 What chemical compounds are present in a chromosome?

Nucleic acids are polymers (very large molecules) built up from many monomers (smaller molecules) called **nucleotides**. A nucleotide itself has three parts. These are, in order of increasing size:
■ a phosphate group;
■ a sugar with five carbons in it (a pentose); and
■ an organic base (containing nitrogen).

In nucleotides which make DNA, the pentose sugar is deoxyribose and the nitrogenous bases are called **adenine** (A), **guanine** (G), **thymine** (T) and **cytosine** (C).

Fig 2 shows the way in which two strands of DNA are arranged as a double helix in a chromosome. Notice the way that A is always opposite T and G opposite C. These are described as complementary base pairs and are important in both the way that chromosomes copy themselves during nuclear division and the way they work in controlling the chemistry of cells.

Q2 What is a monomer?

Q3 What are the three components of a nucleotide?

Q4 Name four organic bases involved in DNA structure.

Q5 What is meant by 'complementary base pairing'?

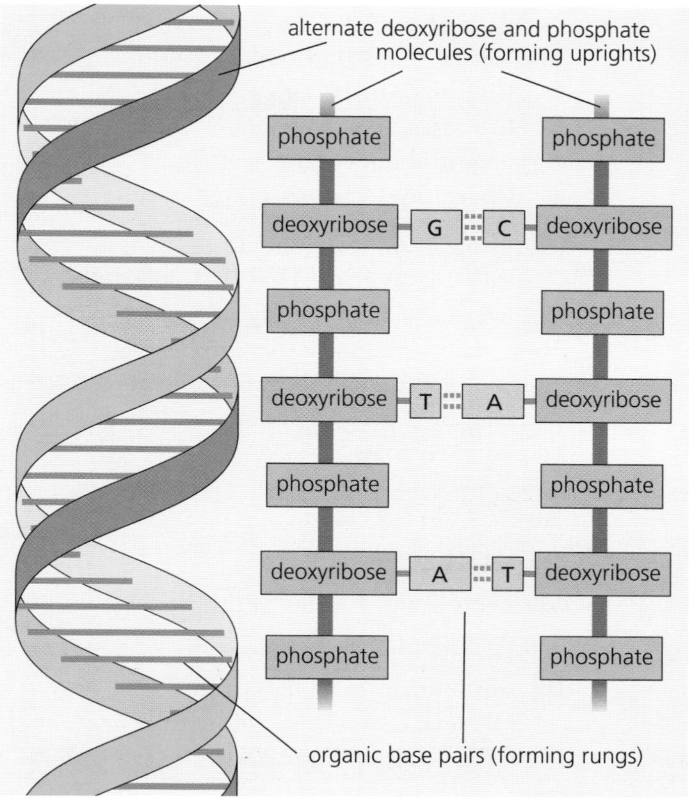

Fig 2 *The DNA double helix*

alternate deoxyribose and phosphate molecules (forming uprights)

phosphate			phosphate
deoxyribose	G	C	deoxyribose
phosphate			phosphate
deoxyribose	T	A	deoxyribose
phosphate			phosphate
deoxyribose	A	T	deoxyribose
phosphate			phosphate

organic base pairs (forming rungs)

Each chromosome will have bases arranged along its length in a particular order. The base order acts as a chemical code. The code prescribes the chemistry which goes on in a cell. It therefore determines what a cell does.

The nucleus of a fertilised egg (zygote) must have all the coding it will ever need for the whole organism.

Fig 3 *Electron micrograph of a sperm fertilising an egg*

Q6 What is the 'chemical code' in the nucleus?

Q7 What does the 'chemical code' control?

A short section of the code controls a specific part of the chemistry of a cell. This bit of DNA is a **gene**. One way of picturing a chromosome is as a long string of genes. During nuclear division, the DNA, and therefore the chromosomes, are copied. This produces sets of chromosomes (and their genes) which can be passed on to the next generation of cells. It is in this way that genetic characteristics are inherited.

Q8 Chromosomes are sometimes compared to 'strings of beads'. What do you think the 'beads' are supposed to represent?

Q9 How would you describe the structure of a gene?

6 Mitosis

In this unit you will learn the answers to these questions:

■ **What is mitosis?**
■ **How does it work?**
■ **Why is it important?**
■ **Where does mitosis take place?**

Every one of us starts life as a single cell called a **zygote**. The 10^{14} cells that we have in our body all come from that original cell. This vast increase in the number of cells is achieved by a process of cell division known as **mitosis**.

Mechanism of mitosis

Mitosis involves a series of processes. These are:

1 **replication** (copying) of the DNA of each chromosome to form a pair of chromatids;

2 **spindle formation** to enable separation of chromatids;

3 **contraction of spindle fibres** to separate the chromatids to form two sets of chromosomes;

4 **division of the cytoplasm** to produce two daughter cells each with a set of chromosomes, identical to each other and to the parent cell. The way in which cellular division is achieved differs in plant and animal cells.

Q1 Name four processes involved in mitosis.

Q2 What does the term 'replication' mean?

Q3 What is a chromatid?

The diagrams show what happens to one of the chromosomes in a nucleus. The same happens to each of the others.

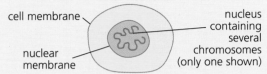

cell membrane
nuclear membrane
nucleus containing several chromosomes (only one shown)

The chromosome is replicated to form a pair of chromatids. Chromatids shorten and thicken.

pair of replicas/copies, each called a chromatid
centromere, holding chromatids together

Nuclear membrane breaks down. Spindle fibres form at two poles. Each chromatid pair is attached to spindle fibres by centromere.

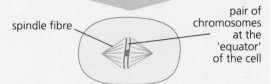

spindle fibre
pair of chromosomes at the 'equator' of the cell

Centromere divides. Spindle fibres contract. Chromatids (now called chromosomes) dragged to their poles.

spindle fibres contracting

Cell membrane 'pinches in' to separate 'daughter chromosomes'. Nuclear membranes form around chromosomes at each pole.

cell membrane 'pinching in'

Two daughter cells produced, each with an exact copy of the genetic material of the parent cell.

one of the two daughter cells
nuclear membrane
chromosome gets longer and thinner

Fig 1 *Mitosis in an animal cell*

Cell division usually follows nuclear division. This is where mitosis in animal and plant cells is different. In plant cells the two daughter nuclei are separated into two daughter cells by the formation of a new cell wall. This is formed across the 'equator' of the dividing cell. In animal cells they are separated by the surface membrane 'pinching in' at the equatorial region. When the surface membrane meets in the centre the cytoplasm is divided into two and two cells are formed.

> **Q4** What is the 'spindle' and when does it form?
>
> **Q5** How are the chromatids dragged apart?
>
> **Q6** How is cell division achieved in plants?
>
> **Q7** How is cell division achieved in animals?

Importance of mitosis

Mitosis produces copies. As a result it is important in three major areas. These are:

1 growth;

2 repair; and

3 asexual reproduction.

Growth. Most animal cells retain the ability to divide throughout their life span. When growth of a tissue becomes necessary, the cells present in the tissue divide. It is essential that the cells formed are genetically the same since they will have the same function to perform. Mitotic divisions provide the copies. Growth occurs and the nature of the tissue stays the same.

Growth in plants differs in that only certain cells retain the ability to divide. These are described as **meristematic cells** and the regions where they are found are called **meristems**. Meristems are found, for example, at the tips of roots and stems.

Repair. When a tissue is damaged it is important that it is repaired. It is important also that damaged cells are replaced by cells of the same type. Mitotic division does this.

Asexual reproduction. Simple animals and most plants can reproduce asexually (without sex). Unicells, for example, undergo mitosis to produce two daughter cells. Pieces broken off multicellular plants, either by natural causes or deliberately by us, grow into whole plants by repeated mitotic divisions. Examples of this include the formation of bulbs, corms or stem tubers. These structures will have the same genetics as their parent plants (see Unit 44 on cloning).

> **Q8** Which feature of mitosis is important in growth?
>
> **Q9** How does growth in plants differ from growth in animals?
>
> **Q10** Which cells are capable of mitosis in plants?
>
> **Q11** Name two plant reproductive structures produced asexually.
>
> **Q12** What will be true about the genetics of offspring produced by asexual reproduction?

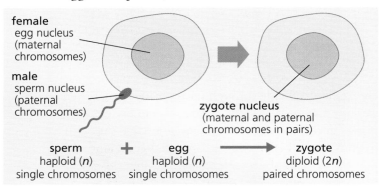

7 Meiosis

In this unit you will learn the answers to these questions:
- What is meiosis?
- Why is it important?
- Where does it take place?
- What happens during meiosis?
- How does meiosis differ from mitosis?

All organisms keep a specific number of chromosomes in the nuclei of their body cells from generation to generation. The nuclei of human body cells, for example, have 46 chromosomes present as 23 pairs.

Sexual reproduction involves the fusion of nuclei at fertilisation. Therefore individual gametes must have half the body cell chromosome number, e.g. 23 singles in human eggs and sperms, if the characteristic chromosome number is to be maintained. The zygote formed at fertilisation will therefore possess one complete set of chromosomes from the male gamete (paternal chromosomes) and one complete set from the female gamete (maternal chromosomes) (Fig 1).

female
egg nucleus (maternal chromosomes)

male
sperm nucleus (paternal chromosomes)

zygote nucleus (maternal and paternal chromosomes in pairs)

sperm	+	egg	→	zygote
haploid (*n*)		haploid (*n*)		diploid (2*n*)
single chromosomes		single chromosomes		paired chromosomes

Fig 1

Meiosis reduces the number of chromosomes from the **diploid** state to the **haploid** state. It is, as a result, sometimes referred to as **reduction division** and occurs in the formation of gametes in animals and spores in most plants.

Q1 Why does a zygote have twice as many chromosomes as the egg from which it was formed?

Q2 Which are the paternal chromosomes in a zygote?

Q3 Why is meiosis sometimes called 'reduction division'?

Q4 Where would you expect to find meiosis taking place in humans?

Mechanism of meiosis (reduction division)

Fig 2 shows the process of meiosis in an animal cell.

The importance of meiosis

1 Reduces chromosome number in gametes. This avoids constant doubling-up of chromosome number at each new generation.

2 Pieces of chromosomes can be exchanged between the paternal and maternal chromosomes of the same pair. The material exchanged will be responsible for the

The diagrams show what happens to one pair of chromosomes in a nucleus. The same happens to each of the other pairs.

All the chromosomes present in the nucleus are replicated/copied. Each chromosome then exists as a pair of chromatids.

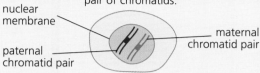

nuclear membrane

paternal chromatid pair

maternal chromatid pair

Nuclear membrane breaks down. Paternal and maternal chromatids pair up and lie above and below the equator. Centromeres are attached to spindle fibres.

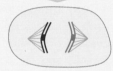

spindle fibre

centromere

Spindle fibres contract. Pairs of chromatids are dragged apart.

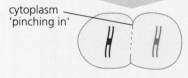

Paternal and maternal chromatid pairs are separated. Cytoplasm 'pinches in' at equator to form two cells.

cytoplasm 'pinching in'

Spindle fibres set up to separate chromatids. Centromere attached to spindle fibres.

Spindle fibres contract. Chromatids separated. Each chromatid is now a chromosome in its own nucleus. Four cells are formed from the parent cell. Each has half the chromosome number of the parent cell.

Fig 2 Meiosis in an animal cell

same general genetic characteristics but the **details will differ**. This leads to a new combination of characteristics.

3 The arrangement of the pairs of chromosomes at the equator early in meiosis provides an opportunity for **variation** (difference) to arise. Each pair may take up one of two positions at the equator, paternal to 'migrate north' and maternal to 'migrate south', or the opposite. This is true for each chromosome pair in the cell and each pair behaves independently of the others. This is called **random assortment**. Consequently there can be a very large number of ways of separating the individual members of all the pairs into two groups, one group to the north pole of the cell and the other to the south. For example, in humans with 23 pairs there are 2^{23} possible groupings. This works out to over 8 million different possible combinations. It is not surprising that every gamete gets its own, unique, combination of genes.

The table compares meiosis and mitosis (see Unit 6).

Feature	Meiosis	Mitosis
Where does it occur?	gamete formation in sex organs	during growth and repair
Why does it happen?	to halve the number of chromosomes	to make exact copies
How many cells are produced per division?	four	two
How many chromosomes present in the nucleus?	half the number present in the parent cell nucleus	same number as in the parent cell nucleus

8 Nutrients – the chemistry of food

In this unit you will learn the answer to this question:

- What does our food contain?

Carbohydrates and **fats** contain the elements carbon, hydrogen and oxygen. **Proteins** have these three elements too, but in addition contain the element nitrogen.

Carbohydrates

The human diet commonly contains a variety of carbohydrates. One of the simplest is a sugar called **glucose**. Glucose molecules can combine together in pairs (**condensation**) to form **maltose**. Enzymes can reverse this change, forming glucose once more. The reversal of condensation is called **hydrolysis**. This is the type of chemical change which goes on in the gut during the digestion of food (see Unit 12). The reversible reaction between glucose and maltose is summarised in Fig 1.

$$\text{glucose} + \text{glucose} \underset{\text{breaking down (hydrolysis)}}{\overset{\text{combining together (condensation)}}{\rightleftharpoons}} \text{maltose} + \text{water}$$

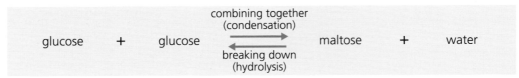

Fig 1 *Maltose formation / breakdown*

This adding together of similar molecules is called **polymerisation**. If many units are added, a large chain can be produced. These are called **polymers**. One example of a glucose polymer is called **starch** and another is **glycogen**. Fig 2 shows the polymerisation of glucose to form starch. Sugars are soluble in water. Starch and glycogen are insoluble in water.

$$\text{glucose} + \text{glucose} + \underbrace{\ldots\ldots}_{\text{many glucose molecules}} + \text{glucose} \underset{\text{breaking down}}{\overset{\text{combining together}}{\rightleftharpoons}} \text{starch} + \text{water}$$

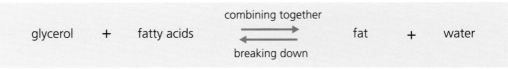

Fig 2 *Starch formation / breakdown*

Fats

Fat molecules are formed by two types of molecules combining together. These are **glycerol** and **fatty acids**. Once more this reaction can be reversed. Fig 3 summarises these changes. A fat molecule contains a very large number of carbon and hydrogen atoms but in different amounts to carbohydrates. Fat is a very high energy food material because of this.

$$\text{glycerol} + \text{fatty acids} \underset{\text{breaking down}}{\overset{\text{combining together}}{\rightleftharpoons}} \text{fat} + \text{water}$$

Fig 3 *Fat formation / breakdown*

Proteins

Proteins are polymers too. This time the simpler molecules (monomers) are **amino acids**. Amino acids combine to form large chains called **polypeptides**. Proteins are formed from one or more of these polypeptides. When protein chains are broken up amino acids are re-formed (Fig 4).

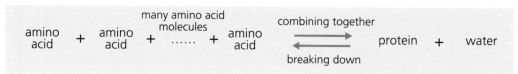

Fig 4 Protein formation/breakdown

Vitamins

Vitamins are a group of complicated compounds. Chemicals in this group show a wide variety of molecular size and shape. The compounds we call vitamins have chemical names but are usually known by letters of the alphabet. You are likely to have heard of some of them, e.g. vitamin C.

Minerals

Humans need a large variety of mineral ions. These fall into two groups, namely the **macronutrients** and the trace elements or **micronutrients**. Calcium in the form of calcium ions (Ca^{2+}) is an example of a macronutrient. Iron as ions (Fe^{2+}) is a micronutrient. Essential minerals are needed in very small quantities.

Dietary fibre

This is the material which humans cannot digest, mainly made up of cellulose, plant cell walls. It is often referred to as **roughage**.

Water

Water forms about 75% of the protoplasm of cells and as such is the most important inorganic molecule in living systems.

The table shows common sources for some of the food materials mentioned in this unit.

Food material	Source (examples)
glucose	grapes
maltose	malt
starch	potatoes, rice, wheat flour
glycogen	liver
fat/oil	milk, butter, fish oils, plant oils
protein	lean meat, cheese, peas
vitamin C	citrus fruits
vitamin B complex	liver
vitamin A	vegetables, fruit, liver
vitamin D	liver, dairy products
calcium	dairy products, green vegetables
iron	liver, green vegetables
dietary fibre	vegetable matter, wholemeal flour

Q1 Name the three elements found in all carbohydrates, fats and proteins.

Q2 Name an additional element found in all proteins.

Q3 How is starch formed?

Q4 Name the two types of compound involved in the formation of a fat.

Q5 Name the monomers involved in protein synthesis.

Q6 Name the two groups of mineral nutrients.

Q7 Name a single food source containing vitamins B, A and D.

Q8 Name a single food source containing both calcium and iron.

Q9 Name a good source for dietary fibre.

9 Human diet

In this unit you will learn the answers to these questions:
- What should we eat?
- How much should we eat?
- What is a balanced diet?
- What happens when the balance is wrong?

The human diet must include carbohydrates, fats, protein, vitamins, mineral salts, water and dietary fibre.

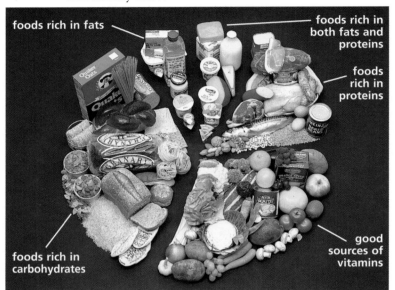

foods rich in fats

foods rich in both fats and proteins

foods rich in proteins

good sources of vitamins

foods rich in carbohydrates

Carbohydrates such as sugars and starch provide the body with energy. Glucose is usually the main source of energy. Respiration of glucose makes the energy of food available for use by the body. Some sugar is stored as glycogen in the liver, and a little in the muscles. Glycogen acts as a glucose source when blood glucose levels are low. Any sugars left over are stored as fat.

Fats release more energy than carbohydrates during respiration and due to this they make very good storage products. Fats also act as heat insulation and waterproofing. Fat is deposited in a variety of places in mammals, particularly under the skin.

Proteins are described as 'body building' foods and are important in the production of new cells. Digested proteins supply the body with amino acids, the raw materials for the manufacture of the new amino acids and proteins which the body needs at that time. There are some amino acids which the body must have, 'ready-made'. These are '**essential amino acids**', essential if health is to be maintained. Proteins have a wide range of uses in the body. They are found in bones, nails and hair. Haemoglobin is one of many very important blood proteins. Enzymes are proteins.

Vitamins are required in very small quantities. They are involved in a variety of ways in the body, each having a particular part to play in maintaining health. The table lists sources and uses of various vitamins.

Vitamin	Good source	Use
A	green vegetables, butter, egg yolk, fish oils	healthy skin and membranes
B complex	yeast extract, liver, wholemeal bread	variety, particularly respiration
C	citrus fruits, blackcurrants, vegetables	healthy skin, strong capillaries
D	butter, egg yolk, synthesised in skin	uptake and controlled use of calcium

Mineral salts are also required in very small quantities. They are employed in the body in a variety of ways, as shown in the table.

Element	Good source	Use in body
Ca (calcium)	cheese, milk	bones and teeth
F (fluorine)	toothpaste	affects hardening of tooth enamel
Fe (iron)	liver, green vegetables	part of haemoglobin molecule
I (iodine)	table salt additive, sea-food	part of thyroxine molecule
K (potassium)	green vegetables	nerve and muscle function
Na (sodium)	table salt	nerve and muscle function
P (phosphorus)	milk	ATP production, bones and teeth

Plant cells have walls made of cellulose. This is the main component of **dietary fibre**. Humans cannot digest cellulose and this, together with other indigestible fibrous plant material, adds bulk to our diet. It gives the gut muscles something to work on, making digestion more efficient. **Peristalsis** (see Unit 10) is improved and the gut is more likely to remain healthy. Dietary fibre helps to retain water in the gut cavity and prevent diseases such as constipation and bowel cancer.

Water is the most important inorganic molecule in living systems. It makes the largest contribution to the mass of living protoplasm (approximately 75%) and is therefore a vital component of any diet. Water has many important jobs. It acts as a solvent, transports substances and provides the medium where reactions take place.

Q1 Why are some amino acids described as 'essential amino acids'?

A **balanced diet** must provide all of the substances described above for growth and repair, and contain sufficient energy to maintain the body's activities. It must provide essential health factors. To be balanced the substances must be in the correct amounts.

Clearly not everybody's demands are the same. For example, growth rate varies with age. Younger people are therefore more likely to need greater quantities of those food materials required to support growth. Some occupations and lifestyles demand greater energy reserves. People whose work involves long spells of physical activity, such as builders, are likely to need a larger carbohydrate intake than those in more sedentary jobs in offices. The same will be true for those who take part in more sporting activities. They too will have a higher energy demand than those who are not so active.

Malnutrition is the condition which exists when an individual's diet or eating pattern is 'out of balance'. It is possible to eat too little or too much of particular parts of the diet. **Obesity** resulting from an excessive intake of carbohydrate is one obvious example. This may lead to heart disease, shortened life span and poor health in old age.

Anorexia nervosa and **bulimia** are two eating-related disorders. The deliberate, minimal intake of food over prolonged periods of time leads to anorexia nervosa. One of the symptoms of bulimia is the intake of huge amounts of food and then getting rid of it by induced vomiting. Both conditions can ultimately be fatal.

10 The human digestive system

In this unit you will learn the answers to these questions:
- What happens to food in our gut?
- How is the gut designed to deal with our food?

We get our food by eating other animals and plants. Our digestive system helps us to break down the complex food into its simpler parts which we are then able to use.

There are five basic processes through which food has to go before it ends up being available for use inside the cells of a human.

1 Food material has to be put into the mouth. This process is called **ingestion**.

2 Large, complex, insoluble food chemicals are converted into simpler, soluble molecules. This process is called **digestion**. Digestion includes both mechanical and chemical digestion.

3 The products of digestion are then taken from the gut into the circulatory system. This process is called **absorption**.

4 Absorbed food chemicals are then put to use in the body. This process is called **assimilation**.

5 The remaining undigested waste left in the gut is pushed out of the body as faeces. This process is called **egestion**.

The gut is a single, continuous tube starting at the mouth and ending at the anus. Different parts are adapted to perform different functions and in doing so carry out the five processes listed above.

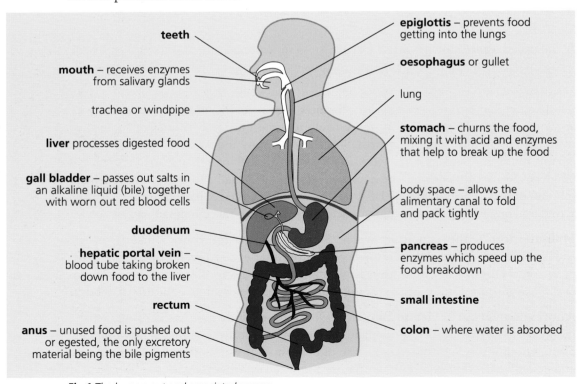

teeth

mouth – receives enzymes from salivary glands

trachea or windpipe

liver processes digested food

gall bladder – passes out salts in an alkaline liquid (bile) together with worn out red blood cells

duodenum

hepatic portal vein – blood tube taking broken down food to the liver

rectum

anus – unused food is pushed out or egested, the only excretory material being the bile pigments

epiglottis – prevents food getting into the lungs

oesophagus or gullet

lung

stomach – churns the food, mixing it with acid and enzymes that help to break up the food

body space – allows the alimentary canal to fold and pack tightly

pancreas – produces enzymes which speed up the food breakdown

small intestine

colon – where water is absorbed

Fig 1 The human gut and associated organs

There are several structures close to the gut which, although not actually part of it, play a very important part in the way food is processed. For example, the **salivary glands** are linked to the mouth. The **pancreas** and **liver** release materials into the small intestine. The liver also stores material received from the gut.

Food starts its passage through the gut at the **mouth**. Those animals which eat meat have **sharp, pointed teeth**, good at puncturing and slicing. Those animals which feed on plant materials, particularly grasses, have **flatter teeth** which are better suited to grinding up vegetation. Most humans eat a mixture of plant and animal material. The teeth we have show features somewhere between the two. Some of our teeth are sharp and chisel-like, some have flattened tops similar to the grinding teeth of plant eaters.

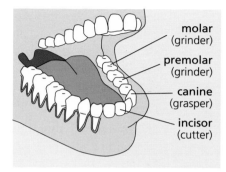

Fig 2 Human teeth

Q1 In what way are teeth adapted to the job they do?

The shape and form of a tooth will determine what it can do. There are four types of teeth in the human mouth. These are **incisors**, **canines**, **premolars** and **molars**.

The **oesophagus** (gullet) and the **trachea** (windpipe) have entrances quite close together. It is important that food enters the oesophagus and not the trachea. A flap-like structure called the **epiglottis** moves across and blocks the entrance to the trachea. This prevents food from passing into the air passages and prevents the person from choking. After swallowing, the food is moved along the gut by muscle action. The first part of this journey, from the mouth to the stomach, passes along the oesophagus.

The wall of the gut is muscular. Circular muscle contraction makes the cross-section of the tube smaller. The result is a bit like squeezing a tube. The opposite occurs when the longitudinal muscles contract. The two sets work together, in opposition, as an antagonistic pair. This process, called **peristalsis**, is responsible for moving food from one end of the gut to the other.

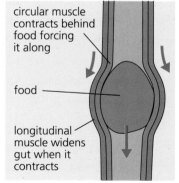

Fig 3 Peristalsis

Food leaves the oesophagus and enters the **stomach**, a large, bag-like structure which acts as a food store. The increase in diameter in this part of the gut slows down the passage of food. Secretory cells in the wall of the stomach release digestive factors known as **gastric juice** (see Unit 11).

Food leaves the stomach, entering the **small intestine**. The structure of the small intestine is modified to its dual function of digestion and absorption (see Unit 12).

During its passage through the gut large quantities of water are added to the food in the form of digestive juices. Water is taken back into the bloodstream in the **large intestine**, particularly in the **colon**.

The gut contents become more firm as a result of the removal of water. The undigested remains of food, together with gut bacteria, form the faeces. This is stored in the **rectum**, the final section of the gut, before being egested via the **anus**.

11 Digestion in the human gut

In this unit you will learn the answers to these questions:
- Why does food have to be digested?
- Is different food digested in different parts of the gut?
- Why have we got acid in our stomach?

Food passes through the gut from the mouth to the anus. Anything swallowed but which remains chemically unchanged emerges at the other end. Before food materials can be of real value to us they have to leave the space within the gut and enter the body cells. At the very least, they must enter the cells lining the gut cavity. Better still, they enter the blood or lymph vessels close to the gut space. They can then go off to living cells anywhere in the body and be of some use (see Unit 12).

There are two things which make this difficult. The first is that the membranes surrounding the cells lining the gut are only partially permeable (see Unit 3). The second is that many food molecules are too big to diffuse easily through the membranes of the gut lining which encloses them.

The problems are overcome by the process known as **digestion**. Chewing food in the mouth and the churning effect of the stomach help to break up food. These are not, however, enough on their own.

Large, insoluble molecules are broken down chemically by **enzymes** in the gut cavity. The final products are small, soluble molecules. These can cross the membranes of the cells lining the gut and enter the fine branches of the body's transport systems. As a result, food can leave the gut for use elsewhere.

The enzymes involved in digestion are produced by cells present in the lining of the gut or in cells of organs near to it. They are released onto food in the gut cavity and therefore work 'outside the body'. Enzymes of this type are called '**extracellular**' enzymes, to distinguish them from '**intracellular**' enzymes which work inside cells.

Saliva contains the enzyme **amylase**. This speeds up the breakdown of starch to the sugar maltose. The pH of the mouth is suitable for amylase to work. Starch is a major component of staple diets throughout the world. This enzyme is therefore very important. Salivary amylase stops working when the swallowed food enters the stomach because the pH is too acid. Carbohydrate digestion starts again when the food reaches the small intestine. **Maltase**, another enzyme, brings about the conversion of one sugar, maltose, to glucose, which is a smaller sugar.

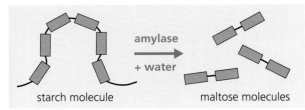

Fig 1 Digestion of starch to maltose

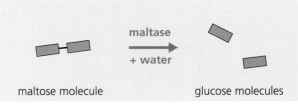

Fig 2 Digestion of maltose to glucose

Protein digestion involves enzymes known as **proteases**. The digestion of proteins starts in the stomach and continues on into the small intestine. Different proteases work in different parts of the gut. The stomach enzymes work in an acid environment and those in the small intestine work in an alkaline environment. Eventually all proteins are converted into amino acids.

The acid present in the stomach creates the correct pH for gastric proteases to work. It also helps to sterilise the food entering the gut by killing many of the bacteria present.

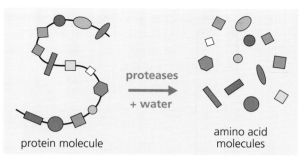

Fig 3 Digestion of protein to amino acids

Lipases are released into the small intestine. They act on the fats present in food. Their job is to convert fats to glycerol and fatty acids. These enzymes work in the alkaline environment of the small intestine. When food enters the small intestine from the stomach it comes into contact with **bile**. Bile is secreted by liver cells and is stored in

the gall bladder. A duct carries and empties the fluid into the duodenum (see Unit 10). Here the bile salts break up the fat in food into a very large number of microscopic droplets. This increases the surface area of the fat for the lipases to work on. The lipases work better as a result.

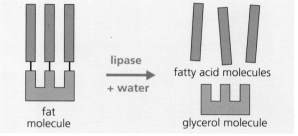

Fig 4 Digestion of a fat to glycerol and fatty acids

The end products of digestion are **glucose**, **amino acids**, **fatty acids** and **glycerol**. These molecules are small enough to pass through the membranes of the cells lining the gut. They are therefore in a form which enables them to enter the circulation and be of use. That is, they are simple, soluble molecules.

The complete process of digestion in the gut is summarised in the table.

Place	Action	Digestive juice	Enzyme	Change
mouth	mechanical digestion			teeth break food into smaller pieces
	chemical digestion	saliva	amylase	starch to maltose
stomach	mechanical digestion			stomach churns the food, mixing it with acid and gastric juice
	chemical digestion	gastric juice	proteases	proteins broken down to smaller chain molecules (polypeptides)
duodenum	physical change	bile from gall bladder (not a digestive juice)		fat broken up into microscopic droplets
	chemical digestion	pancreatic and intestinal juices	amylase	starch to maltose
			maltase	maltose to glucose
			lipases	fats to fatty acids and glycerol
			proteases	proteins and polypeptides to amino acids

Q1 Suggest a reason why cellulose is not digested by humans.

Q2 Digestion involves mechanical as well as chemical action. Where does mechanical digestion take place?

12 Absorption and assimilation

In this unit you will learn the answer to this question:
- **What happens to food after it has been digested?**

Absorption

Branches of the blood system and the lymph system are brought very close to the gut in the region of the ileum, part of the small intestine (see Unit 10). The food material crosses the lining of the small intestine here and enters these systems.

The region of the small intestine where absorption takes place is **very long** in proportion to the rest of the gut. The average length of the small intestine of an adult man is seven metres. The surface of the ileum is **folded**, with each square

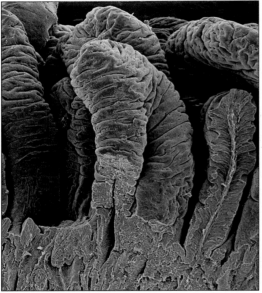

millimetre of surface carrying a large number of finger–like projections called **villi**. These project into the gut space through which the food is passing. Closer examination of their surface reveals that each villus also carries projections. These are called **microvilli**.

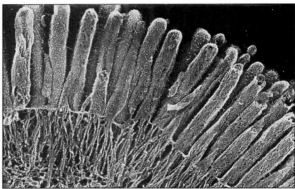

Fig 1 Photomicrograph of a section through the small intestine, showing folding and villi

Fig 2 Electron micrograph of cells from the lining of the small intestine, showing microvilli

folded wall with tiny pieces sticking up called villi

circle of muscle cut across

muscles going round the food canal

muscles running along the food canal

The two sets of muscles produce peristalsis (see Unit 10)

The fact that the ileum is long and narrow means that the food is more likely to be brought close to the absorbing surface for a longer time. The folded internal surface increases the surface area for contact. It also provides a greater surface to carry villi, which in turn carry microvilli. These features provide a **very large surface area**, making the ileum an efficient organ for absorption.

Fig 3 Part of the small intestine, in cross-section. The folds and villi provide a very large surface for absorption

Fig 4 shows the structure of a single villus. The wall is very thin and is permeable to the products of digestion. Branches of the artery which goes to the small intestine form **capillaries** which deliver blood to each villus. Blood drains away from the villus to join blood from other villi before it leaves the small intestine. A **lacteal**, a fine branch of the lymphatic system (see Unit 15), lies in the centre of each villus.

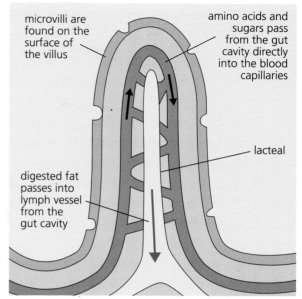

microvilli are found on the surface of the villus

amino acids and sugars pass from the gut cavity directly into the blood capillaries

lacteal

digested fat passes into lymph vessel from the gut cavity

Fig 4 A single villus

Sugars, amino acids, fatty acids and glycerol diffuse across the thin membranes of the villus surface cells. They enter the blood and are carried away. Their immediate removal helps to maintain a diffusion gradient. This makes sure that more can be taken into the blood by diffusion. Some absorption of digested food is by active transport.

Cells at the surface of the villus absorb fatty acids and glycerol. These are used to synthesise fat and the fat droplets formed are transferred to the lacteal. Large numbers of fat droplets in the lacteal give it the appearance of milk. These fats are taken away in the lymph to be transferred to the blood system later.

Assimilation

Food material absorbed from the small intestine is first transported to the **liver**. The link between the gut and the liver is provided by the **hepatic portal vein**. Absorbed food material is put to use in a variety of ways. The liver plays a very important part in controlling what happens to food after it has been absorbed.

1 Sugars are used as the raw material for respiration during which energy is made available to living cells (see Unit 19). The body requires a certain quantity of glucose to be in circulation in the blood at any one time to work satisfactorily.

2 Excess sugar is converted into glycogen in the liver. There is a small temporary store of glycogen in the muscles.

3 The adult liver can store approximately 100 g of glycogen. Any extra carbohydrates are converted to fat which is stored in the liver cells.

4 Fat is stored in tissues under the skin.

5 Amino acids are used to make proteins and are involved in cell growth, repair and as health factors.

6 For other uses see Units 8 and 9.

Q1 Name two transport systems which play a part in absorption.

Q2 List four features of the ileum which increase the efficiency of absorption.

Q3 What is a lacteal and what is its job?

Q4 What does the hepatic portal vein do?

13 Circulatory system

In this unit you will learn the answers to these questions:
- ■ Why is the idea of 'surface area to volume ratio' important in biology?
- ■ Why do we need a circulatory system?
- ■ How are things moved around inside the body?
- ■ What is 'double circulation'?

In order to stay alive an organism must be able to exchange materials with its environment. Animals need to take in nutrients in order to grow. Oxygen is required for respiration. There must be somewhere to deposit waste materials.

The exchange takes place across the surface which separates the organism from its environment. The rate at which material crosses this boundary depends mainly on how fast diffusion takes place. This, in turn, is affected by the surface area available to the exchange process.

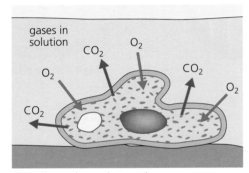

Fig 1 *Gas exchange in* Amoeba

Very small organisms have a larger surface area to volume ratio than larger organisms. In other words, each bit of surface available for diffusion in a very small organism has less organism (cytoplasm) to supply. Single-celled organisms (unicells), e.g. *Amoeba,* have a very high surface area to volume ratio. This will mean that any part of the cytoplasm of a unicell is only a very small distance (the diffusion distance) from a very large exchange surface. It can get its raw materials, get its respiratory gas, and dump its wastes into the environment by diffusion alone.

For larger organisms, animals in particular, diffusion through the outer surface would be *much too slow.* The biochemistry of an active animal would soon run out of essential raw materials. Wastes would soon build up to poisonous levels inside the organism. Diffusion also involves the *random movement of particles.*

A circulatory system overcomes these two problems. It provides the **rapid** movement of materials in the **right direction**.

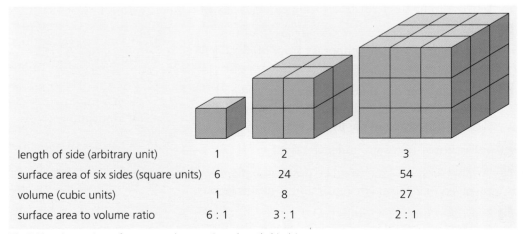

length of side (arbitrary unit)	1	2	3
surface area of six sides (square units)	6	24	54
volume (cubic units)	1	8	27
surface area to volume ratio	6 : 1	3 : 1	2 : 1

Fig 2 *The change in surface area:volume ratio as length (size) increases*

Double circulation in humans

Blood passes from the heart to the lungs where oxygen is added and carbon dioxide removed. It then returns to the heart. The heart–lungs–heart circuit is called the **pulmonary circuit**.

Blood then leaves the heart for the body. Blood is circulated to the organs before returning to the heart. The heart–body–heart circuit is called the **systemic circuit**.

The circulatory system of a human is described as a **double circulation** because there are two circuits. The blood passes through the heart *twice* each time it passes around the whole body.

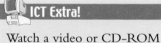

ICT Extra!

Watch a video or CD-ROM showing the circulatory system to help here.

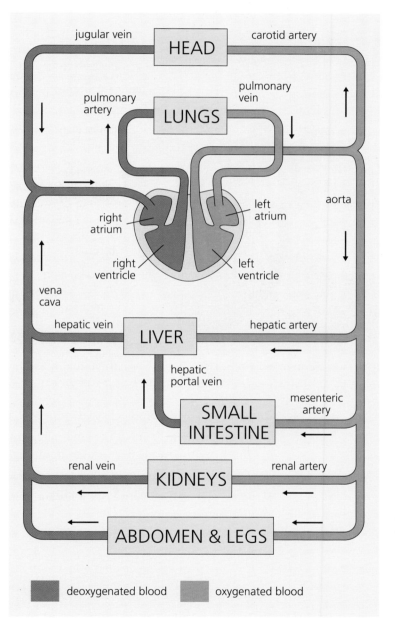

Fig 3 The circulatory system of a human

deoxygenated blood   oxygenated blood

Q1 Why do unicellular organisms not need a circulatory system?

Q2 What would the surface area:volume ratio be for a cube with sides 4 units long?

Q3 State two advantages of having a circulatory system.

14 The heart

In this unit you will learn the answers to these questions:

- What are the parts of the heart called?
- How does your heart work?
- Why does blood only flow one way?
- What can you do to keep your heart healthy?

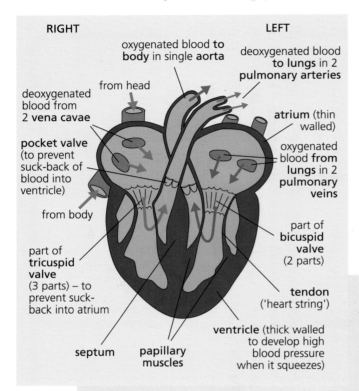

Fig 1 shows a vertical section through a mammalian heart.

Answer the following 16 questions. You will be able to find the answers in Fig 1. This should give you an understanding of the structure of the heart and how it works.

When you have completed this exercise (not before!) compare your answer to **Q16** with the summary given on the next page.

Fig 1 The mammalian heart in section: structure and function

Q1 How many chambers does the heart have?

Q2 What are the thinner walled chambers called?

Q3 What are the thicker walled chambers called?

Q4 Can you see any difference between the two thicker walled chambers?

Q5 The wall thickness depends on how much muscle there is. Which chambers do you think are the most successful at pumping blood?

Q6 How many large blood vessels are linked directly to the heart?

Q7 What are they called? Write out a list and state where the blood in them is coming from or going to.

Q8 Where are the tricuspid and bicuspid valves found?

Q9 Which way would you expect blood to flow through these valves?

Q10 There are valves at the base of the pulmonary artery and the aorta. Which way would blood flow through these valves?

Q11 What do you think would happen to **a)** the tricuspid and bicuspid valves and **b)** the pocket valves if the muscular walls of the ventricles contracted?

Q12 Which chamber would be able to pump blood out at the highest pressure? Give reasons based on your observations of the structure of the heart.

Q13 Suggest a function for the tendons attached to the tricuspid and bicuspid valves.

Q14 Which chambers are associated with the pulmonary circuit?

Q15 Which chambers are associated with the systemic circuit?

Q16 List the order in which the blood vessels, chambers and valves would be involved in one complete circulation of blood around the body and lungs. Remember that blood passes through the heart twice for a complete circuit of the blood system.

Summary of blood flow through the heart

1 Blood is delivered to the heart, from the head and body, in the vena cava. At the same time blood arrives from the lungs via the pulmonary veins.

2 Blood from the body enters the right atrium, stretching the wall outwards. Blood from the lungs enters the left atrium, stretching the wall outwards.

3 Blood collects in the atria until the pressure causes the cuspid valves to open.

4 Blood moves from the atria into the ventricles.

5 Muscles in the walls of the ventricles then contract, increasing the pressure on the blood, with the left ventricle generating the greater pressure.

6 The cuspid valves are closed due to the increasing pressure. This prevents the backflow of blood into the atria. (The tendons prevent the valves from being forced back into the atria.)

7 Eventually, as the pressure continues to rise the pocket valves at the base of the pulmonary artery and the aorta are forced open and blood is pumped out of the heart.

8 The pulmonary artery directs blood to the pulmonary circuit and the aorta directs blood to the systemic (body) circuit.

The effects of exercise, diet, smoking and stress on the circulatory system

The heart is no different from any other muscular organ in that exercise will make it more efficient and increase its size. This means that the heart can beat less frequently and still pump the same amount of blood.

The heart muscle is supplied by two coronary arteries. Blood delivers oxygen and glucose, which are essential for muscular contraction. Blockage of these vessels can starve the heart muscle of oxygen and glucose. This leads to coronary heart disease and possible death.

Three risk factors known to be associated with cardiovascular disease (CV disease) are:

1 diet; **2** raised blood pressure; and **3** smoking.

A diet involving high levels of **saturated fats** (typically animal fats) and **cholesterol** is particularly likely to increase the risk of CV disease. **High blood pressure** makes the heart work harder. It is common in middle-aged and older people and may be made worse by smoking, drinking too much alcohol, lack of exercise and too much stress.

Q17 Can you suggest why fats and oils prepared from plant material are thought to be better for you than animal fats?

15 Blood and lymph vessels

In this unit you will learn the answers to these questions:
- How does blood get to all parts of the body?
- Why does it make sense that some of the blood vessels leak?
- What is the lymphatic system?
- Why are there three types of blood vessel?

Every living cell needs a supply of raw materials to stay alive. These are delivered to the cells via the blood. Blood carrying the raw materials is pumped to each organ in an **artery**. The arteries get smaller in diameter the closer they get to the cells. Each tissue has a system of finely branched **arterioles** (small arteries). Cells produce waste products and heat during metabolism. These are removed by the blood leaving the area. Blood is taken away from the cells in **venules** (small veins) and returned to the heart by large **veins**.

Why do capillaries leak?

For the transport system to be effective, there must be an opportunity for materials to 'get on' and 'get off'. The exchange of materials takes place in very small blood vessels called **capillaries**. Capillaries form the link between **arterioles** and **venules**. Here a fluid leaks into the spaces around the cells. **Plasma** leaks out of the capillaries and bathes the tissues, and so is called **tissue fluid**. Most of the tissue fluid is water, but it contains the materials that the cells need. It also takes away materials the cells need to get rid of.

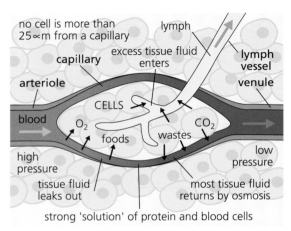

Fig 1 The relationship between blood, tissue fluid, cells and lymph

The **lymph system** is a system of fine tubes found amongst the tissues of the body. The lacteals in the villi (see Unit 12) are one exmple. Small lymph tubes join others to form large lymph ducts. The largest duct connects with the blood system through the main vein of the left arm. Here the excess tissue fluid, which has collected in the lymph system, is returned to the blood.

Blood leaving the heart in the **aorta** will be under very high pressure. The pressure is strong enough to take the blood out to all the organs of the body. Each time the heart contracts, a surge of high pressure passes along the

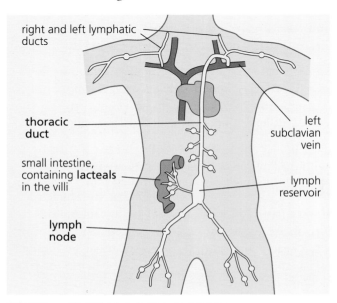

Fig 2 The lymphatic system in Man

arteries. It is this wave of pressure we recognise and record when we take someone's **pulse**. The pressure in the left ventricle is big enough to force the blood through not only the arteries, but also through the capillaries and veins, and so return the blood to the heart. The blood pressure gets lower the further the blood travels away from the heart. Getting the blood through the capillary networks, in particular, results in a large drop in blood pressure. Our upright habit is another factor which affects getting blood back to the heart. Being upright means that for most of the time most of the organs are lower than the heart. Blood returning to the heart in the veins must therefore overcome gravity too. Veins have **valves** in them. These prevent the blood draining down, back towards the tissues it has left.

Ideas and evidence

Harvey (1616) correctly deduced that blood circulated continuously around the body through arteries and veins, with the heart acting as a pump. His theory was not widely accepted at the time. Malpighi (1661) observed and reported the presence of capillaries in lung tissue.

How did Malpighi's research enable Harvey's theory to gain wider acceptance?

Arteries, veins and capillaries show adaptations to the functions which they have to carry out. The table in Fig 3 summarises the differences between the structure of an artery and the structure of a vein.

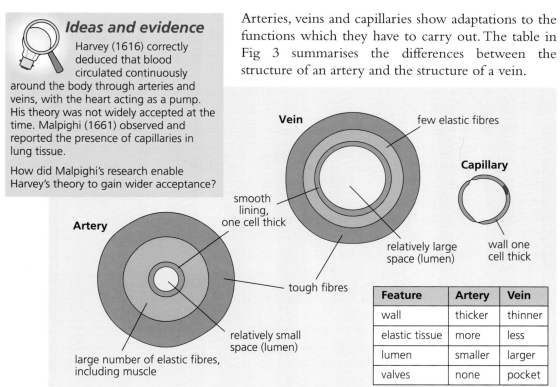

Feature	Artery	Vein
wall	thicker	thinner
elastic tissue	more	less
lumen	smaller	larger
valves	none	pocket

Fig 3 *Cross-sections of an artery, vein and capillary*

The wall of a capillary is only one cell thick. There are spaces between some adjacent cells in the wall. This arrangement allows tissue fluid to escape readily but retains most of the larger structures present in the blood. White blood cells (phagocytes, see Unit 30), however, can squeeze through the gaps and escape from the capillaries. Soluble materials can be removed from or added to the tissue fluid before it passes back into the blood capillaries.

Q1 What are arterioles and venules?

Q2 How does the pressure of the blood change as it goes around the body?

Q3 Why are valves necessary in veins but not in arteries?

16 Composition and functions of blood

In this unit you will learn the answers to these questions:
- **What is blood?**
- **How is its work load divided up?**

Fig 1 shows whole human blood before and after having been spun in a centrifuge. The centrifuged blood shows that whole blood includes a straw-coloured liquid. This liquid component is called **plasma**. The heavier part, which has ended up at the bottom, includes the **blood cells** that were suspended in the plasma. Fig 2 shows a colour photomicrograph of a blood smear.

Fig 1a Whole blood

Fig 1b Whole blood after centrifugation

You should be able to recognise three types of cells and some small fragments called **platelets**. There are **red blood cells** and two types of **white blood cells** (**phagocytes** and **lymphocytes**).

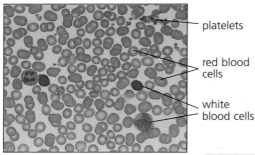
Fig 2 False-colour photomicrograph of a blood smear, showing red blood cells, white blood cells and platelets

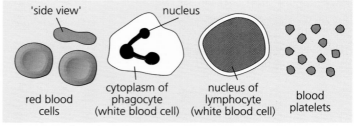
Fig 3 Blood cells and platelets

Q1 What are the names of the three types of blood cell visible in the blood smear?

Q2 Give four ways, other than colour, in which the white cells and the red cells differ.

Plasma

Materials are transported around the body in the blood. Most materials are transported in solution. The plasma acts as both the solvent and the transport medium.

All respiring cells require **glucose**. They will produce **carbon dioxide** as a waste. The plasma delivers glucose from the **liver** to all respiring cells in the body. It removes the carbon dioxide produced in respiration, and takes it to the **lungs** for excretion. **Urea** produced in the liver cells is transported to the **kidneys** where it is filtered out of the plasma for loss as a component of urine. The liver is extremely active chemically and generates **heat** in the process. The heat is distributed around the body in the plasma. Excess heat is taken to the skin surface, where it escapes. The table gives examples of materials transported in the plasma.

Transported in plasma	From	To
carbon dioxide	all cells	lungs
urea	liver	kidneys
products of digestion	small intestine (ileum)	all tissues
hormones	endocrine glands	target cells
heat	all cells – liver and muscles in particular	all parts of the body

Red blood cells

You will have noticed in the photomicrograph of the blood smear (Fig 2) that there are more red blood cells than white blood cells. (This assumes that the blood smear is a representative sample.) There are about 5.5 million red blood cells in each cubic centimetre of blood in a healthy adult. Red blood cells transport **oxygen** to respiring cells. The red cells contain a red pigment called **haemoglobin**. Haemoglobin combines with oxygen to form **oxyhaemoglobin**. The combination is only a temporary one. Whether or not the oxygen stays combined with the haemoglobin depends on the oxygen levels around the red blood cell.

high oxygen availability

oxygen + haemoglobin ⇌ oxyhaemoglobin

low oxygen availability

If the red blood cell is in an area where there is a lot of oxygen it combines with the pigment to form oxyhaemoglobin. In an area where oxygen is scarce or in great demand, oxyhaemoglobin releases the oxygen it is carrying.

Q3 Suggest one area in the body where there is likely to be a lot of 'free' oxygen around.

Q4 Suggest where in the body there is likely to be a constant demand for oxygen and consequently little, if any, 'free' oxygen around.

Q5 Explain why blood travelling in the pulmonary vein is likely to have more oxyhaemoglobin in it than the blood travelling in the pulmonary artery.

The red blood cell – a specialist

The red blood cell offers an opportunity to explore how cells are specialised to carry out a particular function. As you have seen earlier in this unit, the red blood cell's function is to absorb, carry and release oxygen. Mature red blood cells have no nucleus. The whole cell is filled with the pigment haemoglobin, thus carrying as much as possible. The critical process in the way the cell works is the diffusion of oxygen from one side of the cell membrane to the other. The membrane is very thin and is permeable to oxygen. Red blood cells are biconcave discs, thus offering a very large surface area through which oxygen can diffuse. They are relatively small and flexible and this allows them to penetrate and pass through even the smallest capillaries.

White blood cells

There are two main types of white blood cells. They do different jobs. **Phagocytes** take in bacteria and cell debris ('rubbish'). **Lymphocytes** make antibodies. Both play an important part in dealing with disease organisms (pathogens) which enter the bloodstream (see Unit 30).

Blood platelets

Damaged cells release a chemical which starts a chain of reactions leading to the formation of a blood clot. Blood platelets are involved in this process (see Unit 30).

17 Breathing

In this unit you will learn the answers to these questions:
- What's inside the chest?
- How do we get air in and out of our lungs?
- In what way is the air breathed out different from the air breathed in?
- How long can you hold your breath?

Structure of the thorax

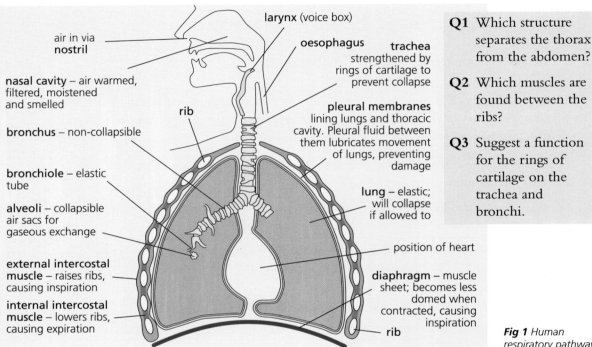

larynx (voice box)

air in via nostril

oesophagus

trachea strengthened by rings of cartilage to prevent collapse

nasal cavity – air warmed, filtered, moistened and smelled

rib

pleural membranes lining lungs and thoracic cavity. Pleural fluid between them lubricates movement of lungs, preventing damage

bronchus – non-collapsible

bronchiole – elastic tube

lung – elastic; will collapse if allowed to

alveoli – collapsible air sacs for gaseous exchange

position of heart

external intercostal muscle – raises ribs, causing inspiration

diaphragm – muscle sheet; becomes less domed when contracted, causing inspiration

internal intercostal muscle – lowers ribs, causing expiration

rib

Fig 1 Human respiratory pathway

Q1 Which structure separates the thorax from the abdomen?

Q2 Which muscles are found between the ribs?

Q3 Suggest a function for the rings of cartilage on the trachea and bronchi.

The mechanism of breathing

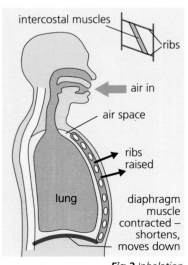

intercostal muscles

ribs

air in

air space

ribs raised

lung

diaphragm muscle contracted – shortens, moves down

Fig 2 Inhalation

The ribs and sternum are raised in order to inflate the lungs. This movement is brought about by the contraction of the **external intercostal muscles**. The **diaphragm** is a tough, fibrous sheet. It forms the floor of the cavity of the thorax. Muscles are arranged around its margin. These contract and gain leverage over the stomach and other abdominal organs. This action flattens the diaphragm. The change in position of the rib cage and diaphragm makes the volume of the thorax bigger. As a result the air pressure inside the thorax is lowered. The air space inside the lungs connects with the atmosphere outside the body. Because of the drop in pressure described above, the pressure outside the body is, at this point, greater than that in the air space of the lungs. Air therefore moves in to inflate the lungs in order to balance up the pressure difference. The person breathes in (**inhalation**).

Breathing out (**exhalation**) results from reversing the actions needed to bring air in. The ribs and sternum are lowered by contraction of the **internal intercostal muscles**. These movements are helped, in humans, by the ribcage dropping under the influence of gravity. The diaphragm muscles relax. The resistance offered by the abdominal organs pushes the diaphragm back into its more dome-shaped position. The change in position of the walls and floor of the thorax reduces the volume of the thorax. Pressure inside the thorax rises above atmospheric pressure. The difference in pressure results in air being squeezed out of the lungs, through the air passages and into the atmosphere.

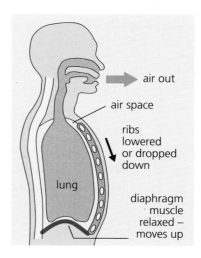

Fig 3 Exhalation

air out

air space

ribs lowered or dropped down

lung

diaphragm muscle relaxed – moves up

Composition of inhaled and exhaled air

Air enters the lungs to provide a source of **oxygen** for the process of respiration. Air leaving the lungs will have had the respiratory waste **carbon dioxide** added to it. This is excreted when the air is exhaled. The **water** content of the atmosphere varies but, because of the moisture inside the lungs, air leaving the body tends to have a higher water content than when it went in. The gas with the largest percentage by volume in inhaled air is **nitrogen**. Nitrogen is a gas which the body does not use. The nitrogen breathed in is breathed out. The table shows the approximate percentage by volume of gases inhaled and exhaled.

ICT Extra!

Link humidity and oxygen sensors to a computer to monitor changes in the composition of re-breathed air.

	Inhaled	Exhaled	Approx. change
oxygen	21%	17%	20% decrease
carbon dioxide	0.04%	4%	100-fold increase
nitrogen	79%	79%	nil

Q4 Which gas is retained by the body?

Q5 What is the change in composition for oxygen and carbon dioxide during breathing?

Q6 Suggest another way in which air breathed out is likely to differ from inhaled air.

Control of breathing

As you know, it is possible to hold your breath for only a short time. You soon have to breathe in, whether you want to or not. Some mechanism overrides your decision not to breathe. The basic rhythm of breathing in and breathing out is maintained automatically. Its control centre is in part of the brain. The part of the brain involved is called the **medulla oblongata**. Cells there are particularly sensitive to changes in the concentration of carbon dioxide in the blood. When the level rises, even slightly, the muscles associated with breathing are instructed to contract more often. As a result the rate and the depth of breathing increases until the extra carbon dioxide is excreted and the blood carbon dioxide concentration returns to 'normal'. Lactic acid has a similar effect on rate of breathing because it changes the blood pH.

Fig 4 Snake divers can hold their breath for a long time

18 Gas exchange and lung structure

In this unit you will learn the answers to these questions:
- How do the lungs work?
- What makes the lungs good at their job?
- How does smoking affect the way the lungs work?
- What is the link between smoking and lung cancer?

Air enters the body through the mouth or the nose. The **trachea** (windpipe) carries air towards the lungs. It divides into two smaller tubes, called the left and right **bronchi** (singular, bronchus). These supply air to the left and right lungs, respectively. The air passages in the lungs form a branched system, which can be likened to the branches of a tree (the **bronchial tree**). The tubes get smaller and smaller in diameter after each division. The smallest branches eventually form dead ends. The tubes between the bronchi and the dead ends are called **bronchioles**. At the dead ends are inflated structures, **air sacs**, known as **alveoli** (see Fig 1 of Unit 17, and Fig 1 of this unit).

Adaptations to promote efficient gas exchange

The branched arrangement of the bronchial tree results in a **large internal surface area**. It has been estimated that this surface, in an adult, is approximately equal to the surface area of a tennis court. Cells lining the air passages are adapted to produce **mucus** which keeps their surfaces moist. The air sacs are very **thin–walled**. Lung tissue has a very **rich supply of blood capillaries**, which are positioned very close to the walls of the air sacs. These factors, working together, provide a very efficient system for the exchange of gas.

Air entering the system through the nose passes into spaces in the bones of the face, where it is warmed. Mucus traps dust particles and other microscopic structures, including bacteria and fungal spores. The mixture of mucus and particles is moved to the back of the throat by microscopic, hair-like structures called **cilia**. It is usually swallowed. When the mucus enters the stomach the acid kills the bacteria and spores.

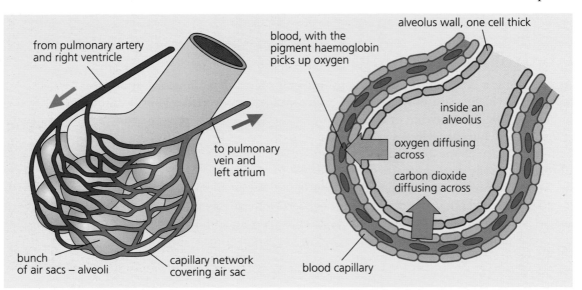

Fig 1a The blood supply to air sacs

Fig 1b Detailed section of one air sac

The cells lining the trachea also produce mucus. They, too, have cilia projecting from their outer surface into the air passage and they have a similar function. Together, the mucus and cilia help to clean the air before it reaches the deeper parts of the lungs. As a result, fewer bacteria and other disease-causing organisms are likely to enter the lungs and do damage.

Effects of smoking on the gas exchange system

Smoke is a complicated mixture of chemicals. The main ingredients which affect gas exchange, however, are **tars** and **carbon monoxide**. The cilia present in the air passages are paralysed by the tars in tobacco smoke (see Fig 2b). This means that mucus containing bacteria and airborne particles is allowed to remain in the system. This leads to respiratory disorders such as **bronchitis**. Tars also damage the walls of the alveoli, causing a disease called **emphysema**. This dramatically reduces the surface area available for gas exchange.

Carbon monoxide combines with haemoglobin. It forms **carboxyhaemoglobin**, which does not break down. As a result, anything up to 15% of the haemoglobin carried by the red blood cells of a smoker can be unavailable for the transport of oxygen. Carbon monoxide also has an effect on 'passive smokers'.

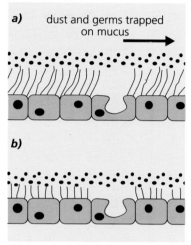

Fig 2a *Normal healthy ciliated cells*
b Ciliated cells of a smoker

Smoking and lung cancer

Cancers arise when the normal pattern of cell division is upset. Cells sometimes divide and increase in number in an uncontrolled way. This leads to the formation of masses of cells, called **tumours**. Tumours which continue to divide and spread are said to be **malignant**. There is considerable evidence to suggest that tobacco smoke encourages the development of tumours. Tobacco smoke therefore must contain **carcinogens** – cancer-inducing agents. The cells lining the air passages are particularly susceptible to tumour development. As a result, by far the commonest form of lung cancer is bronchial cancer.

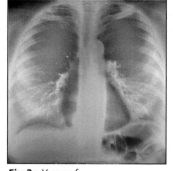

Fig 3a *X-ray of healthy lung*

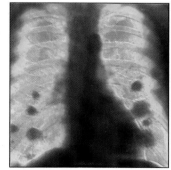

Fig 3b *X-ray of cancerous lung*

ICT Extra!

Use the Internet to search for data on the effects of smoking on human health.

Q1 List four features of lung tissue which enable gas exchange to be efficient.

Q2 What does mucus do in the breathing system?

Q3 What are cilia?

Q4 Name two harmful chemicals in tobacco smoke.

19 Aerobic respiration

In this unit you will learn the answers to these questions:
- Why do we need energy?
- How do we get energy from food?
- What is 'aerobic' respiration?

Living things need a supply of energy to get things done. Energy is obtained from food materials. The release of energy from food is called **respiration**. It goes on in every living cell. The molecules in food have energy 'locked' in their bonds. It is this energy which is made available to a living cell by respiration. The energy is used to make **adenosine triphosphate** (**ATP**). ATP is then used as an 'energy currency' to 'pay' for those changes in a cell which require energy.

Energy released from food is used in many ways. Four examples are listed below.

1 Controlled movement involving **muscular contraction** requires ATP. Figs 1, 2 and 3 show situations where a lot of energy is required.

2 Most muscles have to be stimulated by **nerve impulses** before they will contract. An active nerve cell uses up energy when it transmits such impulses.

Fig 1 Sporting activity requires much energy

Fig 2 Cheetahs can reach speeds of 70 mph over short distances

Fig 3 Terns regularly fly 22 000 miles each year when migrating

3 Some of the energy from food is not locked into ATP but is released as **heat**. This may be used to help maintain body temperature; as in mammals, for example.

4 Plants use ATP in order to absorb ions from the soil by **active transport** mechanisms (see Unit 4).

Some organisms require a constant supply of oxygen in order to respire efficiently. These organisms are respiring aerobically – a process which requires oxygen. **Aerobic respiration** can be compared to the process of burning. Both processes need a fuel and a supply of oxygen. Burning and respiration both produce wastes. The waste products of respiration are **carbon dioxide** and **water**. These wastes are also produced by burning, but burning often produces additional material, seen as smoke. The energy released by burning is released as heat and light. Respiration releases energy as heat, but some of the energy is locked into chemical compounds, as described earlier in this unit.

The table compares aerobic respiration and burning.

Aerobic respiration involves many steps controlled by enzymes (see Unit 98).

Aerobic respiration	Burning
uses food containing carbon, e.g. glucose	uses fuel containing carbon, e.g. coal
uses oxygen	uses oxygen
produces carbon dioxide and water as wastes	produces carbon dioxide and water as wastes
releases energy; some as heat, some locked up in ATP	releases energy; most as heat, some as light

Aerobic respiration can be summarised by the following word equation.

sugar + oxygen ➡ carbon dioxide + water + energy

Glucose is the sugar most frequently used in respiration. Glucose has the formula $C_6H_{12}O_6$. Oxygen is carried to the respiring cells of mammals by the haemoglobin in red blood cells (see Unit 16). Glucose is carried in solution in the plasma.

Fig 4 Aerobic fitness improves the supply of oxygen and glucose to respiring cells

Q1 How do you think 'aerobics' makes someone fitter?

Q2 Why is 'aerobics' such an appropriate name for the type of exercise shown in Fig 4?

20 Anaerobic respiration

In this unit you will learn the answers to these questions:
- What is anaerobic respiration?
- How can energy be released without oxygen?
- How can sprinters run without breathing?
- What has respiration got to do with beer and bread?

Some organisms can survive for a long time without a supply of oxygen. They obtain their energy by an anaerobic process – **anaerobic respiration**.

Human muscle tissue relies on anaerobic respiration when the blood supply can no longer deliver enough oxygen to keep aerobic respiration going. This can only be a temporary option for humans, for example, during exercise.

When oxygen is absent, the reactions in respiration form different products, with the release of only a small quantity of energy. The type of cell respiring determines which products are formed. Cells in plant tissues have enzymes which convert sugar to **ethanol** in the absence of oxygen. Animal cells, for example, muscle cells, produce **lactic acid** instead.

Muscle cells

Anaerobic respiration in human muscle cells can be summarised by the following word equation.

glucose ➡ lactic acid + a little energy

Muscle cells will continue to contract even when the circulatory system and breathing mechanisms cannot keep pace with the demand for oxygen. Under these conditions the muscles continue to work, but get their ATP anaerobically. As a result, the lactic acid concentration increases in the muscles and blood. The build up of lactic acid during exercise is what causes **muscle fatigue**. Muscle cells which have obtained ATP in this way are said to have generated an '**oxygen debt**'. The lactic acid is oxidised later. This is why the breathing rate and the pulse rate stay high after the period of exercise has ended. The removal of lactic acid needs extra oxygen.

Fig 1 Exercise can lead to anaerobic respiration

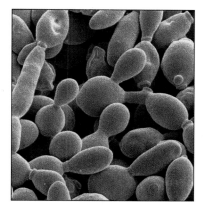

Yeast cells

Anaerobic respiration in yeast cells can be summarised by the following word equation.

glucose ➡ ethanol + carbon dioxide + a little energy

The waste products of anaerobic respiration by yeast have been put to use for many hundreds, if not thousands, of years. Two main uses have been the production of alcoholic drinks by a fermentation process and the baking of bread.

Fig 2 Budding yeast cells

Fermentation

A sweet mixture, called wort, is made from warm water and ground malt. The wort is fermented using special strains of yeast. The yeast converts sugars into alcohol and carbon dioxide. The product is some form of beer. The length of fermentation, the strain of yeast used and the nature and quantity of additives provide the distinctive flavours associated with different types of beers.

Fig 3 A variety of beers and wines

Wine makers take advantage of natural yeasts which are found on the skins of grapes. Different types of grape are associated with different growing areas. The ferment produced by crushed grapes produces wines of different, distinctive flavours peculiar to the region.

Fig 4 Freshly baked loaves

ICT Extra!

Link pH and temperature probes to data-logging equipment to monitor fermentation, e.g. fermentation of milk by lactobacilli.

Baking

The baking industry takes advantage of the carbon dioxide produced in anaerobic respiration. The gas given off by respiring yeast cells gets trapped in the warm dough. Pockets of gas cause the dough to inflate, expand and rise. The resulting bread has a much lighter texture. Some people find this more pleasing to eat than unleavened bread which has not had yeast added. The alcohol, produced while the yeast is making the dough rise, is destroyed during the baking process.

Q1 What are the products of anaerobic respiration in muscle cells?

Q2 What does the term 'oxygen debt' mean?

Q3 What is 'wort'?

Q4 What is the difference between the amount of energy produced by anaerobic respiration compared to aerobic respiration?

21 Senses

In this unit you will learn the answers to these questions:
- What changes are there in our environment?
- How do we recognise change?
- How do nerves work?

The environment in which an animal lives is constantly changing. One obvious change is from darkness to light at the start of the day. Sound levels change. Temperature may increase or decrease. Factors such as light, sound, pressure, temperature and chemicals are known as **stimuli**. Some of the changes may be advantageous, and some disadvantageous. It is important that animals are aware of these changes if they are to live successfully.

Humans have **sense organs**. Sense organs are **receptors**, which are sensitive to stimuli. Receptors have evolved which are sensitive to particular stimuli. The table shows the names of some human receptors and the stimuli to which they are sensitive.

Sense organs / receptors	Stimuli	Sense
eye	light	sight
ear	sound	hearing
	gravity	balance
nose	chemicals	smell
tongue	chemicals	taste
skin	pressure, heat, texture	touch

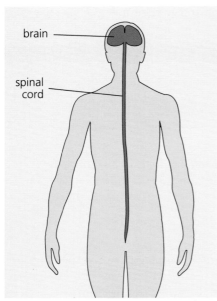

Fig 2 The central nervous system (CNS) of Man

All receptors do basically the same thing. The energy which they receive as a stimulus is converted into a nerve impulse. For example, the energy received by light-sensitive cells of the eye causes nerve impulses to be generated in the optic nerve. In the same way, sound waves entering the ear canal produce vibrations. These vibrations, in turn, lead to the production of nerve impulses in the auditory nerve.

Fig 1 shows the structure of a **neurone** (nerve cell) which could link a sense organ to

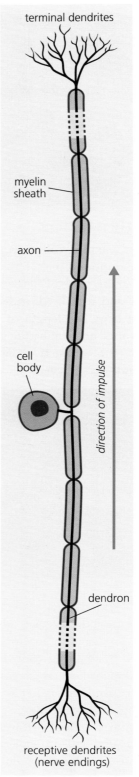

Fig 1 A sensory neurone

the brain. There are several different types of neurones in the human body. The one shown in Fig 1 is called a **sensory neurone**. It carries impulses towards the **central nervous system** (brain and spinal cord). Neurones which form links between the central nervous system, leading impulses away from the central nervous system to muscles and other organs, are called **motor neurones**.

Part of the cytoplasm of the cell body of a neurone is extended into a long fibre. This enables an individual cell to carry messages over a long distance. For example, a motor neurone could link the base of the spinal cord to one of the toes of the foot. A single neurone may therefore be a metre in length.

Fig 3

Other extensions to the cell body provide points where external stimuli are registered, or points where impulses from other neurones in the system are received and passed on. The **myelin sheath** insulates the neurone from other neurones close to it. This ensures that messages get to the right place.

The photograph (Fig 3) shows the start of a race. The changes taking place in the environment and the body of one of the sprinters can be used to illustrate the sequence of events leading up to her response to the starter's gun. The sound waves enter her ears when the gun goes off. The energy of the vibrations that are set up in her ears is converted to nerve impulses in the neurones of the auditory nerve. The auditory nerve conducts the impulses to the brain cells. A chain of impulses then passes through the neurones of the brain, finally passing out of the brain along motor neurones to the muscles of the body. The muscles contract and the athlete moves out of the starting blocks.

ICT Extra!

Use spreadsheets to process data collected from experiments on reaction time.

The sequence involved in a typical nervous response may be summarised as follows:

stimulus ➡ receptor ➡ sensory neurones ➡ CNS (coordinator) ➡ motor neurones ➡ effector ➡ response

Q1 How is it possible that only a few neurones are needed to form a nerve link between the brain and the foot?

Q2 Can you think of any changes you are aware of that are not mentioned in the first paragraph of this unit?

22 Structure and function of the eye

In this unit you will learn the answers to these questions:

- Where does the light go after it enters the eye?
- The lens of a camera moves in and out. Why do our lenses not do the same?
- How do our eyes cope with bright and dim light?

Only the front part of the eye is visible. Most of the eyeball is hidden, set back in a cup-shaped pocket, the eye orbit, in the bone of the skull. The **orbits** provide protection for the eyes. The eyes are further protected by pairs of **lids** and by **tears**, which together cleanse the surface of the eye exposed to the outside world.

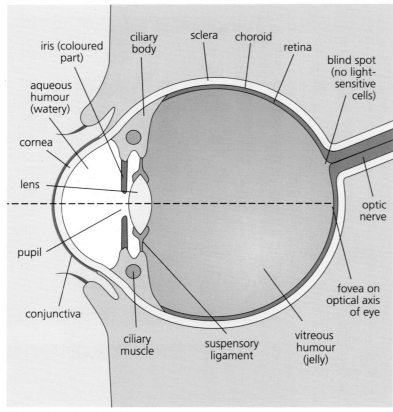

Fig 1 Section through a human eye

Light enters the eye, passing first through the **conjunctiva** and then the **cornea**. The cornea changes the direction of the light rays, bending them to a point on the **retina**. This is where most of the focusing takes place. On the way to the retina the light passes through a **lens**, which makes fine adjustments to the focusing. The image is focused onto light-sensitive cells in the retina. The most sensitive area of the retina is the **fovea**, which has a very high density of these cells. The retinal cells change the light energy into nerve impulses. The nerve impulses pass from the eye to the brain in neurones of the **optic nerve**.

The healthy human eye is able to cope with a wide variety of light intensities and with moving objects. Any change in position will mean that the object is at a different distance from the retina. It will go out of focus. Therefore the eye must make focusing adjustments continuously. The same will be true, obviously, if the viewer stops looking at a nearby object and looks at something further away.

The lens in the human eye is flexible. It is this property which allows adjustments to be made to enable a clear image to be focused on the retina. The lens is suspended by ligaments attached to the **ciliary body** (see Fig 1). When the muscles of the ciliary body contract, the ligaments go slack and the lens has a smaller diameter and is fatter. A fatter, more convex, lens bends the light more and is therefore more effective at focusing light from nearer objects. A thinner lens results when the suspensory ligaments go tight as the ciliary body muscles relax. A thinner lens bends light less and is more effective when the viewer looks at more distant objects. The process which brings about changes in the shape of the lens is called **accommodation**.

The photographs in Fig 3 show the human eye in two different light intensities. The coloured part of the eye, the **iris**, has pigments in it. The pigments absorb the light which falls on them. Light enters the eye through a gap in the iris called the **pupil**. The size of the pupil determines the amount of light which is allowed to enter the eye. Too much light could damage the sensitive retina, while too little would produce a poor image.

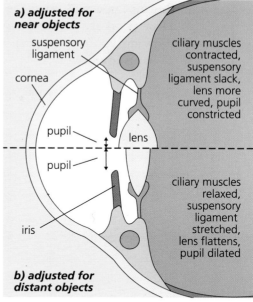

Fig 2 Accommodation

In everyday life we move into and out of areas of different light intensity. The eye can adapt to these changes automatically. A reflex system (see Unit 23) operates to adjust to these differences. There are two sets of muscles in the iris. These are **circular** and **radial** muscles. When the circular muscles contract, the iris is constricted. This causes the pupil to decrease in size and become smaller in diameter (see Fig 3a). These muscles are activated when the light intensity increases. The radial muscles operate when the light intensity decreases. Their role is to draw back the margin of the iris, dilating the pupil by increasing its diameter. In this way more light is allowed to enter the eye (see Fig 3b).

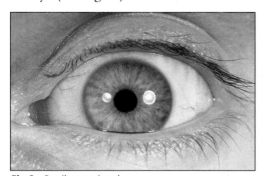

Fig 3a Pupil constricted

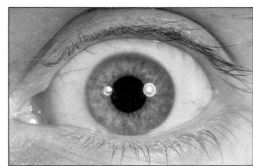

Fig 3b Pupil dilated

There are two types of light-sensitive cells in the retina. These are **rods** and **cones**. The rods are sensitive to low light intensity, but only allow black and white vision. The cones provide detail and colour vision, but only in bright light. The cones are concentrated in the fovea, with the rods distributed throughout the rest of the retina.

Q1 In which tissue is light converted into nerve impulses?

Q2 What is the most sensitive region of the retina called?

Q3 What do rods and cones do?

23 Reflex action

In this unit you will learn the answers to these questions:
- How good are your reactions?
- How do you react so fast without thinking?
- What is a reflex arc?

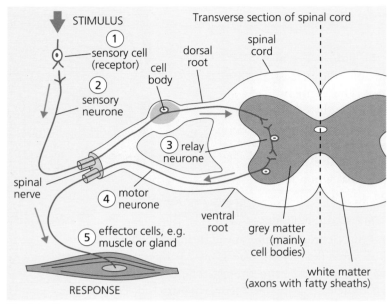

Fig 1 A reflex arc

When you touch something hot you remove your hand very quickly. Fig 1 shows the pathway in the nervous system which allows you to do this. It is described as a **reflex arc**.

Heat stimulates **pain receptors** in the skin. Nerve impulses pass along the neurones in a **sensory nerve**. The sensory nerve enters the **spinal cord** through the dorsal (upper) root of the spinal nerve involved. In the grey matter of the spinal cord the information is passed onto other **intermediate** or **relay neurones**. Their job is to pass the information to a third group of neurones. Some of these 'inform' the brain, others bring about an immediate response in **effectors** (muscles or glands). **Motor neurones** leave the central nervous system via the ventral (lower) root of the spinal nerve. These neurones conduct impulses which stimulate muscles to contract. Contraction of the muscles brings about the **response** – in this case an immediate withdrawal of the hand.

The three types of neurones involved work together to bring about the response. However, they are not in direct contact with each other. There is a microscopic space between the ends of each pair of communicating neurones in the arc. The space is called a **synapse** (see Fig 2). When impulses arrive at the end of a neurone, chemical changes take place in the synapse. The chemicals released into the space stimulate the next neurone in line to produce impulses. These changes allow a continuous flow of messages to take place.

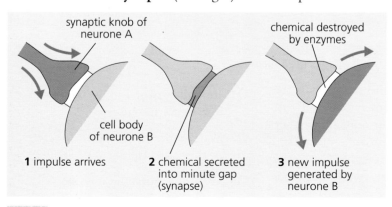

Fig 2 Passing a 'message' at a synapse

Despite the brain being 'informed' of the pain and danger to the hand, the muscular response is **automatic**. This saves valuable time and prevents unnecessary damage. You do not have to think about what to do. This is a common feature of reflex action. You may be consciously aware of the action or response, but you have not had to take decisions about whether, or how, to deal with the situation.

Most of us are aware of the uncontrollable, explosive sneeze we experience when we get something like pepper or pollen in our nose. Not all reflex actions are as obvious as sneezing (Fig 3) or the protective reflex described in Fig 1. Fig 4 shows a doctor checking for another reflex. The iris muscles, described in Unit 22, normally respond to stimulation by a reflex, in order to protect the eye from dangerous light intensities.

Fig 3 Sneezing

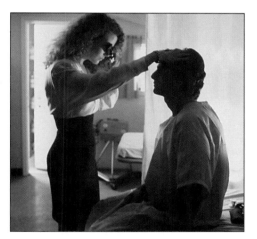

Fig 4 Doctor checking the iris reflex

The table summarises some human reflexes.

Reflex	Stimulus	Value
blinking	foreign particle on cornea	protects the eye
iris	change in light intensity	protects retina
sneezing	foreign particles in nose	protects the lungs
coughing	irritants in throat	protects the lungs
knee-jerk	tendons below knee cap stretched	maintains posture (balance)
withdrawal	pain	withdraws limb from danger

Fig 5 shows a doctor carrying out one of the routine tests which follow the birth of a baby. The fact that the baby has probably only just been born tells you something else about reflexes. Unlike much of our behaviour, most reflexes are not learned. You are born with them.

Fig 5 Checking the grip of a newborn baby

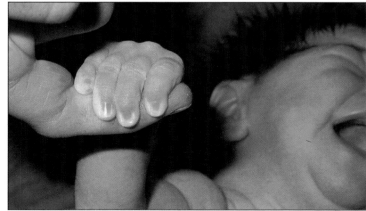

Q1 List the structures in the order in which they appear in a reflex arc. Start with 'stimulus' and end with 'response'.

Q2 What do **a)** sensory neurones and **b)** intermediate neurones do in a reflex arc?

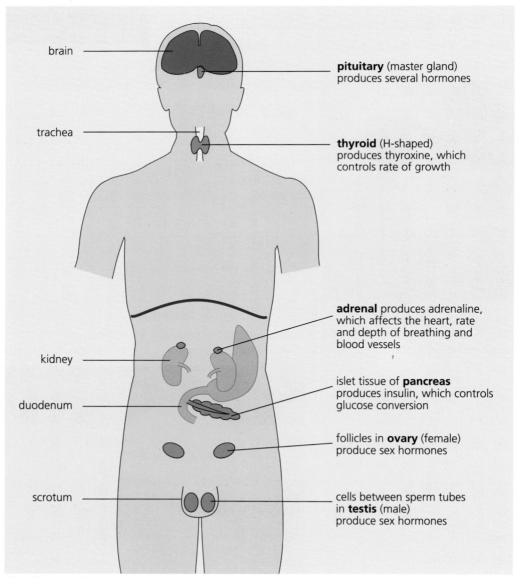# 24 Hormonal control

In this unit you will learn the answers to these questions:
■ What are chemical messages?
■ How do cells 'know' who the message is for?
■ What are the differences between hormonal and nervous control?

Units 21, 22 and 23 have introduced the way in which the nervous system is involved in getting things in the human body to work together. There are some processes which are coordinated in a different way. These are processes which involve **hormones**.

> **Hormones are chemicals produced by specialised glands in the body.**

There are basically two types of glands in the human body, ducted and ductless.

brain

pituitary (master gland) produces several hormones

trachea

thyroid (H-shaped) produces thyroxine, which controls rate of growth

adrenal produces adrenaline, which affects the heart, rate and depth of breathing and blood vessels

kidney

islet tissue of **pancreas** produces insulin, which controls glucose conversion

duodenum

follicles in **ovary** (female) produce sex hormones

scrotum

cells between sperm tubes in **testis** (male) produce sex hormones

Fig 1 The endocrine system in humans

The tear gland (see Unit 22) secretes a fluid used to cleanse the surface of the eye. Tears are delivered to the surface of the eye by the tear duct. The tear gland is described as a **ducted gland** or **exocrine gland**. The secretions of ducted glands are delivered directly to the specific place where they will have their effect. The table lists various human ducted glands.

Gland	Ducted to
tear	eye
salivary	mouth
liver (bile)	duodenum
pancreas	duodenum
sweat	skin surface

There are some glands in the body whose secretions are not delivered in this way. These are the **ductless glands** or **endocrine glands**, which produce hormones. Fig 1 shows the position of the major hormone glands of the body.

Hormones are chemical messengers which bring about changes in the body, often some distance from where they are made. In some cases their effect is felt throughout the whole body. Endocrine glands have very well developed blood supplies. Their tissues have very close contact with the circulatory system, with large numbers of blood capillaries. Secretions from endocrine cells pass into the blood plasma. They are distributed throughout the body, being delivered to every cell having access to blood.

The blood plasma will therefore carry hormones produced by a whole range of endocrine glands (see Fig 1). This is obviously different from the very specific, directness of nervous communication. A neurone will carry impulses from one specific point to another. Despite the 'blanket distribution' of hormones by the bloodstream, each hormone affects particular cells, and influences one or more specific processes.

Cells affected by a specific hormone are described as **target cells**. The surface membrane of a target cell can 'recognise' the hormone and interact with it. Consequently only those cells that can do this are affected by the hormone.

The table summarises the differences between hormonal and nervous coordination.

Feature	Hormonal	Nervous
message	chemical	electrical
source	hormone gland	receptor
aimed at	target cells	effector
carried by	bloodstream	neurone
speed	slow	very fast
duration	long lasting	brief
precision	general effect	very specific

Q1 What arrangement makes it certain that bile produced in the liver cells (see Units 10 and 11) gets to where it is needed?

Q2 Why do you think the term 'blanket distribution' was used to describe the way hormones are delivered?

Q3 What is a 'target cell'?

25 Insulin and sex hormones

In this unit you will learn the answers to these questions:
■ What does insulin do?
■ What do the sex hormones do?

Insulin, glucagon and the control of blood glucose levels

Glucose absorbed from the gut in the small intestine enters the bloodstream. The concentration of **glucose** in the bloodstream will therefore *increase* some time after a meal. Living cells use blood glucose as a raw material for respiration and other metabolic processes. These processes will *decrease* the concentration of blood glucose. Cells will only work properly if the glucose concentration is kept around a particular level. It is important therefore that some controlling mechanism exists to take account of the variations described above.

The **liver** plays a role in the regulation of blood glucose concentration. The **pancreas** is also involved. Liver cells absorb glucose from the blood and convert it to **glycogen**, for storage in the liver. Glycogen can be broken down later to re-form glucose, which can be returned to the bloodstream.

The basic pattern of meal times may be fairly constant, but the carbohydrate content of the food is likely to vary. Similarly, day-to-day physical activities, which demand glucose as a source of energy, are also fairly constant. No two days are likely to be exactly the same, however, and there will be occasions when more food is eaten or more exercise taken. These variations have to be monitored, and the conversion of glucose to glycogen, and vice versa, adjusted. The liver cells must be informed of the changing levels of glucose occurring in the rest of the body.

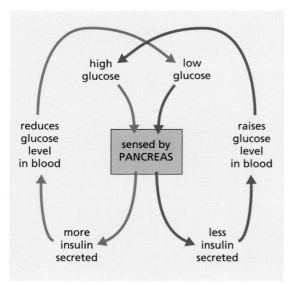

Fig 1 *How feedback controls blood glucose level; if too little insulin is secreted, glucose level is not self-correcting and diabetes results (see Unit 27)*

When blood glucose concentration rises above normal (about 0.1%), a particular group of cells in the pancreas register the increase, and secrete the hormone **insulin** (see Unit 24). Insulin causes liver cells to convert soluble glucose to insoluble glycogen. Blood glucose concentration falls. If blood glucose concentration falls below the normal level, this too is registered by the cells of the pancreas and insulin secretion is reduced. When blood glucose concentration falls below 0.1% different cells in the pancreas produce a second hormone, called **glucagon,** which encourages liver cells to convert glycogen to glucose. This action restores the blood glucose concentration to its normal level.

Q1 What parts do the liver and pancreas play in controlling blood glucose level?

Sex hormones

Testosterone is one of a group of hormones called **androgens**. They are the **male sex hormones**. Testosterone is produced by cells in the **testes**. This hormone is responsible for controlling the development of the male sex organs and later, at puberty, the **male secondary sexual characteristics**, e.g. production of sperm.

The **female sex hormones** are the **oestrogens** and **progesterone**. The **ovaries** secrete oestrogens. Oestrogens are responsible for controlling the development of the **female secondary sexual characteristics**, e.g. production of eggs. Progesterone maintains the lining of the uterus in a state suitable to support a developing embryo.

The sequence of events from the production of one egg to the next is called the **oestrus cycle**. Each month in sexually mature females, an **egg follicle** starts to develop in an ovary. The follicle produces the egg and secretes **oestrogen**. This affects the lining of the uterus. It becomes thicker and spongy, and numerous blood vessels grow into it. Once the egg is released from the follicle at **ovulation** the follicle becomes the **corpus luteum**. Oestrogen production then stops and the corpus luteum secretes a second hormone, **progesterone**.

If an embryo buries itself in the lining of the uterus a **placenta** forms. Production of progesterone is then taken over by the placenta. Continued production of progesterone has two effects. Firstly, the lining of the uterus is not shed and, secondly, no further ovulation takes place.

If the egg released is not fertilised then blood progesterone level drops and the lining of the uterus breaks down. The tissues are lost, via the vagina, over a period of about five days with a considerable amount of blood. This is **menstruation**. The **menstrual cycle** (see Fig 2) usually takes about twenty-eight days but can vary considerably from one person to another.

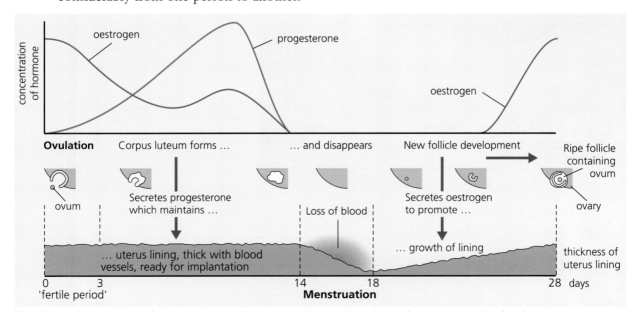

Fig 2 The main changes in the ovary, uterus and hormones which take place during the oestrus/menstrual cycle

26 Medical uses of hormones

In this unit you will learn the answers to these questions:
- What happens when the message goes wrong?
- How can we change the message?
- Why do some people have to inject insulin?
- How can someone who cannot conceive be helped to have babies?

Hormonal treatment and diabetes

Some people do not produce enough insulin. Specific cells in the pancreas do not work properly. This may be a condition which they have inherited or may be a result of the ageing process. As a result they are unable to control the amount of glucose in circulation in their bloodstream. This results in a condition called **diabetes** and the individuals who experience it are described as **diabetics**. It is important that blood glucose levels are kept around the normal level of 0.1% otherwise cells suffer damage. Brain cells in particular are sensitive to blood glucose levels. Failure to put right the deficiency of insulin can eventually result in coma and death.

Diabetes is not curable but is controllable. Since the problem results from too much glucose one approach is to be careful about how much carbohydrate is taken in the **diet**. Foods containing high levels of 'potential' sugar must be kept to a minimum. Another way is to raise the level of insulin artificially.

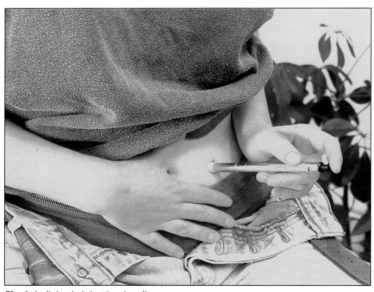

Fig 1 A diabetic injecting insulin

Insulin is a protein. This poses a problem. It can not be taken by mouth because it would be digested with other proteins in the gut. As a result **insulin** has to be **injected**. It is difficult to know exactly how much to inject because the demand for glucose varies (see Unit 25). Too much insulin leads to a glucose level which is too low for normal function. However, diabetics learn to recognise symptoms which suggest their glucose levels are too low. They can make up for this by taking extra sugar, either as sugar itself or by eating food rich in sugar.

Other, more novel, ways to approach the problem of diabetes are being researched:

1 transplantation of the whole pancreas;

2 living insulin-secreting cells have been isolated from a normal pancreas and introduced into the abdominal cavity, where they continued to secrete insulin.

Hormonal treatment and human fertility

Female sex hormones control egg production and the menstrual cycle (see Unit 25). The **contraceptive pill** contains chemicals identical to these hormones. Consequently when the pill is taken the ovaries and uterus behave according to this artificial hormonal programme.

Correct doses of the appropriate hormone, progesterone, will inhibit ovulation. Therefore sexual intercourse cannot result in pregnancy, as there is no egg to be fertilised.

Some couples who wish to have children are biologically unable to do so. This may be for a variety of reasons. Here sex hormones may be used to encourage the chance of conception, not to prevent it.

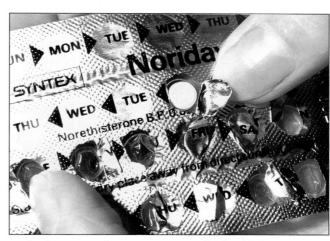

Fig 2 *A pack of contraceptive pills, showing the bubblepack day sequence*

One possibility is that the woman is not producing enough eggs on a regular basis. In these circumstances hormones can be used to treat infertility. Hormones are given to the woman to increase egg production. This increases the probability of fertilisation taking place.

In some cases the man does not produce enough sperms or they may not be strong enough to reach the oviduct where fertilisation usually takes place. One approach to overcome this problem is to arrange for the fertilisation to take place outside the woman's body. This is called **in vitro fertilisation** (**IVF**). The woman is given hormones to encourage her ovaries to produce eggs. Often the amount given means that many eggs are released. These are collected from the ovary during a surgical operation. The eggs are placed in a sterile Petri dish and the man's sperms are added to them. If the process is successful several embryos may be formed. The woman is given hormones to make her uterus receptive to the embryos and they are surgically introduced into the uterus. Here, if the transplant is successful, they will develop in the normal way. Several embryos may be transplanted to make sure that at least one will be successful. Sometimes this can lead to multiple births.

ICT Extra!

Produce a DTP report or a Powerpoint presentation on 'Hormonal treatment and human fertility'.

Q1 Why do some people have to inject insulin?

Q2 How does a contraceptive pill work?

Q3 Suggest two biological reasons why some couples who want to have children cannot.

Q4 What do the initials IVF stand for?

Q5 Which hormones might be used to make an IVF patient's uterus receptive to embryos?

27 Homeostasis

In this unit you will learn the answers to these questions:
- Why is it important for the surroundings of a cell to stay the same?
- How is a 'steady state' achieved by humans?

Living things have two environments, one external and the other internal. The external environment is provided by their surroundings. The internal environment surrounds each and every one of their cells.

Fig 1a *External environment*

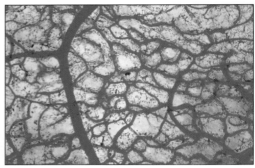

Fig 1b *Internal environment*

Living cells put constant demands on their immediate environment. In humans this will be the **tissue fluid**. Cell activity will lead to a constant need for raw materials. These are removed from the tissue fluid. The cell produces materials which it releases into the tissue fluid. If the cell is to continue to work efficiently, and in a balanced way, the raw materials, such as glucose and oxygen, must be available in the correct concentrations at all times. Similarly, waste products, such as carbon dioxide and urea must be removed. The heat generated must be distributed and the appropriate temperature maintained. Other factors in the tissue fluid which may vary are water content and salt concentration.

The ability, which complex animals such as humans have, to control their internal environment is described as **homeostasis**.

> **Homeostasis is the maintenance of a steady state, providing a stable environment for cells.**

Animals which can do this effectively are at a considerable advantage. They can live in places where factors in the external environment vary considerably. Animals unable to cope with these fluctuations could not survive.

Fig 2a *Penguins in Antarctica*

Fig 2b *Gerbil in a desert*

Tissue fluid is formed when blood plasma leaks from capillaries. Therefore the systems in the human body which are active in homeostasis often operate by regulating the composition of the blood. (Units 17, 25, 28 and 29 will look specifically at those systems which are involved in the control of levels of blood glucose, oxygen, water and salt, and temperature.)

One idea which needs to be explored, before looking at particular examples of homeostasis, is the principle of **negative feedback**. An electric oven is a good example of a non-biological system which will help to explain how negative feedback works.

Temperature is the factor to be kept constant. The oven includes a **sensor**, a device which, in this case, monitors temperature. This sensor is a thermostat. A thermostat works as a switch which is sensitive to temperature. The temperature source is a heating element which increases the temperature of the oven.

The oven temperature is set. Electricity flows through the element and raises the temperature in the oven. This continues until the thermostat 'senses' that the oven has gone above the set temperature. At this point the electricity supply to the heating element is switched off. The oven then cools. If the temperature of the oven drops below the setting, the thermostat 'senses' this and switches the element back on. Repeated 'sensings' keep the oven at a fairly stable temperature. The thermostat allows the temperature to rise to a point where the system switches itself off. By increasing the temperature, the source eventually causes its own shut-down. This is why it is described as negative feedback.

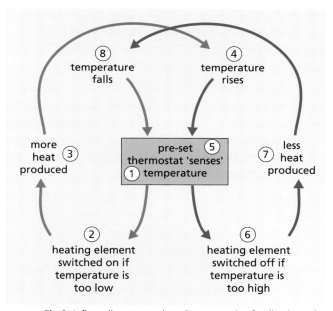

Fig 3 A flow diagram to show how negative feedback works. Start with ① and follow the numbered sequence

The main systems which maintain a constant internal environment are summarised in the table. To get more detailed information about these systems you will need to read Units 17, 25, 28 and 29.

Homeostatic process controlling	Structures involved
body temperature	part of the brain and skin
water balance	part of the brain and kidney
breathing rate	part of the brain and muscles associated with breathing
blood glucose concentration	liver and pancreas

Q1 What other non-biological negative feedback systems have you in your home?

Q2 How does the environment around a cell get 'out of balance'?

28 The kidney and homeostasis

In this unit you will learn the answers to these questions:
■ What jobs do kidneys do?
■ How do kidneys work as excretory organs?
■ How do we maintain our water balance?

The chemical processes going on in living things add up to what is called metabolism. Metabolism includes those chemical processes which build things up and those which break things down.

metabolism = anabolism + catabolism
(building up)   (breaking down)

Metabolic processes produce wastes. Some of these are poisonous. All of them become dangerous if they are allowed to build up to levels above the needs of the organism.

Humans eat **protein** as part of a balanced diet. Usually we consume more than enough amino acids to meet our needs. Any amino acids left over, called **excess amino acids**, can not be stored because of their nitrogen. Excess amino acids are broken down in the **liver**. The nitrogen is removed from the amino acid molecule and built into molecules of another compound, called **urea**. Urea is poisonous and cannot be allowed to accumulate in the body. It has to be removed from the body. It has to be **excreted**.

Urea dissolves in the tissue fluid surrounding the liver cells. The **kidney** is the organ which can remove urea and other excretory materials from the blood plasma. Blood is delivered to each kidney through a **renal artery** and taken away in a **renal vein**. The human kidney contains a very large number of blood capillaries and tiny tubes called **nephrons** (see Figs 1 and 2).

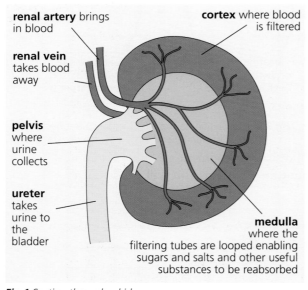

renal artery brings in blood

cortex where blood is filtered

renal vein takes blood away

pelvis where urine collects

ureter takes urine to the bladder

medulla where the filtering tubes are looped enabling sugars and salts and other useful substances to be reabsorbed

Fig 1 *Section through a kidney*

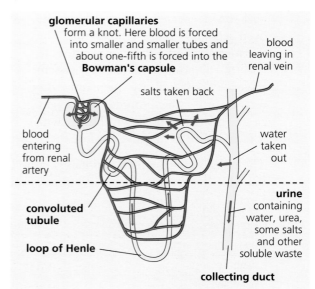

glomerular capillaries form a knot. Here blood is forced into smaller and smaller tubes and about one-fifth is forced into the **Bowman's capsule**

blood leaving in renal vein

salts taken back

blood entering from renal artery

water taken out

convoluted tubule

loop of Henle

urine containing water, urea, some salts and other soluble waste

collecting duct

Fig 2 *Diagram of a single kidney tubule (nephron)*

The nephron has four recognisable regions. These are the Bowman's capsule, the first convoluted tubule, the loop of Henle and the second convoluted tubule. The nephrons finally join together to form a collecting duct.

Capillaries supply blood to each nephron from the renal artery and return 'treated' blood to the renal vein. The table summarises what the nephron does to the blood plasma delivered to it.

Substance	Plasma/%	Urine/%
water	90	95
protein	8	0
glucose	0.1	0
urea	0.03	2
other nitrogen-containing wastes	0.005	0.13
sodium ions	0.32	0.34
other inorganic ions	0.40	2.53

The capillaries do two things. They deliver blood to the Bowman's capsule and they reabsorb materials from the tubule.

Blood is filtered in the Bowman's capsule and materials passing down the tubule are reabsorbed or not, depending on the needs of the body. The end product is **urine**. Urine passes from each nephron into a collecting duct. It eventually leaves the kidney along a **ureter** for storage in the **bladder**.

The capillaries associated with the Bowman's capsule form a capillary knot called a **glomerulus**. The arteriole (see Unit 15) delivering blood to the Bowman's capsule has a wider bore than the venule leaving it. As a result the pressure, generated by the heart, builds up. The blood plasma is separated from the space in the Bowman's capsule by thin membranes. These membranes are selectively permeable. Cells and large molecules such as blood proteins cannot pass through the membranes. Smaller molecules such as water, salt, glucose and urea do. The pressure build-up, described above, forces these molecules through the membranes into the space inside the nephron. Since the process involves separating molecules and ions it is sometimes described as **ultrafiltration**.

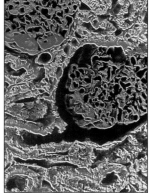

Fig 3 Photomicrograph of a Bowman's capsule

At this stage in the process urea has been separated from the blood. Unfortunately it is accompanied by many molecules the body cannot afford to lose. Glucose and the correct amount of salt and water are essential if the body is to work properly. These must be removed from the urine and put back into the blood. This is achieved in the other parts of the tubule which are in close contact with the blood capillary network. This is **selective reabsorption**.

Water enters the body as part of the food. Respiration produces water as a waste product. Water loss occurs every time air is exhaled. It is also lost as sweat, tears, in faeces and as a major component of urine. A homeostatic system operates to achieve balance and thus avoid dehydration.

Cells in the brain called **osmoreceptors** act as **sensors**. They monitor how much water is in the blood plasma. When the water content drops below the normal concentration, a hormone, **antidiuretic hormone** (**ADH**), is released into the bloodstream. Three things happen as a result. The kidney tubules reabsorb more water, less urine is produced and the amount of water in the plasma increases. The osmoreceptors register the increase. Negative feedback (see Unit 27) causes less ADH to be released, less water is reabsorbed, more urine is produced and the amount of water in the plasma decreases. In this way the body restores the water balance.

Q1 List the jobs carried out by the kidney.

29 Skin and homeostasis

In this unit you will learn the answers to these questions:
- Which structures in the skin are involved in temperature control?
- How does the skin help to keep our body temperature constant?

The body temperature of a healthy human being remains fairly constant, at about 37°C. This is so despite temperature changes in both our external and internal environments. This phenomenon is described as **homiothermy** (same heat). Humans are said to be **homiothermic** animals.

Heat gain and heat loss

The way the human body gains and loses heat is summarised in the table.

The **core** (internal) **temperature** of a human being must be maintained around 37°C if a stable environment is to exist for chemical change and an efficient metabolism. Control systems exist to try to achieve this.

Heat gain	Heat loss
cell respiration	breathing out warmed air
muscle activity	lost with urine and faeces
eating hot food and drink	heat loss by conduction and radiation
Sun's heat absorbed	

Skin and temperature balance

The skin is the main surface of contact which humans have with their environment. As a result the skin plays a very important part in heat exchange. It shows several features which are involved in maintaining a constant body temperature.

The skin is involved in temperature control in three main ways. These are:

1 the ability to raise and lower hairs; **2** sweating; and **3** variable blood flow.

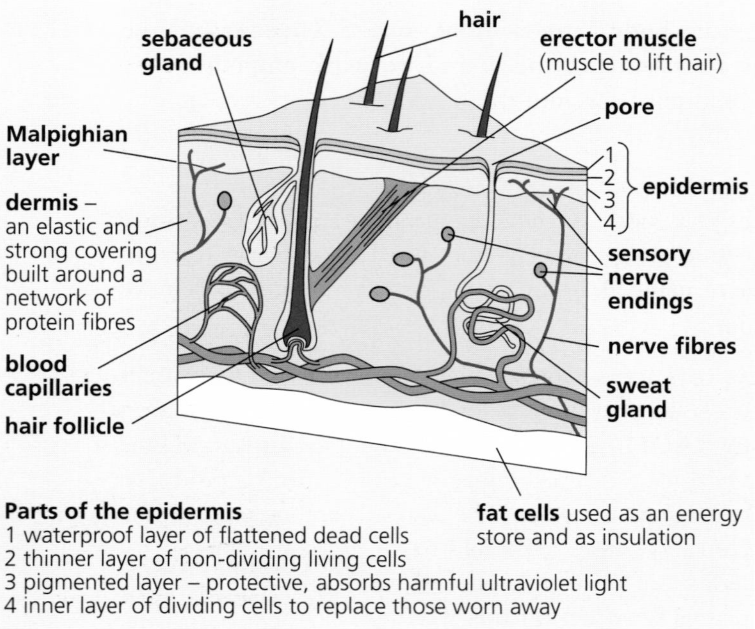

Malpighian layer

dermis – an elastic and strong covering built around a network of protein fibres

blood capillaries

hair follicle

sebaceous gland

hair

erector muscle (muscle to lift hair)

pore

1
2
3
4 } epidermis

sensory nerve endings

nerve fibres

sweat gland

fat cells used as an energy store and as insulation

Parts of the epidermis
1 waterproof layer of flattened dead cells
2 thinner layer of non-dividing living cells
3 pigmented layer – protective, absorbs harmful ultraviolet light
4 inner layer of dividing cells to replace those worn away

Fig 1 Diagram of a wedge of skin showing its internal structure

Hairs in the skin can be raised or lowered. Each hair has an **erector muscle** attached near to its base. When the muscle contracts the hair is pulled away from the surface of the skin and made to stand up, not necessarily at right angles to it, but in that direction. Raised hairs trap a thicker layer of air. Conduction of heat from the skin to this layer of air warms it up. The layer of air then acts as insulation and reduces further heat loss. This occurs when body temperature is falling. Hairs remain flat, close to the surface, when the body temperature is steady or increasing. The insulating layer is reduced in thickness and therefore does not hinder heat loss to the environment.

Sweat glands secrete sweat onto the surface of the skin. Sweat contains water. Water in the sweat evaporates from the skin's surface (**sweating**). The water molecules have to gain a certain amount of energy before they will evaporate. Sweat absorbs heat energy from the skin. When the sweat has absorbed enough heat, the water evaporates, taking away the heat energy in the process. Therefore the skin and underlying tissues cool down.

When the temperature of the body rises above the desired norm (around 37°C) the sweat glands secrete more sweat onto the surface of the skin. This leads to greater heat loss than normal and helps to restore the temperature balance. Lower than normal body temperatures will be accompanied by a reduction in the quantity of sweat secreted. Less heat is then lost by this means.

Blood flowing through capillaries in the skin is brought close to the surface. Heat is lost from the blood to the surrounding tissue and ultimately, on land, to the air. Any increase in **blood flow** through this region will be followed by increased heat loss. Conversely, decreased blood flow will be accompanied by a reduction in heat loss at the skin's surface.

Fig 2 Exercise raises body temperature causing sweating and reddening of the skin

When the body temperature exceeds the norm, changes occur in the capillaries in the skin. They get wider in bore, becoming dilated. This process is called **vasodilation**. **Vasoconstriction** is observed when the body temperature falls. Here the capillaries are constricted and show a narrowing of the bore. Vasodilation leads to increased flow of blood near to the skin's surface and encourages heat loss. Vasoconstriction decreases blood flow and consequently leads to reduced heat loss.

Body temperature is **monitored** by particular cells in the brain (in the **hypothalamus**). These are sensitive to very small changes in blood temperature. When stimulated, they set up changes in the nervous system which lead to the starting up of the processes described above.

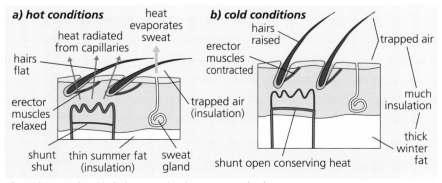

a) hot conditions
heat radiated from capillaries
heat evaporates sweat
hairs flat
erector muscles relaxed
trapped air (insulation)
shunt shut
thin summer fat (insulation)
sweat gland

b) cold conditions
hairs raised
erector muscles contracted
trapped air
much insulation
thick winter fat
shunt open conserving heat

Q1 List those structures in the skin which are involved in temperature control.

Q2 Where are the feedback sensors for temperature regulation found?

Fig 3 The way the skin helps to maintain a constant body temperature

30 Defence mechanisms of the body

In this unit you will learn the answers to these questions:
- What part does the skin play in defence?
- How do blood clots form?
- What do tears and stomach acid have in common?
- How do white blood cells help to keep us healthy?

Fig 1 in Unit 29 shows the structure of the human skin. The **epidermis** is relatively tough and provides an almost continuous **barrier** for the surface of the body. Unless it is punctured, for example by a cut, then it stops things getting into the tissues of the body. Bacteria and other microscopic disease-causing organisms (pathogens) are kept out.

When the skin surface is broken the blood starts to **clot** in the damaged region. When the clot has formed, further loss of blood is kept to a minimum and the wound is sealed. This process also prevents the entry of potential pathogens. The clot acts as a barrier against infection.

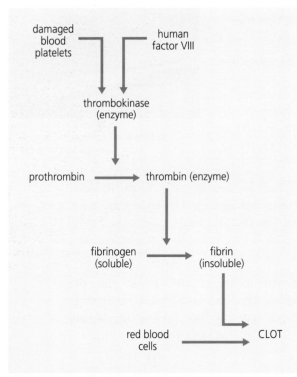

Fig 1 Summary of the clotting mechanism

Blood **platelets** start off the clotting mechanism. This mechanism attempts to prevent further loss of blood and prevent the entry of pathogens. When the skin is cut or firmly knocked the breakdown of platelets results in the release of an enzyme called **thrombokinase** into the blood. This acts on **prothrombin**, which is present in the plasma at all times, changing it to **thrombin**. Thrombin promotes the change of **fibrinogen** to **fibrin**. Fibrinogen is a soluble fibrous protein which is also present in the plasma at all times. Fibrin forms the clot. The clot is composed of a mesh of fibrin in which red blood cells become trapped. As the clot dries it forms a **scab**, thus preventing both further loss of blood and the entry of potential pathogens. **New skin** is formed under the scab, and the scab eventually falls away.

The sequence of events is summarised in the flow diagram shown in Fig 1.

Some parts of the body have a surface layer which is less effective at keeping bacteria out. One area which is vulnerable is the eye. The part of the eye which is in contact with air, the **conjunctiva**, is particularly delicate (see Unit 22). Bacterial infection here may cause 'red eye' or **conjunctivitis**. This is usually prevented by **tears** which wash away dust and potential pathogens before infection can take place. Tears also contain a substance which kills bacteria called **lysozyme**. Occasionally, however, abrasive particles get into the eye and the damage they cause may allow bacteria to become established.

Bacteria and other pathogens can enter the body through the mouth and nose. These are trapped in the **mucus** secreted into the air passages by cells lining the tubes

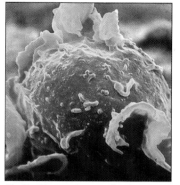

(see Unit 18). The mucus is swallowed and enters the stomach. **Hydrochloric acid** secreted by cells in the lining of the stomach kill the bacteria.

White blood cells are involved in protecting the body against infection. There are two types of white cells involved. These are **phagocytes** and **lymphocytes**.

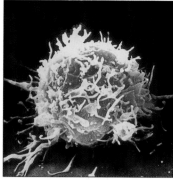

Fig 2a *Photomicrograph of a phagocyte*

Fig 2b *Photomicrograph of a lymphocyte*

Phagocytes protect the body by eating bacteria. The feeding process in phagocytes is described as **phagocytosis** (see Fig 3).

1 Phagocytes squeeze out of capillaries and feed on bacteria and cell 'rubbish' on the surface of cells.

2 A food vacuole is formed inside a phagocyte when its surface membrane comes into contact with bacteria.

3 The bacteria are taken into the food vacuole (engulfed).

4 The phagocyte secretes enzymes into the food vacuole.

5 The bacteria are killed and digested.

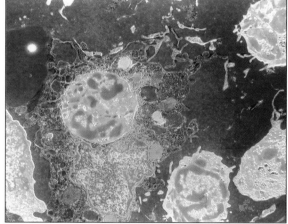

Fig 3 *Phagocytosis – the phagocyte (green/blue) has engulfed a bacterium (shown in pink)*

Lymphocytes are white cells which are active when 'foreign material' gets into the blood system. Pathogens, such as bacteria and viruses, are recognised as 'foreign material' and the lymphocytes react to them. Pathogens contain substances called **antigens**. When lymphocytes come into contact with antigens they produce molecules called **antibodies**.

There are several ways in which antibodies work in an attempt to protect the body from infection. Some antibodies kill bacteria directly by causing them to burst. Others affect the surface membrane of the bacteria causing them to clump together. This may make it easier for phagocytes to kill them. Some pathogens release poisonous chemicals into the plasma. These are called **toxins**. The antibodies which protect humans against these are **antitoxins**. These combine with the toxins and neutralise their effects.

Q1 How does the skin protect us from infection?

Q2 Name two body secretions which are protective.

Q3 What is phagocytosis?

Q4 What are antibodies?

31 Effects of solvent and drug abuse

In this unit you will learn the answers to these questions:
- What are drugs and solvents?
- How do they harm us?
- Drinking or driving?

What are drugs and organic solvents?

Drugs may be chemicals obtained from living things which affect the behaviour and function of a human being or other animal. They may also be chemicals made to copy the effects of these naturally occurring substances. These are synthetic drugs.

Organic solvents are chemicals made to dissolve substances which are not soluble in water.

Examples of drugs and organic solvents are listed in the table. Except for alcohol, caffeine and tobacco (nicotine), all of the drugs listed in the table are illegal.

Alcohol and tobacco are readily available drugs, but there are laws which restrict their sale. Anybody can buy drinks containing caffeine, i.e. tea, coffee, cola and cocoa. Many homes will have some alcohol around and many people smoke. Few people think of these three substances as drugs. Most houses will have a selection of household products of the type listed as organic solvents. It is far more likely, therefore, that if abuse is going to occur, then it is legal drugs and solvents that are abused, and not substances such as cocaine and heroin.

Drugs	Organic solvents, used in
alcohol	butane gas
amphetamine	correcting fluid
caffeine	dry-cleaning fluid
cannabis	hairspray
cocaine	oven-cleaners
ecstasy	paintspray
heroin	pain-relieving sprays
LSD	polishes
tobacco (nicotine)	solvent-based glues
valium	

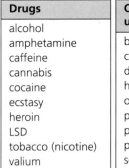

ICT Extra!

Use spreadsheets to process data collected from experiments on the effect of caffeine on pulse rate.

What are the possible effects of drug and solvent abuse on the body?

The effects vary, but all drugs affect the way the user feels and behaves, by altering the way the brain and nerves work. In addition to these effects, there are physical effects which can arise from long-term substance abuse. Some of the effects of drug and solvent abuse are listed in the following table.

Substance	Effect
alcohol	liver cells are poisoned and the liver does not work efficiently; brain damage
nicotine	destroys cells lining the air passages; bronchitis; increases risk of cancer (see Unit 19)
solvents	damage to brain, liver, kidneys and heart; some solvents have cancer-causing properties

Drinking or driving?

When a drink containing alcohol is swallowed the alcohol enters the bloodstream. It starts to go into the blood in the mouth and throat. A larger part enters the circulation from the stomach, and any which is left is absorbed in the small intestine. The amount of alcohol in the blood, the blood alcohol concentration (BAC), can be measured.

Different drinks have different amounts of alcohol in them. The effect they are likely to have on the body can be measured according to the number of units of alcohol they contain. One **unit of alcohol** will on average raise the BAC by **15 mg per 100 ml of blood.**

Fig 1 Examples of drinks that each contain one unit of alcohol

Alcohol is a **sedative** drug. It makes you feel sleepy, your reactions slow down and your ability to take decisions is not as good. There is an obvious danger if a person drinks and then drives. The **legal driving limit** in the UK is a BAC of **80 mg per 100 ml of blood**. Alcohol escapes from the blood passing through the lungs. A driver can be breath tested to see how much alcohol the exhaled air has in it. This indicates whether the driver's BAC is likely to be 'over the limit' or not.

Drugs used wrongly are harmful and often **habit forming**. When the body gets used to having a drug in the circulation the person has to keep taking it otherwise they suffer from **withdrawal symptoms**. A person in this state is **physically dependent** on the drug. Withdrawal symptoms are what happens, the way the body reacts, when the cells are not getting the drug any more. Sometimes people think that they need to keep on taking the drug in order to cope with life. This is described as **psychological**

Fig 2 A driver being breathalysed

dependence. One of the many problems linked to drug abuse is that the body's **tolerance** to the drug increases. This means that ever larger 'doses' are needed to get the same effect.

Q1 What is a drug?

Q2 How many units of alcohol are there in two pints of beer?

Q3 What does BAC stand for?

Q4 What is the legal BAC driving limit?

ICT Extra!

Gather information from the Web on the incidence of drink-related accidents or drink-related crime.

32 Photosynthesis and leaf structure

In this unit you will learn the answers to these questions:
- What do plants need to make food?
- What makes leaves good at photosynthesis?

Green plants do not feed in the same way that animals do. Animals take in ready-made food. Plants make their own. They make food by a process known as **photosynthesis**.

Photosynthesis

The raw materials for photosynthesis are **carbon dioxide** and **water**. The energy source used to 'power' this process is **light**.

Plants get the carbon dioxide for photosynthesis from two sources. The carbon dioxide produced in the plant cells as they respire can be used in photosynthesis. This is not enough on its own. Plants take in extra carbon dioxide from the air or water around them. Water is absorbed by the roots of a land plant and transported to the leaves where some of it can be used for photosynthesis (see Unit 38). In the natural world light for photosynthesis comes from the Sun but this is often supplemented by artificial light in commercial practice.

Most plants are green. This is due to the presence of a coloured chemical, a pigment, called **chlorophyll**. Chlorophyll is usually present in the leaves of plants, even when the leaves appear to be a different colour, e.g. copper beech leaves. Chlorophyll is a very important compound. This chemical absorbs light energy and passes it to the process of photosynthesis. Plants which never have any chlorophyll have to feed like animals do, or die.

The fact that most plants appear to be green means that they are reflecting green light. The really important point is that plants are not absorbing green light. This must mean that they are not using the energy from it. White light is made up from the whole spectrum of colours. Some wavelengths of light (colours) are used more effectively in photosynthesis than others.

The plant uses carbon dioxide and water to produce **carbohydrate**. Photosynthesis produces the sugar **glucose**, which is converted into **starch**. The starch is stored for use as and when needed. **Oxygen** is produced as a **waste product**. Oxygen not used by respiration in the plant is released into the environment around the plant.

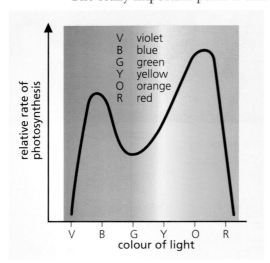

V violet
B blue
G green
Y yellow
O orange
R red

relative rate of photosynthesis

colour of light

Fig 1 The effect of different coloured light on the rate of photosynthesis

The process of photosynthesis can be summarised in a word equation:

$$\text{carbon dioxide} + \text{water} \xrightarrow[\text{chlorophyll}]{\text{light}} \text{glucose} + \text{oxygen}$$

Photosynthesis is carried out by most plants in the leaves. All leaves have the same basic structure. This is shown in Fig 2.

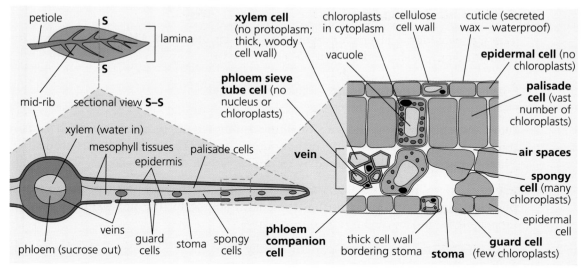

Fig 2 *Leaf structure*

The leaf as an organ for photosynthesis

A leaf shows many adaptations to the process of photosynthesis. It needs to have a **large surface area** in order to absorb the maximum possible amount of light. Most leaves have a large, flat surface to do this. Large numbers of **chloroplasts** containing **chlorophyll** are concentrated in the **palisade mesophyll tissue**, positioned near to the leaf surface.

Carbon dioxide diffuses into the leaf through microscopic pores, known as **stomata**, on the surface of the leaf. The thin walls of the cells of the **spongy mesophyll** offer a large, moist surface for gas exchange. Carbon dioxide dissolves in the water on the gas exchange surface and diffuses to the chloroplasts where photosynthesis takes place. Oxygen, produced during photosynthesis, diffuses out of the leaf along the same pathway but in the opposite direction. Glucose is formed in the chloroplasts. It may be stored as **starch grains** in storage structures in the cell or exported, as sucrose, to other parts of the plant in the **phloem** tissue (see Unit 39). Water is delivered to the leaf in the **xylem** (see Unit 38).

Photosynthesis must involve gas exchange. Any surface which lets in carbon dioxide and lets oxygen out will be permeable to water. This creates water conservation problems. The leaf is adapted to counter this. The **upper epidermis** is covered by a **waterproof**, waxy layer called the **cuticle**. In broad-leaved plants the stomata are concentrated on the lower surface of the leaf and close when water loss gets too high (see Unit 38).

Q1 Name two raw materials for photosynthesis.

Q2 What traps light energy for photosynthesis?

Q3 Which two areas of the spectrum (colours of light) give relatively high rates of photosynthesis?

Q4 Suggest three ways in which leaves are adapted for photosynthesis.

33 Limiting factors and photosynthesis

In this unit you will learn the answers to these questions:
- ■ What keeps photosynthesis in check?
- ■ What is a limiting factor?

The rate at which a plant photosynthesises can be measured. The word equation for photosynthesis, established in Unit 33 is:

$$\text{carbon dioxide} + \text{water} \xrightarrow[\text{chlorophyll}]{\text{light}} \text{glucose} + \text{oxygen}$$

One way of measuring the rate of photosynthesis is to record how much carbon dioxide or water a plant is using, or how much starch or oxygen a plant is producing. Photosynthesis is usually measured by recording carbon dioxide uptake.

Plants need to be in the light for at least part of the day if they are going to photosynthesise. Light is essential as the energy source for the process. If there is no light at all the process will not go on.

It is possible to demonstrate experimentally that plants give out a fairly constant volume of carbon dioxide if they are kept in darkness. Carbon dioxide is produced as a respiratory waste. Measurement of the carbon dioxide released by a plant in darkness will therefore give an indication of its rate of respiration under the controlled, experimental conditions.

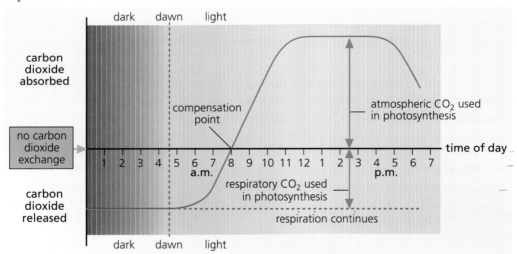

Fig 1 Carbon dioxide exchanged by a plant from midnight until 7 p.m. on a day in summer

Fig 1 shows the sort of results obtained when the carbon dioxide exchange of a plant is measured over the course of a typical summer day. During the hours of darkness a plant gives out carbon dioxide. This will be respiratory carbon dioxide. At dawn the plant starts to give out less carbon dioxide. The plant must respire at all times, therefore, presumably, the carbon dioxide that should be released is being used somewhere else. It will be used for photosynthesis. As the light intensity increases during the morning the amount of carbon dioxide given out decreases to a point where none is exchanged. At this point the carbon dioxide produced by respiration exactly balances the carbon dioxide needed to support photosynthesis. The rate of photosynthesis is equal to the rate of respiration. This point is called the **compensation point**. Photosynthesis has made up for the sugar used in respiration. After this point increasing amounts of sunlight result in increased uptake of carbon dioxide. In other words, the rate of photosynthesis increases with increasing light intensity.

Fig 2 shows a simpler graph of rate of photosynthesis against light intensity. In section A to B (phase I) of the curve in Fig 2, increasing the light intensity increases the rate of photosynthesis. Between B and C (phase II) increasing the light intensity begins to have less effect. After C (phase III) the photosynthetic rate does not change even though the light intensity continues to increase.

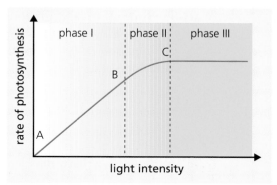

Fig 2 *The relationship between the rate of photosynthesis and light intensity*

During phase I of the above curve, each time the plant is given more light it photosynthesises better. This must mean that the plant's photosynthetic process is being held back, restrained or **limited** by the lack of light. In phase II light is not holding the process back as much. It is not such a **limiting factor**. In phase III light intensity is not limiting the process at all. At those light intensities, it doesn't matter how much light is received by the plant, it doesn't photosynthesise any quicker. Something else must be limiting the photosynthetic rate.

Measuring the effect of carbon dioxide concentration on the photosynthetic rate of plants gives a similar curve. Increasing the concentration of carbon dioxide available to a plant, up to a particular level, gives increased photosynthesis. Beyond that concentration, no further gain is shown.

Carbon dioxide can be a limiting factor for photosynthesis, as can temperature or any other factor involved in the process. For example, magnesium ions will limit photosynthesis if the concentration is too low to make sufficient chlorophyll.

Greenhouse keepers can manage the environment inside a greenhouse. They attempt to get maximum yield from their crop. They can increase the amount of light or carbon dioxide if either are likely to be limiting the growth of their plants.

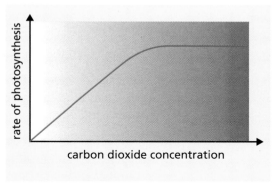

Fig 3 *The relationship between the rate of photosynthesis and carbon dioxide concentration*

Q1 Which factors can be used to measure photosynthesis?

Q2 Name two limiting factors for photosynthesis.

 ICT Extra!

Use modelling software to examine the effect of changing variables on photosynthetic rate.

34 Plant mineral nutrition

In this unit you will learn the answers to these questions:
- Which elements do plants need for healthy growth?
- How do we recognise mineral deficiencies?
- How do farmers improve the mineral content of their land?
- Inorganic or organic fertilisers?

Carbohydrates, **fats** and **proteins** all contain the elements **carbon**, **hydrogen** and **oxygen**. These three groups of compounds, together with **water**, provide most of the matter in the nucleus and cytoplasm of a cell. **Nitrogen**, **phosphorus** and **potassium** are also **essential elements** for plant growth.

Nitrogen is used by plants to make amino acids, proteins and nucleic acids. Deoxyribonucleic acid (DNA) contains the bases adenine, guanine, thymine and cytosine. These organic bases have nitrogen in them and are often called nitrogenous bases.

Phosphorus is used to make nucleic acids. It is also found in the molecule adenosine triphosphate (ATP), which you may have met in Units 19 and 20.

Nutrient	Deficiency symptoms
nitrogen	poor growth – little protoplasm made
sulphur	poor growth – little protoplasm made
calcium	faulty cell division
iron	pale leaves – lack chlorophyll
magnesium	pale leaves – lack chlorophyll
phosphorus	poor growth – lack of ATP for synthesis of protoplasm
potassium	poor growth – dehydration

Potassium plays an important role in the formation of cell membranes.

Sulphur is an important element in some amino acids and the proteins they form.

Magnesium is essential for the manufacture of chlorophyll.

Plants require a whole range of other elements for healthy growth. They are required in very small quantities. The table above shows the names of mineral nutrients required by plants and what happens to the plants if the nutrients are not provided.

The yield which farmers and horticulturists get from their crop plants depends on the health of the plants and the health of the environment in which they grow. Even the healthiest, potentially high-yielding crop will not be a commercial success if one essential mineral nutrient is limiting.

Limiting factors were discussed in Unit 33. Magnesium was given as an example of a factor which limits photosynthesis. If a crop plant is grown in soil with a magnesium deficiency its yield will be reduced and the cash return on the crop unsatisfactory. This is summarised in the flow diagram in Fig 1.

Modern farming practice often involves **monoculture**. Here, one type of crop plant is grown, usually on a very large scale. All the plants are the same. All the plants will put the same demands on the environment. They will all want the same factors, the same resources. It is easy to see how a particular mineral nutrient could become scarce, particularly if the same

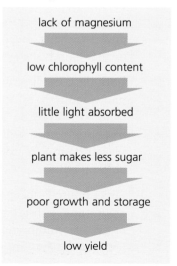

lack of magnesium

low chlorophyll content

little light absorbed

plant makes less sugar

poor growth and storage

low yield

Fig 1 *Magnesium as a limiting factor in the yield of a crop plant*

crop is grown in consecutive years. One mineral nutrient could easily become a limiting factor. This can be avoided by crop rotation, the application of fertilisers or, preferably, both.

Fertilisers

There are two types of fertiliser. **Organic fertilisers** are those produced by animals and plants. These are composts and manures and are often called natural fertilisers. **Inorganic fertilisers** are made by the chemical industry. These are the artificial fertilisers which you may have seen stored in plastic bags with the initials NPK on them. The initials are significant. It means that the users know exactly what they are getting. They

Fig 2 East Anglian 'prairie' – wheat monoculture

are getting a fertiliser which will supply the nutrients nitrogen, phosphorus and potassium. Natural (organic) fertiliser such as manure will also have nitrogen, phosphorus and potassium in it, but not in as concentrated a form. There will be many other things there too, which might not be needed in a particular situation. The table below compares organic and inorganic fertilisers.

Application of fertilisers will allow something approaching maximum yield to be achieved, provided that no other factor is limiting.

There are some problems associated with the use of inorganic, artificial fertilisers. For example, artificial fertilisers do not return to the soil the fibrous material and important organic compounds needed to maintain the physical

Feature	Organic (e.g. farmyard manure)	Inorganic (e.g. artificial fertilisers, NPK pellets)
cost	cheap	expensive
user friendliness	smelly, sticky, bulky	easier to handle, dry powder or pellets
nutrient release	slow	fast
effect on soil structure	good	poor
environmental risk	low	may lead to 'run off' – eutrophication

structure of the soil. A soil's crumb structure can be lost if artificials and only artificials are used continuously. The topsoil can get blown away as dust in extreme cases.

Many artificial fertilisers dissolve quickly. This is a benefit because the crop plants can start to absorb them sooner. This does mean, however, the nutrients are more easily **leached** out of a soil into natural watercourses such as drains, ditches, streams and rivers. Left unchecked, the high levels of nitrogen and phosphorus, entering a stream for example, can lead eventually to its ecosystem being destroyed (see Unit 106). The process during which high levels of nutrients get into water systems in this way is called **eutrophication**. It also means of course that natural sources of water for human consumption are also vulnerable to contamination.

Q1 Name one plant use for each of N, P and K

Q2 What does the term 'monoculture' mean?

Q3 Suggest one way organic fertilisers are better than inorganic fertilisers.

Q4 What are the problems associated with artificial fertilisers?

35 Use of photosynthetic products

In this unit you will learn the answers to these questions:
- What do plants make with the glucose produced by photosynthesis?
- Which plant chemicals do we make use of?

The first products of photosynthesis are **glucose** and **oxygen**. Plant cells can use the glucose and oxygen as raw materials for their respiration. Any oxygen not used in this way is released into the atmosphere. This becomes part of the oxygen reservoir in the atmosphere on which all aerobic, non-photosynthetic organisms depend.

Growth takes place in the shoot and root tips. **Sucrose** formed from glucose in the leaves is transported to the shoot and root tips, where it is used to promote their growth. Leaf and flower buds use the sucrose as a source of energy and as a starting material for the manufacture of other chemicals used to build new cells. Some sugar may end up as **nectar**. Plants which reproduce sexually form **fruits**. Many of these have food reserves built into them. Succulent fruits such as grapes, peaches and tomatoes have food stored in them to act as attractants to aid their dispersal and more particularly the dispersal of the **seeds** inside them. The food stored in a seed supports the embryo.

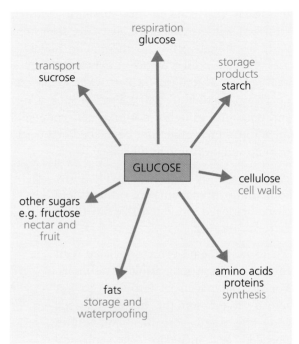

Fig 1 Glucose, made in photosynthesis, is the key to other substances

Potatoes store **starch** in underground stems. A carrot plant stores its reserves in a swollen tap root. Extra carbohydrate produced during the summer by an onion plant ends up at the base of its leaves, causing them to swell up and form a bulb.

Photosynthesis is the single process which builds new organic molecules from carbon dioxide and water. It is the only way in which extra carbon gets fixed into the system (see Unit 52). Each carbon atom found in any other organic molecule, i.e. another carbohydrate, or a fat or a protein, must at some time have been part of a glucose molecule made by photosynthesis. Glucose molecules are the starting material for the manufacture of all other compounds in the plant body. Other elements need to be imported by the plant. For example, nitrogen atoms must be taken in from the environment if the plant is to make amino acids, proteins or nucleic acids.

Chemical pathways exist in plants which enable them to rearrange the atoms of glucose molecules. Different combinations of other elements are added, to produce a huge number of different organic compounds. Humans take advantage of the variety of materials produced by plants. The table shows some of the plant chemicals humans use.

Plant products
beverages, e.g. tea, coffee
cosmetics
drugs
food
food colouring
gums
oils
perfumes
rubber
tannin
textile dyes
timber

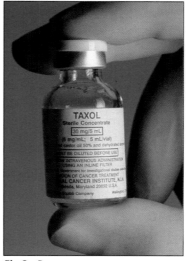
Fig 2a Drugs

Fig 2b Rubber tyres

Fig 2c Coffee

Fig 2d Furniture

Fig 2e Food

Q1 Which carbohydrate is usually transported around a plant?

Q2 Suggest two uses for carbohydrates in plants.

Q3 How do plants make proteins from carbohydrates?

36 Control of plant growth

In this unit you will learn the answers to these questions:
- What are plants sensitive to?
- What do plant hormones do?

The photograph in Fig 1 shows a potted plant which had been left on a window sill for several days. The plant is responding to the **stimulus** of **light**. The shoots appear to 'bend' towards the window. They have not bent. They have grown into that position. The response is a **growth response** called a **tropism**. The light is stronger outside the window and the plant has grown into that position in response to it. It has shown a positive response. It is said to be a positive response because it has grown towards the light. The shoot system is showing **positive phototropism**. Roots, on the other hand, grow away from light and are described as **negatively phototropic**.

Germinating seeds always produce roots which grow away from the soil surface down into the soil. The developing plumule (embryonic shoot) always grows towards the surface of the soil. This time the stimulus is **gravity**. On this occasion the root is showing a positive response because it is growing towards the stimulus. **Roots** are said to be **positively geotropic** (geo-, gravity) and **shoots** are **negatively geotropic**.

Fig 1 Plants 'grow' towards the light

Tropic responses are of benefit to a plant

Roots, by showing a positive geotropic response, grow into a region where there is likely to be more water. They also become embedded in a better position, to anchor the plant.

A phototropic response allows a plant shoot system to grow into a position where it will gain maximum light for photosynthesis. Plants which grow close together are in competition with each other for a variety of factors. An obvious one is light. A plant which is overshadowed by another will not photosynthesise well. It usually responds by growing out of the shaded area into a more brightly lit one. It will grow into a new position to do this. This is what makes it look as though the tissue which was already in place has simply bent. The old tissue however, has to stay where it was originally formed. It will be the new tissue, produced by growth, which creates the bend or curvature.

Plants produce chemicals that regulate growth and development. These substances behave in the way that the hormones found in mammals and other animals do. These are the **plant hormones** or **plant growth substances**.

One group of plant hormones is called **auxins**. Shoots which show the type of growth curvature described above have an uneven distribution of auxins. Auxins are produced in the shoot tip and in a plant evenly lit on all sides the auxin diffuses down the stem evenly. Uneven lighting changes the distribution of auxins in the shoot, with more being found on the shaded side. The growth substance promotes faster growth on the shaded side and as a result that side grows further. Growth curvature is the end result.

Fig 2 *A gardener pinching out the tip of a plant*

Shoot tips produce substances that stunt the growth of side shoots. This is demonstrated when the lead–shoots in a hedge are cut. Removal of the tips removes the source of inhibition and side shoots develop, making the hedge thicken out and become more bushy.

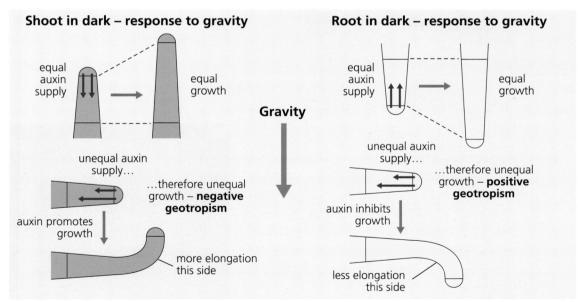

Fig 3 *Geotropism in roots and shoots*

Q1 What is a tropism?

Q2 What does 'positively geotropic' mean?

Q3 In what way does a plant benefit from positive phototropism?

37 Uses of plant hormones

In this unit you will learn the answers to these questions:
- How does rooting powder work?
- What are selective weedkillers?
- How do we grow seedless fruits?

Rooting powders

One way in which gardeners can increase their stock of plants is by means of **stem cuttings**. This method of asexual reproduction, a form of reproduction which does not involve gametes or fertilisation, involves cutting a piece of shoot from a plant and getting the detached piece to grow into a 'new' plant. The cutting must be encouraged to produce roots quickly if it is to survive. One way in which this can be speeded up is to use a plant growth hormone. Before the cutting is potted-up, its base is dipped into a commercially produced **rooting powder** containing **growth-promoting chemicals**. The treated cutting is then inserted into a suitable soil or compost and allowed to develop. The hormones present in the powder promote the production of root tissue from cells present in the cut stem. Roots are formed in this way and the cutting can then absorb water, anchor itself in the soil and become an established plant.

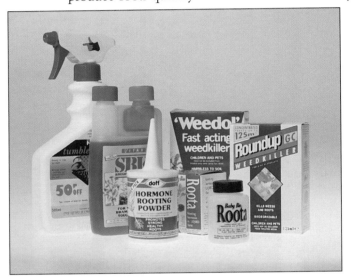

Fig 1 Rooting powders and selective weedkillers

Selective weedkillers

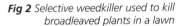

Fig 2 Selective weedkiller used to kill broadleaved plants in a lawn

Herbicides are chemicals which kill plants. Some herbicides kill all the plants they come into contact with. Others only kill some types of plants. This type of herbicide is described as a selective herbicide or, more commonly a '**selective weedkiller**'. Some of them are based on the naturally occurring plant growth substances such as an auxin (see Unit 36). A gardener, wishing to improve the appearance of a lawn by destroying the broad-leaved 'weeds', must kill the weeds but not the grasses. A selective weedkiller will do this (see Fig 2). Cereals, such as wheat and barley,

are narrow-leaved 'grasses' too. Therefore, selective herbicides of this kind have an obvious application, on an agricultural scale, for cereal producers.

Seedless fruit

Sexual reproduction in plants usually involves **pollination** followed by **fertilisation** and the development of **seeds** and **fruits**. Growth substances are involved in this process. Pollen grains produce auxins.

If a flower is not pollinated it soon ages and falls off because it lacks the growth promoters supplied by pollen. Spraying with the correct concentration of auxin will therefore help to keep the flowers on the plant. This will increase the chance of successful fruiting and a bigger crop.

Fig 3 *Mechanical spraying of a fruit crop to set fruit*

Auxins, produced by the pollen grains, influence the development of the embryo and the fruit following successful pollination. The flowers of fruit crop plants can be sprayed with auxins. Such sprays will effectively replace those auxins normally introduced into the flowers by pollen grains. The result is that the flowers stay on the plant and set fruit without pollination having taken place. This commercial practice will reduce the risk of low pollination rates, due perhaps to bad weather or few pollinators (e.g. bees), and secure a better yield from the crop.

Another advantage of using auxin sprays in this way follows from the fact that no pollen is involved. Pollen delivers male gametes to the ovary to bring about fertilisation and the formation of seeds. If there are no pollen grains, fertilisation cannot take place. If fertilisation does not take place, no seeds will be formed. Fruits will develop, therefore, which are **seedless**. This practice is sometimes employed in grape and citrus crop production.

Q1 What do gardeners use rooting powder for?

Q2 What does a selective weedkiller do?

Q3 How are seedless grapes produced?

38 Uptake of water and transpiration

In this unit you will learn the answers to these questions:
- How does water get into the roots of a plant?
- How does water get up to the leaves?
- What is transpiration?
- How do plants maintain their water balance?

Roots are the organs which **anchor** plants and allow them to **absorb water** from the soil. Most of the water enters the root through specialised surface cells, called **root hair cells**. Their outer wall is extended to form a long projection which penetrates between the soil particles. The wall is thin and this allows water to pass through it easily. The root hair cells of an entire root system provide a **very large surface area** for the absorption of water.

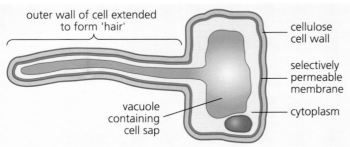

Fig 1 Root hair cell

The membrane just inside the cell wall of a root hair cell is selectively permeable (see Unit 3). The cytoplasm and cell sap (in the vacuole) of a root hair cell contain many solutes dissolved in water. Water found outside the cell, amongst the soil particles, contains solutes too, but at a much lower concentration. The root hair cell gains water from the soil by **osmosis** (see Unit 4).

Evaporation of water from the cells of the shoot system of a plant (the leaves in particular) to the atmosphere is called **transpiration**. The continuous flow of water through the xylem of the plant is called the **transpiration stream**.

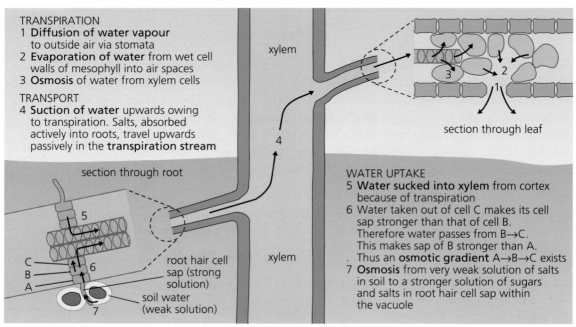

Fig 2 Water uptake, transport and loss in a flowering plant

The rate at which transpiration takes place is affected by environmental conditions. Any factor which affects evaporation will also affect transpiration. Factors which affect transpiration are **air humidity**, **temperature**, **air movement** and **light**. An increase in air humidity decreases the transpiration rate because the diffusion gradient for water between the leaf and the air is less steep (see Unit 4). An increase in temperature and air movement increases the rate of transpiration by making the diffusion gradient steeper. Light has its effect indirectly. The guard cells of stomata, through which most water loss occurs by transpiration, are sensitive to light intensity. They open during periods of light and close as the light intensity falls. These changes allow transpiration either to occur or not.

Stomatal pores are formed between pairs of **guard cells**. Guard cells are specialised. The wall bordering the pore is thicker than the others. When a guard cell swells or shrinks, owing to the gain or loss of water, the thickened wall is the only one to retain its shape. As a result when the two guard cells swell, they are drawn apart, opening the pore. When the two guard cells shrink, they move towards each other, closing the pore. Water enters or leaves the guard cells by osmosis. The degree and direction of movement of water is influenced by several factors, one of which is **light**.

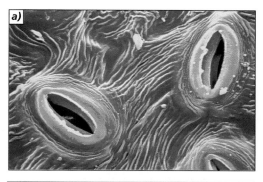

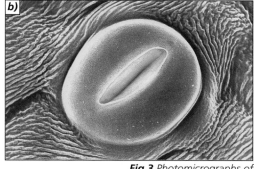

Fig 3 Photomicrographs of *a)* two open stomata and *b)* one closed stoma

Another factor which affects whether stomata remain open or closed is the **water balance** of the plant. If a plant continues to lose more water to the air than it can gain from the soil, the stomata eventually close. This reduces water loss by transpiration and allows the plant time to restore its water balance.

Plants show **adaptations** to **conserve water**. Leaves, in particular, may show modifications. These include extra wax in the cuticle, e.g. holly, or reduced surface area, e.g. pine, cactus. Some plants have their stomata at the bottom of 'wells' in the leaf surface to protect them from wind, e.g. pine. One type of grass which grows on sand dunes has leaves which roll up when the plant's water balance goes wrong.

The water inside plant cells keeps them blown up and turgid (rigid). Turgid cells play an important role in supporting the plant. When **turgor** is lost the plant **wilts**.

 ICT Extra!

Use a balance linked to a computer to measure water loss from a plant. Also use other data-logging devices to monitor water loss under different ambient environmental conditions.

Q1 In what ways are root hair cells specialised for water uptake?

Q2 What is transpiration?

Q3 Why does a plant wilt if it is not watered?

39 Transport in plants

In this unit you will learn the answers to these questions:
- What tissues are found in roots and stems?
- Which tissues are used to move substances around in plants?
- What are 'conduction' and 'translocation'?

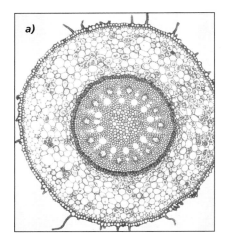
a)

Figs 1a and 1b show the internal structure of a typical plant root and stem in cross-section.

b)

Fig 1 *Photomicrographs of transverse sections of **a)** root and **b)** stem of a dicotyledonous plant*

The tissues which are involved in the transport of materials around the plant are concentrated in regions known as **vascular bundles**. There are two tissues involved in transport. These are **xylem** and **phloem**. The vascular bundles provide a continuous link between the root, stem and structures formed on the stem such as leaves, flowers and fruits. This means that water taken in by the root can pass to all other parts of the plant. Sugars manufactured in the leaves can be transported to the roots, stem, flowers and fruits.

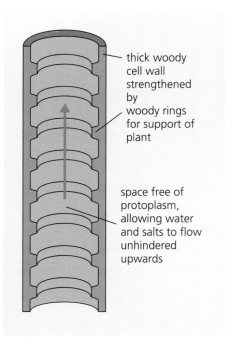

thick woody cell wall strengthened by woody rings for support of plant

space free of protoplasm, allowing water and salts to flow unhindered upwards

Xylem cells (vessels) are long, tubular cells. The walls of xylem cells are made from cellulose, like other plant cells, but as they get older another chemical, known as **lignin**, is added. Lignin **waterproofs** and **strengthens** the walls. The added strength is important because xylem plays an important part in supporting the plant. A plank of wood is part of what was the xylem tissue of a tree.

Once a xylem cell has lignin in its walls, water containing sugars and other essential materials cannot get into the cell. As a result a mature xylem cell is dead. The cytoplasm dies, leaving an empty tube through which water can travel. Xylem vessels are arranged in series, one after another, and water passes from vessel to vessel, along the line.

Most of the water moves around a plant in the xylem. This process is known as **conduction**.

Fig 2 *Sectioned vessel cell of xylem*

Phloem cells are elongated and arranged end to end to form a tubular system. Phloem cells differ from xylem cells in several important ways. Their cellulose walls are not modified chemically, and remain permeable to water at maturity. They are alive, not dead. The phloem tube is not hollow or empty. It contains cytoplasm, but no nucleus. The nuclei of phloem tissue are found in smaller cells, closely associated with the phloem tube cells. The smaller cells are called **companion cells**. Sucrose formed from the glucose made in photosynthesis enters the phloem in the leaves. Phloem cells transport the sucrose from the leaves up and down the stem. This process is known as **translocation**. This means that cells in the growing points in the tips of the shoot and the root have access to a supply of food. Some of the sucrose can also find its way in the phloem to other structures, e.g. flowers, fruits or storage organs below ground.

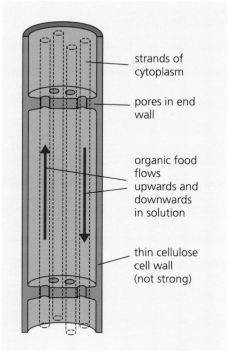

strands of cytoplasm

pores in end wall

organic food flows upwards and downwards in solution

thin cellulose cell wall (not strong)

Fig 3 Sectioned vessel cell of phloem

The table summarises the differences between xylem and phloem.

Feature	Xylem	Phloem
nature	dead	alive
wall	lignified	cellulose
permeable wall	no	yes
transports	water + dissolved minerals	sucrose and other organic molecules
direction of transport	up the plant	up and down the plant
supporting ability	considerable, e.g trunk wood	turgor only

Q1 Where are the vascular bundles found in the roots and shoots of plants?

Q2 State two ways in which phloem cells differ from xylem cells.

Q3 What are 'conduction' and 'translocation'?

Q4 Suggest a function that the companion cells associated with phloem cells might carry out.

Q5 Why is it important that translocation moves sucrose upwards and downwards in a plant?

40 Variation

In this unit you will learn the answers to these questions:
- How do living things differ?
- What causes the variation?

Students in a teaching group at school may all be the same age, but, as individuals, they show different characteristics. They will differ in height, eye colour, skin colour, hair colour, blood group, and possibly gender, to mention but a few. An individual's characteristics illustrate what is described as **variation**.

There are two types of variation. These are **continuous** and **discontinuous** variation. The heights of a group of pupils in a class (all born in the same year) are recorded in the table. A histogram of the results is shown in Fig 1.

Height class/cm	121–125	126–130	131–135	136–140	141–145	146–150
Number of pupils	2	3	5	6	3	1

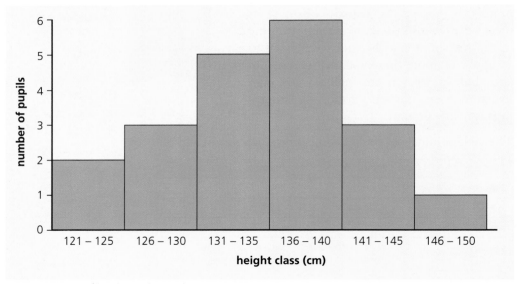

Fig 1 Histogram of heights in the teaching group

As you might expect, there were one or two who were much taller than the others. Some were shorter, but the majority were around the 'average' for the class. The histogram in Fig 1 is based on a small number of students. If a much larger sample is taken then a curve similar to Fig 1 is produced, but which is much 'smoother'. This is described mathematically as a '**normal distribution**' curve. Body mass, index finger length and span are other examples which would produce data giving a normal distribution curve for a large group of individuals of the same age. Variation which produces a normal distribution within a population is called **continuous variation**. An individual will lie somewhere between the minimum and maximum on the scale for that characteristic.

Some characteristics fall into very distinct groups. Individuals are either male or female. Their blood group is either A, B, AB or O. There are no 'in-betweens'. Variation of this kind is called **discontinuous variation**.

All of the characteristics shown by an individual are the result of information inherited from their parents. Genetic material is passed on from generation to generation during reproduction. The potential to grow to a particular size, in terms of height and body mass, is already there at the start. It is determined by the genes present in the sperm and egg or, for an asexually produced organism, by the genetic material already present. Whether an individual reaches their potential growth rate and final size, for example, does depend on other things. The 'other things' will be factors in the environment. Continuous variation is a result of both genetic and environmental conditions. Data from twin studies, where identical twins have been brought up in two different situations, for example, in two different family groups, have shown this to be so.

Fig 2 Experimental plots showing pure-breeding plants that have been grown under different regimes

Plants also clearly demonstrate the importance of the part the environment plays in the way an individual turns out. The photograph in Fig 2 shows the results of field trials for a fertiliser on a pure-breeding crop plant. Some plants have received a different quantity of fertiliser, with obvious effects.

On the other hand, the outcome of the genetic information any individual has concerning gender, blood group, eye colour and other examples of discontinuous variation is not influenced by the environment. Someone who is born blood group O will remain so whatever the environment. Discontinuous variation is the result of genetics alone.

Q1 What are the two types of variation shown by living things? Give two examples for each.

41 Reproduction and mutation

In this unit you will learn the answers to these questions:
- How is a new human being produced?
- What happens at fertilisation?
- What makes us individuals?
- How are twins formed?
- How do mutants arise?

The structures of the sexual reproductive organs of a human were introduced in Unit 2.

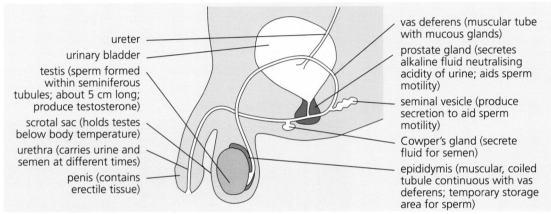

ureter
urinary bladder
testis (sperm formed within seminiferous tubules; about 5 cm long; produce testosterone)
scrotal sac (holds testes below body temperature)
urethra (carries urine and semen at different times)
penis (contains erectile tissue)

vas deferens (muscular tube with mucous glands)
prostate gland (secretes alkaline fluid neutralising acidity of urine; aids sperm motility)
seminal vesicle (produce secretion to aid sperm motility)
Cowper's gland (secrete fluid for semen)
epididymis (muscular, coiled tubule continuous with vas deferens; temporary storage area for sperm)

Fig 1 *Male reproductive organs, side view*

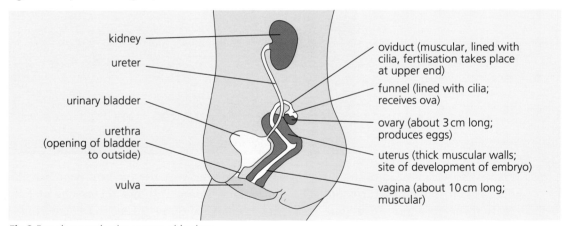

kidney
ureter
urinary bladder
urethra (opening of bladder to outside)
vulva

oviduct (muscular, lined with cilia, fertilisation takes place at upper end)
funnel (lined with cilia; receives ova)
ovary (about 3 cm long; produces eggs)
uterus (thick muscular walls; site of development of embryo)
vagina (about 10 cm long; muscular)

Fig 2 *Female reproductive organs, side view*

The function of the **testes** is to produce male gametes (sex cells) called **sperms**. The **ovaries** produce **eggs**, the female gametes. The equivalent organs in the flowering plants are the **anthers**, part of the **stamens** (male), and the **ovary**, part of the carpel (female). The anther produces **pollen grains**, which in turn produce the male gametes. The ovary produces one or more **ovules**, each of which contains a female gamete.

Fertilisation

Fertilisation in humans usually occurs high in the oviduct. Sperms surround the egg as it travels down the oviduct towards the uterus. One of the sperms penetrates the egg membrane. Once a sperm has penetrated the membrane, changes take place in the membrane which prevent any others getting in. The nucleus of the 'successful' sperm fuses with the egg nucleus. The **fertilised egg nucleus** becomes the **zygote**. The **embryo** develops from the zygote. The embryo will have genetic information from both gametes and therefore inherits characteristics from both parents.

Fertilisation is a random process. One human ejaculation (about 1.5 cm³) contains about 100 million sperms. Each sperm will have its own unique combination of genes (see Unit 7). Only one of these combinations will join the combination, also unique, of genes in the egg. This point explains, in part, how easy it is for different 'individuals' to arise in organisms that reproduce sexually.

Twins

Occasionally two or more eggs are released in one month. If two eggs are fertilised, two zygotes result and twins may develop. Two, separate eggs are involved, each fertilised by a different and therefore genetically unique sperm. As a result each of the embryos will inherit a different combination of genes. These are **non-identical twins**.

Less frequently, an embryo may divide into two during its early stages. Each part then develops normally to produce two individuals. Both individuals will have arisen from the same fertilisation, one egg fusing with one sperm. Consequently twins which are conceived in this way have identical genetics. They will be **identical twins**.

Mutation

Chromosomes are copied during meiosis. Occasionally the copying process goes wrong. Genetic information is written in chemical code in the nucleic acid of chromosomes (see Unit 5). The code may break and join up again the wrong way round. Bits of information may be lost or added. The message carried as a result may not necessarily be 'wrong', but it will certainly be different. Changed genes arising in this way will be formed randomly. They are called **mutant genes**, and the process is known as **gene mutation**.

Sometimes a whole chromosome may 'go missing' or 'turn up' during the formation of gametes. One example of this is responsible for **Down's syndrome**. Here the zygote receives an extra chromosome, usually from the egg. The individual therefore has a chromosome number of 47, not the usual 46. As a result, physical and mental development is not normal.

Mutations occur naturally. The rate at which they occur may be accelerated by specific environmental agents. These agents are called **mutagens**. Ionising radiation and particular chemicals are mutagens. Mutations may lead to abnormal cell growth, producing **tumours** or **cancers**. Mutagens of this kind are called **carcinogens**. Exposure to too much **sunlight** during sunbathing can lead to an increased risk of skin cancer. Over-exposure to **nuclear radiation** sources may induce tumour formation. Some of the chemical compounds in **tobacco smoke** are carcinogens.

Q1 What happens when an egg is fertilised?

Q2 How are non-identical twins formed?

Q3 What are mutations?

KS4 42 Monohybrid inheritance

In this unit you will learn the answers to these questions:
- What do all these genetic terms mean?
- How do you write out a genetic cross?
- What does a 3 : 1 ratio mean?
- How is sex inherited?

Genetic information is passed from one generation to the next in the nuclei of gametes. The zygote formed at fertilisation has in it all the information that will ever be needed to allow a new individual to develop. The inherited characteristics, included in the code, produce a new member of the species. The way these characteristics show up from one generation to the next can be studied.

Genetic terms

It is worthwhile spending some time sorting out the terminology (specific words) used in describing genetic crosses. We can then look at the way a particular characteristic might be inherited.

Allele The gene for a particular characteristic may exist in more than one form. Each form is known as an allele.

Gene A section of the nucleic acid of a chromosome which, on its own or with other associated genes, is responsible for a particular characteristic.

Locus The specific position on a chromosome occupied by a gene (gene locus).

Dominant A dominant allele always expresses itself (works), whether it is partnered with another like itself or with a recessive allele.

Recessive A recessive allele works only when it is partnered by another like itself.

Homozygous A condition where both the alleles for a particular gene are the same.

Heterozygous A condition where the alleles for a particular gene are different.

F_1 generation The first generation of offspring produced by two parents.

F_2 generation The second generation of offspring. In a human study, the F_2 offspring would be the children of parents who were members of the F_1 generation. F_2 offspring would be grandchildren of the original parents studied.

Genotype Symbols representing the alleles present for a particular gene.

Monohybrid Feature controlled by a single gene.

Phenotype The outcome of a particular gene. The feature that can be observed.

There are very few examples of human external features which are controlled by single genes (**monohybrid** inheritance). One human characteristic which is controlled by a single gene is the ability to taste a chemical called phenylthiocarbamide (PTC). About 70% of the population in the UK find a very dilute solution (0.01%) of PTC very bitter in taste. These people are described as 'tasters'. The other 30% ('non-tasters') cannot taste anything unpleasant at this concentration. Response to PTC provides us with an example of discontinuous variation and a useful example of monohybrid inheritance.

Monohybrid cross

As you read through the next few paragraphs it may be helpful to refer back to the list of terms defined above.

ICT Extra! Use computer simulations to model breeding experiments.

When writing out genetic crosses it is usual to represent the dominant allele by a capital letter. The 'taster' allele is dominant with respect to the 'non-taster' allele and therefore will be represented by '**T**' and the recessive allele by '**t**'. Since each gamete contains only one allele for a particular characteristic, the zygote will have two.

Therefore the possible genotypes involved here will be **TT**, **Tt** or **tt**. People who have the genotypes **TT** or **Tt** will have the phenotype 'taster', and those with the genotype **tt** will have the phenotype 'non–taster'.

When a couple have children it is possible to predict the likely outcome as far as this gene is concerned. If one of the parents is a taster and the other a non–taster there will be two possible crosses which need to be considered. These are drawn out in Figs 1a and 1b.

If both parents are tasters there are three possibilities which need to be considered. These will be (i) **TT** × **TT**, (ii) **TT** × **Tt** and (iii) **Tt** × **Tt**. All of the gametes produced by both parents in cross (i) will have the single dominant allele **T**. Every fertilisation will produce **TT**. All the offspring will be tasters. Crosses (ii) and (iii) are drawn out in Figs 2a and 2b.

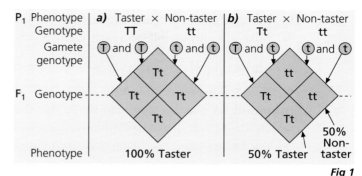

Fig 1

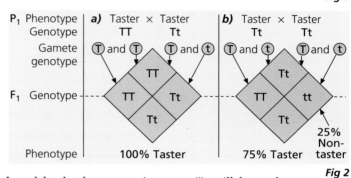

Fig 2

Outcomes are probabilities not certainties

It is important to remember that the phenotypic ratios seen above, that is the 1:1 ratio in Fig 1b and the 3:1 ratio in Fig 2b are achieved only when very large numbers of offspring are involved. They are only probabilities.

Inheritance of sex

The nuclei in the human testis and ovary have 23 pairs of chromosomes. One of the pairs is the **sex chromosomes**. A **female** has two sex chromosomes which look the same and are represented by the symbols **XX**. A **male** has two chromosomes, and one is shorter than the other. These are represented by the symbols **XY**. Fig 3 shows the way in which sex is inherited. The phenotypic ratio is 1:1.

Q1 What does monohybrid mean?

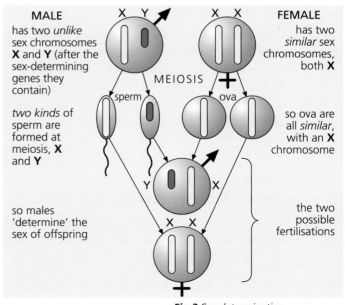

Fig 3 Sex determination

43 Inheritance and disease

In this unit you will learn the answer to this question:
- Why is it impossible to catch haemophilia?

Sickle-cell anaemia

Sickle-cell anaemia is caused by a **recessive allele**. The recessive allele results from a **mutation** of the haemoglobin gene. An abnormal form of haemoglobin is made which forms crystal-like structures in the red blood cells when oxygen concentrations are low. This changes the shape of the red blood cells.

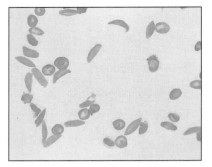

Individuals who are **homozygous** for the allele have a variety of problems. They have **fewer red blood cells** because the red cells may be destroyed. This leads to **anaemia** and general weakness. Also, because their shape is changed, the red cells tend to block capillaries and **clotting** is common. This may lead to heart failure, brain damage and the failure of other vital organs. The symptoms show up in early infancy and the death rate in infancy is very high.

Fig 1 *Photomicrograph of a blood smear of sickle-cell blood*

Individuals who are **heterozygous** for the sickle-cell allele do show sickling of red blood cells and have up to 50% of their haemoglobin in the abnormal form. Apart from that they appear normal. Such individuals are called **carriers**. Carriers have an advantage in that they have some resistance to the malarial parasite.

Cystic fibrosis

Cystic fibrosis (CF) is also caused by a recessive allele. The gene affects the cells which produce mucus. They produce an abnormally thick and sticky mucus. Organs which are particularly affected are the lungs, gut and pancreas. As a result this leads to a variety of distressing disorders.

The mucus blocks the air passages to the lungs. **Chronic lung congestion** occurs. This can be relieved temporarily by regular physiotherapy. Congestion of the lungs increases the risk of **respiratory infections**. These have to be combated by antibiotic treatment. The gut and the **pancreatic duct** can become blocked and foods normally digested by pancreatic enzymes remain undigested. Cystic fibrosis sufferers are often **diabetic** (see Unit 26).

Children who are cystic fibrosis sufferers are usually children of parents who are carriers, both parents being heterozygous for this allele. Sadly there is no cure.

Sex-linked inheritance

Some disorders, such as red–green colour-blindness, are more frequent in males (**XY**) than females (**XX**). These are examples of **sex-linked inheritance**. Most of the sex-linked genes are on the **X chromosome**. If the recessive alleles which cause red–green colour-blindness are present on the **X** chromosome, and the normal alleles are on the partner **X** chromosome, a woman will have normal colour vision. In males there are no functioning partner alleles on the **Y** chromosome. Therefore the recessive allele, on the **X** chromosome, will be expressed and the man will be colour-blind. A colour-blind woman must be homozygous recessive for these alleles. In the heterozygous condition she will have normal colour vision but be a carrier.

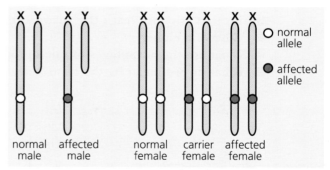

Fig 2 *The possible genotypes for red–green colour-blindness*

Duchenne muscular dystrophy

Duchenne muscular dystrophy is a disease caused by an **X-linked recessive**. Young boys with this condition have difficulty walking and in particular climbing stairs. The muscles gradually weaken and waste away. Sufferers are usually wheelchair-bound by the time they are about 10 years of age. **Muscle wastage** continues with consequent effect on vital systems. Breathing becomes increasingly difficult, ultimately impossible. Duchenne muscular dystrophy sufferers usually die from pneumonia. A life expectancy of 20 years is usually the maximum.

Females who are heterozygous for the allele suffer no disability but are carriers. This will mean that there is a one in two chance of any sons they might have, having this disease.

Haemophilia

Haemophilia is caused by another **X-linked recessive**. A male with this disorder lacks the blood clotting factor, **factor VIII** (see Unit 31). This means that any **bleeding**, either internal or external, will continue unchecked. Consequently the sufferer can become **anaemic**. Bleeding also takes place into **joints,** leading to considerable pain.

Haemophilia can be treated successfully by regular injections of human factor VIII. At the moment, most of this is prepared from human blood donations. Sufferers feel safer, however, using genetically engineered factor VIII, thus avoiding possible HIV contamination.

Q1 What will be the genotype of a sickle-cell anaemia carrier?

Q2 Why do CF sufferers often have respiratory infections?

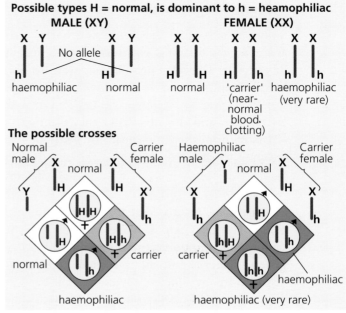

Fig 3 *Inheritance of haemophilia*

44 Cloning and selective breeding

In this unit you will learn the answers to these questions:
- What is a clone?
- What are the advantages of micropropagation?
- What do we mean by the term 'selective breeding'?

Asexual reproduction

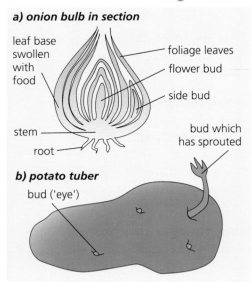

a) onion bulb in section

leaf base swollen with food

foliage leaves

flower bud

side bud

stem

root

bud which has sprouted

b) potato tuber

bud ('eye')

Fig 1 Perennating organs also act as asexual reproductive organs

Most flowering plants reproduce by sexual means. They develop **flowers**, which are in turn **pollinated** and set **seeds**. Some plants produce structures which allow them to stay alive over the winter. Food is stored in specialised structures (**perennating organs**) such as **bulbs** and stem **tubers**. These organs also allow the plants to reproduce.

Onion bulbs and potato tubers have **buds**. Buds are found between the swollen leaves of a bulb and on the surface of a potato. The potato buds are the 'eyes' of the potato. When more favourable conditions arrive, after the winter is over, stored food is used to promote the growth of one or more of the buds. New stems develop, and later roots, and a 'new plant' is produced from each of the buds involved. These will replace the original plant which has probably died back, before or during the winter. As a result, where one bulb or potato was planted one year, several may 'appear' in the next growing season. The plants will have reproduced themselves, but without producing any flowers. This is **asexual** or **vegetative reproduction**.

Some plants, for example strawberry, reproduce asexually by forming **runners**. In this case food is diverted to **lateral buds**. These grow to form side branches and form new plants when they contact the soil. This process is shown in Fig 2. Once they are established and independent, the plantlets can be separated from the parent plant by decay or a gardener cutting through the runner.

Fig 2 Runners from strawberry plants

Cloning

Onion bulbs, potato stem tubers and strawberry runners are all parts of established plants. The cells which make up their structure will have been formed by mitotic divisions. It is important to remember that each time a mitotic division takes place, the genetic material present is copied (replicated) (see Unit 6). Therefore all the cells involved in any of these structures will have the same genetics as their 'parent' plant. The same will be true when a gardener or horticulturist takes leaf or stem cuttings from any other plant. It will have been **cloned**.

Micropropagation

Micropropagation is a technique which is now being used to produce plants commercially. A very large number of 'copies' of the required plant can be grown from a single piece of a stock plant. A stock plant is one which has all the desired characteristics. All the 'copies' will have the same genetics, and therefore the same features, as the stock plant. It may be a very popular house plant or it may be a high-yielding crop plant.

Micropropagation has obvious commercial applications. It is possible to get large numbers of plants ready for special occasions such as Christmas, Easter or Mothering Sunday. The time of year will not matter. Plants can be produced to order whatever the season. There are also biological advantages. It is possible to develop a pure-breeding line of plants using this technique. There is no risk of introducing variation at the pollination stage. Some plant species do not lend themselves to easy propagation by normal vegetative means. Some plants do not produce many seeds. Micropropagation allows these difficulties to be overcome.

Selective breeding

Selective breeding involves taking an organism with the required characteristic and cross breeding it with another of the same species which has a different special feature. The offspring, the F_1 generation, will show variation (see Units 8 and 41) and hopefully among them there will be some specimens showing a combination of the desired features. These can be selected and used as parents. Selection over a number of generations will hopefully produce an inbred line with the required characteristics.

Any aspect of life today which involves animals or plants will provide examples of selective breeding. Cows, sheep, pigs, hens, wheat, oats, grapes and hops will all have been produced over many years of animal and plant breeding where specific features have been selected. The starting point will have been, and continues to be, wild (undomesticated) animals and plants. Some of the features which have been selected for are summarised in the table.

Organism	Feature selected
chickens	rapid weight gain
cattle	milk yield
wheat	fungus resistance
peas	height of plant
roses	scent and colour

Selective breeding has not been confined to the development of food animals and plants. Dog breeders, racehorse breeders and rose breeders will all have employed selective breeding to meet their own particular requirements (see Fig 3).

Q1 Why are cloned plants always the same?

Q2 What are the advantages of micropropagation?

Q3 Where did all our crop plants come from originally?

Fig 3 *Different breeds of dog*

45 Control of cell activity

In this unit you will learn the answers to these questions:
- How do cells know what to do?
- How can we make use of biological systems, organisms and processes?
- What are the applications and implications of biotechnology?

Biochemical control

Cells are chemical systems. To work efficiently their chemical processes have to be controlled. Control of the cell's chemistry is carried out by catalysts known as **enzymes** (see Unit 98).

Biotechnology

Biotechnology has been defined as the **application of organisms** (often, but not always, microorganisms), biological processes and systems **to make things** for us or to provide us with a **service**.

Ideas and evidence

In 1973 Cohen and Boyer demonstrated how DNA could be 'cut' and 'rejoined' using enzymes. In 1981 genes from one organism were successfully transferred to another.

Do you think that scientists should be completely free to pursue research in these areas, or should genetic engineering be strictly regulated? Support your answer with reasons.

Enzymes help us in our everyday lives. They are useful chemical tools. Microorganisms are grown and their enzymes extracted. We can then put them to use for our benefit (see Unit 98).

Biotechnology is being employed to combat crime. DNA profiles are being used to help solve crimes by providing '**genetic fingerprints**'.

Fig 1 Checking DNA profiles

Biotechnology has much to offer in the field of **medicine**. The table shows some of the areas which are currently being researched.

Development	Use
antibiotics	kill microorganisms
biosensors	rapid detection of small amounts of chemicals, including drugs
DNA probes	early diagnosis of disease
genetic tests	genetic counselling provides advice on inheritable diseases
gene therapy	correcting genetic defects
hormone production	provides patients with human hormones rather than those from other animals (see opposite)
monoclonal antibodies	counter a specific antigen
vaccines	protection against infection

The **farming industry** is also benefiting from biotechnological advance. Crop plants and animals can be improved by genetic engineering (see opposite). Strains of nitrogen-fixing bacteria are being developed to associate with plants other than leguminous species (see Unit 53). Most of the staple food crops, e.g. wheat and rice, do not have nitrogen-fixing bacteria which associate with them. Animal disease control has benefited from the production of vaccines and antibiotics.

Biotechnology provides us with **new sources of food** and **fuel**. Single-cell protein (SCP), where microorganisms are the raw material, can be used either as food for humans or as animal feed. Cholesterol-free, protein meat substitutes, with a high fibre content, have been produced from the fungus *Fusarium*.

Biotechnology has been used for a long time in **sewage disposal**. Microorganisms are employed to break down a variety of materials and in the process purify waste water.

Fig 2 Sewage treatment works

Some parts of the world have little, if any, fossil fuel resources. **Fuel alcohol**, made from sugar cane, is providing some of these areas with an alternative to petrol. Methane is produced by intestinal bacteria which digest cellulose. Domestic and farmyard sewage provide a readily available raw material for these bacteria to generate '**biogas**'. As fossil fuel reserves eventually disappear in the future, biotechnology may help to provide a solution to the problem of generating new sources of fuel.

Genetic engineering involves selecting a gene which provides a desirable product or provides a needed service, isolating it and transferring the gene to another organism. DNA (see Unit 5) extracted from an individual of species A is broken up into smaller fragments. Selected fragments can then be attached to the DNA of a 'carrier', for example a plasmid (a small loop of DNA found in bacterial cells), or a virus. The carrier then has its own nucleic acid and the introduced DNA. This is **recombinant DNA**. An individual of species B is then 'infected' with the recombinant DNA. Individual B can now carry out the chemistry encoded in the genes from individual A.

Transferred genes are replicated (copied exactly) each time the host cell divides. For example, a population of bacteria containing the gene which directs human insulin production can be cultivated. Each of these cells would be a clone (see Unit 44) and the technique is called **gene cloning**. Under suitable conditions these cells could produce a reliable source of human insulin. This could then be used in the treatment of diabetes (see Unit 26).

The table summarises some of the benefits and problems resulting from the advances being made in biotechnology.

ICT Extra!

Produce a DTP report or a Powerpoint presentation on the pros and cons of biotechnological advances.

Q1 List ways in which modern farming has benefited from biotechnology.

Q2 What are the advantages of the use of SCP rather than meat as a source of protein?

Q3 What would be the benefits resulting from the development of a strain of nitrogen-fixing bacteria which would work with wheat?

Benefits	Problems
alternative fuel sources	morally wrong to genetically engineer organisms
extraction of metals by microorganisms	
improved farming	escape of genetically engineered organisms and subsequent competition with natural forms
improved medicene	
improved veterinary science	
provide enzymes for a variety of processes	
solve world food problems	how do you patent 'discoveries'?
waste disposal	

99

46 Evidence for evolution

In this unit you will learn the answers to these questions:
- How did life on Earth begin?
- What evidence have we got?

Evolution

How did life on Earth begin? Have the animals and plants we see around us and in natural history films always existed? One of the things which such films often stress is the fact that we are losing many species of plants and animals, almost on a daily basis. On the other hand we see, hear or read reports of new strains of bacteria which are resistant to antibiotics, for example, or of new strains of wheat which are resistant to fungi.

It would appear that the animals and plants of our world are changing now, and therefore are likely to have changed in the past.

One widely accepted scientific theory suggests that today's plants and animals have a common ancestry. The earliest records of living cells, bacterial cells, date back over 3000 million years. The theory argues that, since then, new organisms have developed in response to changes in the world around them, while some have died out. Those that have died out have become extinct.

The theory referred to above is that of **evolution**. What evidence have we got to support the theory? One line of evidence comes from the past by the study of **fossils**.

Fossil evidence

When a plant or animal dies its body, or parts of it, may be eaten. Bacteria and fungi cause the rest to decay. The fossils which we can see in museums, quarries or sea cliffs are the remains of plant and animal bodies where this has not happened.

Sometimes animals and plants die in conditions where they are not eaten, and decay is slowed down, if not stopped altogether, with perhaps only the softer tissues being affected. As a result only the harder parts, such as shells, teeth and bones, are likely to have remained from the past as fossils (see Fig 1).

Fig 1 The fossil skull of a Tyrannosaurus rex

One way in which this can happen is for an organism to be covered by a sediment. When animals die in rivers, lakes or the sea they may sink to the bottom. If they are covered by silt and mud quickly enough, other animals cannot get at them. The silt and mud keep out oxygen, and decay is slowed down or prevented. It is under conditions like these that the fossils which we now see may have formed. Since such conditions do not occur everywhere, fossil formation was and is a relatively uncommon event. It also means that we are more likely to find fossils of some types of organism than others.

Fossils can be formed by:

1 casting; 2 impression; 3 petrification (turn to rock); or 4 whole preservation.

Fig 2 shows the way in which an organism may be fossilised by forming a **cast**. Fossils of this type are found in sedimentary rocks. This type of rock shows layer upon layer of sand and silt deposits. Animals dying at the time when the layers were being formed could be trapped and casts formed later.

Marks such as dinosaur footprints or leaf prints in mud have also been preserved. Here the organism left an **impression** in the mud before it was preserved by the sediment laid down above it.

Sometimes water rich in mineral salts may get into the tissues of an organism before they decay. This eventually leads to the formation of rock, preserving the layout of the tissue. This process is called **petrification**. One example of this type of fossil is shown by the petrified forest in Arizona, which has petrified coniferous trees estimated to be about 170 million years old (see Fig 3).

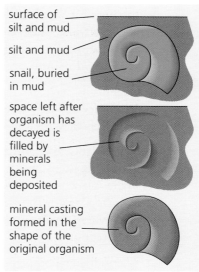

surface of silt and mud

silt and mud

snail, buried in mud

space left after organism has decayed is filled by minerals being deposited

mineral casting formed in the shape of the original organism

Fig 2 *Fossilisation by casting*

Fig 3 *Arizona petrified forest*

Detailed preservation of soft tissues in fossil remains is rare. For **whole preservation** to occur the process of decay must have been stopped very quickly. The conditions which had to be present in nature in the past have to be similar to those used today to preserve food. Woolly mammoths found in Siberian soils have been preserved in a natural deep-freeze. Their muscles remained intact, as did their gut and the food in it. Woolly rhinoceros remains have been found preserved in tar in Poland. Fossilised resin from conifer trees is called amber. Occasionally amber contains perfectly preserved insects, such as ants, which were trapped in the resin.

Other evidence

Vertebrate limbs are all built to the same basic plan. The arrangement of the bones in the front leg of a frog or lizard, the wing of a chicken or the human arm are all very similar. This suggests that perhaps the animals have some common ancestry. Other anatomical features show similarity, but also characteristic differences. The hearts of fish, frog, bird and mammal show one possible line of development. There are two chambers in the heart of a fish, three in an amphibian and four in birds and mammals.

Much of the basic chemistry which goes on in living cells is the same which ever organism the cell represents. Most cells have the same basic set of organelles, for example nucleus and mitochondria. Analysis shows that the DNA (see Unit 5) from different organisms has a lot of common coding.

Unit 47 includes information which supports the idea that evolution has taken place and is still continuing.

Q1 What is our earliest record of living cells?

Q2 Why is the fossil record not a very reliable line of evidence for evolution?

Q3 What evidence other than fossils supports the theory of evolution?

47 Natural selection

In this unit you will learn the answers to these questions:
- What parts do variation and competition play in natural selection?
- How might an organism evolve?
- Why do some organisms become extinct?

Organisms have to reproduce if their species is to continue. Those species which reproduce sexually need to produce at least one male and one female as replacements for when they, themselves, die.

Most plants and animals produce more than two offspring. Good examples which make this point are the field poppy, where the average number of seeds formed by a single plant is 170 000, the cod, where a female will produce a vast number of offspring from the several million eggs released at a single spawning, and the frog, where a pair produces a melon-sized ball of spawn and most of the eggs hatch to form tadpoles.

The individual offspring of sexually reproducing organisms show **variation** (see Unit 7).

Young plants need space to develop. They need light, water, mineral salts and carbon dioxide to photosynthesise. Animals, too, need food and space to grow and breed. All the offspring of a particular species, as individuals, are likely to want the same basic things from their surroundings. The habitats into which 170 000 poppy seeds or several million young cod are released are unlikely to be able to support such a massive increase in demand for space, light and other specific factors. The young poppy plants, cod, frogs, blue tits, rabbits or whatever will be in **competition** with each other for these resources.

Fig 1 A blue tit feeding a nestful of offspring

This is where variation plays its part. Among the offspring there will be those who are different from the rest. If this difference gives them an **advantage** over others of their generation in getting what they want from their environment, then they are more likely to survive. The difference need only be slight. The animal may be slightly faster, the plant slightly taller. Both cases could offer an advantage in feeding. On the other hand, the animal might be prey for a carnivore and be able to escape. This line of argument is summed up in the idea of the '**survival of the fittest**'.

Fig 2 Dark (melanistic) and light (leucistic) forms of the peppered moth (Biston betularia) *on the bark of a tree*

Those individuals who have the combination of characteristics which favours them in a particular set of environmental conditions will **survive** and **reproduce**. This will mean that the genes for these particular characteristics are passed on to the next generation. Over long periods of time and many, many generations, the animal or plant becomes adapted to survive in that particular habitat. **Failure to adapt** to a changing environment leads to an animal or plant species failing to survive and becoming **extinct**.

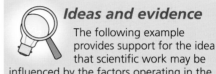

Ideas and evidence

The following example provides support for the idea that scientific work may be influenced by the factors operating in the science arena and in society as a whole at the time.

Darwin and Wallace lived and worked thousands of miles apart but came to the same detailed conclusions about the nature of evolution. They had never met or communicated with each other.

Over several generations the proportion of individuals with the 'favoured characteristics' will increase in a population. This will be because the others are likely to be less successful. The organism may gradually, but continuously, change in response to the environment. The genotype of the organism provides the potential for change. The environment determines which aspects of that potential are expressed, i.e. determines the phenotype (see Unit 42). The organism changes, over many generations, by a process of '**natural selection**'. Some genotypes lead to survival, others to extinction. This is the hypothesis which Darwin used to explain evolution.

Q1 Why is the sea not full of cod?

Q2 What does the term 'competition' mean?

Q3 What does the term 'natural selection' mean?

Q4 What does the term 'survival of the fittest' mean?

Q5 Refer to Fig 2, showing two forms of the same species of moth on a tree. Which form do you think would have the advantage in an industrial area? Why?

48 Adaptation and competition

In this unit you will learn the answers to these questions:

- What is a 'predator–prey' relationship?
- Why are some plants avoided by grazing animals?
- How are animals adapted to survive in extreme climates?
- How do human beings affect the balance of nature?

What makes a good predator?

A **predator** is a carnivorous animal. The animal or animals that it eats are its **prey**. Usually the predator is bigger than its prey. Sometimes, however, smaller predators hunt in groups and are then able to take prey much larger than themselves.

Predators have well developed senses in order to locate their prey. It is obviously important that the prey remain unaware of the predators presence as long as possible. One way this is achieved is by predators having good camouflage.

Good hunting strategies are also employed. Larger cats, such as the lion, approach their prey from downwind so that their scent is not detected. Lions often hunt in a group, known as a pride, with different individuals appearing to play different roles in the capture.

Fig 1 A lion bringing down its prey

A successful approach brings the predators close enough to the prey to attempt a capture. Up to this point in the hunt the predators will have been moving slowly and with great care to avoid being detected by their prey. It is at this point that the lion's ability to sustain a short burst of speed becomes important.

Predatory animals, as a group, have a wide variety of 'weapons' at their disposal. These include, as examples, webs, pitfall traps, poisons, and specialised beaks, claws and teeth.

The lion shown in Fig 1 is using its claws to grip its prey and weaken it by causing bleeding. The large canine teeth penetrate the prey's skin, causing damage to internal organs, more blood loss and at the same time enable the predator to 'hang on'. The arrangement of muscles in a carnivore's skull are adapted to cope with this. The prey may be killed rapidly or it may die from blood loss and exhaustion.

Fig 2 An osprey with beak and talons showing

How are prey animals adapted to avoid capture?

Animals which are prey to carnivores often live as members of a large group. This adaptation provides individuals with the benefit which we sometimes refer to as 'safety in numbers'. Warning signals have evolved to alert members of the group to anything threatening their safety (Fig 3).

Good camouflage is as important to the prey as it is to the predator. The ability to run fast is an obvious adaptation for survival for a prey animal. Also some prey have large, sharp horns which they can use to fend off attack by predators.

Fig 3 *The white tail of the rabbit running acts as a warning signal to other rabbits*

How to avoid being eaten when you can't run

Plants can't run away. Having a low growth form, spines, long hairs, stinging hairs or unpleasant tasting chemicals in their tissues are examples of adaptations shown by some plants to avoid being eaten.

Adaptation to life in extreme climates

The adaptations shown by a polar bear allow it to survive the low temperatures experienced in its polar habitat. The animal is large. It has a low surface area to volume ratio. This means that it will cool down more slowly than a smaller animal would. The fur insulates the animal, as does a thick layer of fat under the skin. Polar bears also show behavioural adaptations to the extreme cold. They hibernate, avoiding the period of most extreme weather.

A camel is adapted to survive the extreme water loss that all living things experience in a desert. They can survive losing the equivalent of one-third of their total body mass. In a desert, opportunities for camels to replace water loss are few and far between. This is less of a problem because when water is available camels can drink an incredible amount at one time, replacing as much as one-third of their body mass in 10 minutes. Camels are adapted to conserve water. Their kidney tubules are extremely efficient at reabsorbing water. Camels do not sweat or pant very much – processes that involve water loss. Sweating starts at a much higher internal body temperature than in other mammals. A camel's internal body temperature varies quite considerably (between 34.5°C and 40.5°C), but they are adapted to tolerate this.

Humans and the balance of nature

Sometimes humans have upset the natural balance by introducing a new species into a community of plants and animals. Examples of this include the introduction of the grey squirrel into Britain and the rabbit into Australia. The competition caused problems for the native species in both cases.

Q1 How are animals adapted to be predators?

Q2 How have plants evolved to avoid being eaten?

49 Our impact on the environment

In this unit you will learn the answers to these questions:

■ Who is to blame for acid rain?
■ What is the greenhouse effect?
■ What is wrong with global warming?
■ Are pesticides good or bad?

One of the things which makes human beings very different from other animal species is our ability to have much greater control over the way we live. We live in houses or flats. When the climate is too cold we can buy fuel and produce heat. When it gets dark we use artificial lighting. Distance is no problem. We no longer have to go everywhere on foot or use animal power. We have cars, buses, lorries, ships, aeroplanes, and even spacecraft. We can get food all the year round whatever the season. We can even get fresh food grown in different parts of the world if we wish. If we need something we can make it, grow it, or buy it from someone else.

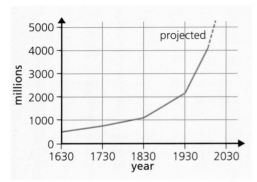

Fig 1 *The growth of the human population*

Whenever we meet problems we try to devise means to solve them. This is a natural consequence of our evolution. We are using our abilities, our skills and intellect. We are adapting to change and to need. So what's the problem? It is a problem principally because the human population is increasing so quickly (see Fig 1). This is accompanied by increasing consumption of resources and increasing pollution. Also, there are other organisms on the planet and what we do affects their environment, as well as our own. For example, rural and urban land–use alters habitats.

In order to illustrate the impact of human activity, this unit will concentrate on four issues. These are the **greenhouse effect**, **acid rain**, the **destruction of tropical rain forests** and the **use of pesticides**.

Energy is required to heat a home, to get a car to move or to harvest a crop. Worldwide, industry and agriculture need huge amounts of energy every day. Most of this comes from the burning of fossil fuels. These are coal, oil and natural gas. Energy may be supplied to industrial and agricultural users as the fossil fuel itself (or a derivative of it, e.g. petrol or diesel), or, more likely, as electricity. Electricity is generated in power stations, many of which are coal, oil, or gas fuelled.

Waste products are formed when fossil fuels are burnt. Carbon dioxide, sulphur dioxide and nitrogen oxides are three of particular concern here. Together these gases cause the greenhouse effect and acid rain.

Fig 2 *Generating electricity by burning fossil fuels*

The concentration of carbon dioxide in the atmosphere has increased dramatically during the last century. The atmosphere allows sunlight to pass through it and fall on the Earth. A proportion of this is used in photosynthesis, some of it heats up the planet and the rest is reflected back into space. The heat radiated from the Earth should pass through the atmosphere and out into space. However, an increase in carbon dioxide concentration in the atmosphere reduces this loss and more of the heat is trapped than was normal in the past. This is the **greenhouse effect** and the problem which follows is **global warming**. Rising temperatures could cause the polar ice caps to melt, raising sea levels. Large areas of land currently above sea level could be flooded if this rate of warming is maintained.

Other pollutants, for example CFCs used in aerosols and refrigerators, have a part to play in this process. They destroy the ozone layer. The ozone layer filters out some of the ultraviolet light from the Sun by acting as a global heat shield. Loss of ozone means that more heat gets through, thus increasing the rate of global warming.

Sulphur dioxide and nitrogen oxides react with water in the atmosphere and form sulphuric acid and nitric acid. These are deposited in solution when it rains. **Acid rain** affects the balance of metal ions in the soil. It raises the concentration of aluminium and lowers the concentrations of calcium, magnesium and potassium. Aluminium is poisonous to plants and the other three are essential plant nutrients (see Unit 34). Rainwater drains into lakes, streams, rivers and the sea. Acid rain has its major environmental effect on plants growing in soils where the rain falls and in the freshwater habitats in that area. Coniferous trees are particularly sensitive to acid rain, as are salmon and trout. The acidity also causes damage to buildings by erosion.

Fig 3 The effect of acid rain on a forest

Vast areas of tropical forest have been cleared as a result of a demand for hardwoods and land clearance schemes. **Destruction of the rain forests** worldwide, but particularly in South America, is a cause of considerable concern for a number of reasons. First, the loss of tropical forest means that more carbon dioxide (a greenhouse gas) will remain in the air. Second, the specialised habitat provided by the rain forests is reduced. Third, fewer rain forest organisms will survive and their genetic material may be lost through extinction. Fourth, the potential to develop new varieties of organisms for our own use is reduced, for example as food plants or as the source of new drugs.

 ICT Extra!

Produce a DTP report summarising man's effect on the environment, OR produce a fuller report concentrating on one aspect.

Modern farming uses chemicals, called **pesticides**, to improve the yield of crops. These prevent losses during and after crop production. Pesticides used in agriculture include herbicides, insecticides and fungicides. However, there are disadvantages in using pesticides. For example, they contain potentially poisonous chemicals which can get into food chains (see Unit 51). Not all pesticides are selective. Also, pests become resistant to the pesticide as a result of natural selection.

Q1 Why is the burning of fossil fuels such a significant environmental issue?

50 Sustainable development

In this unit you will learn the answers to these questions:
■ What is sustainable development?
■ How can Science help to achieve sustainable development?

More of the Earth's resources are being used than ever before. The environment has to accept more wastes than ever before. More and more people accept that this trend is unsustainable and must be reversed.

Q1 Why are we using more resources and producing more wastes?

What sort of problem have we got?

The problem is very complicated and serious. It involves many environmental and social issues. The problem involves the whole world — it is global. It will require full international co-operation to solve it.

Fig 1 *Tokyo city*

Global environmental issues
■ Renewable resources are being used faster than they can be replaced.
■ Increasing rural and urban land use is removing natural habitats. The biodiversity (varieties and numbers of plants and animals) they contain is getting less.
■ All parts of the world are being encouraged to develop economically. This leads to the increasing use of chemicals, production of waste, environmental contamination and disposal problems.
■ Global use of energy resources is running at an unsustainable level.
■ Greenhouse gas production is too high.

Global social issues
■ The people of the world are generally healthier and wealthier than they were in the past, but there are still major problems.
■ The gap between the richest and poorest is getting greater.
■ There is enough food in the world, but it is not shared equally. Poverty and malnutrition are already endemic in many regions.
■ Chemical pollution, together with the destruction and misuse of agricultural and environmental resources is leading to greater human health risks.

Is it totally our fault?

Consider a couple of examples.

Q2 Name three greenhouse gases.

Global climatic change

The fact that natural cycles of climatic change occur on Earth has been accepted for a long time. The time-scale for these cycles is many hundreds to many thousands of years. One example would be a complete cycle of **glaciation** and **deglaciation**. This type of cycle, with its consequent climatic change, has taken place during the last 160 000 years.

However, the current interglacial period is being made warmer and at a faster rate than it would be without our involvement, due to the greenhouse effect (see Unit 49). This could have a significant effect on global climate. For example, evaporation rate and consequent precipitation rates could be affected. Average global precipitation rates would increase. Some regions could experience accelerated reduction in soil moisture levels and increased, intense, rainstorms.

Loss of biodiversity

A species may become extinct as a natural result of evolution. Small changes in climate, habitat, or levels of competition may be enough to bring this about. Extinctions of this type are called **background extinctions** and have been occuring throughout time. Others have become extinct due to **mass extinctions**, which have occurred periodically throughout the history of life on Earth. It is suggested that well over 99% of the species that have ever lived have become extinct. Suggested causes for mass extinctions include major climatic changes, and natural catastrophes such as the Earth being hit by a large meteorite. Some scientists argue that the Earth is entering another period of mass extinction, this one due entirely to human activity.

In 1992, some 150 Heads of State of the world's Governments met in Rio de Janeiro, Brazil. This '**Earth Summit**' produced a document called '**Agenda 21**'. This is a detailed action plan. It *may* provide a route towards **sustainable development**.

Q3 Why is it important that all countries are involved in this programme?

What does 'sustainable development' mean?

Sustainable development is a programme of development that lets people live their lives fully. At the same time it protects, conserves and maintains the following features:

- life support systems (e.g. nutrient and water cycles, soils and the atmosphere);
- biodiversity;
- material and energy resources;
- the economic welfare of all of the peoples of the world.

Q4 What is biodiversity?

How can Science help to solve these problems?

Science can help by providing relevant information. This should mean that better decisions are made. This is important where the choices affect the environment.

The list below includes some examples of the ways scientists are helping to solve the problems:

- keeping a closer watch on the various global cycles (e.g. soil and water cycles), air pollution, and the climate-controlling aspects of the atmosphere;
- developing computer software to enable predictions about natural disasters to be made;
- keeping a close watch on freshwater quantity and quality, particularly in developing countries;
- developing data-logging systems to provide advanced warning of natural disasters;
- researching into efficient use of current resources (including energy) and possible alternatives.

Q5 Write down three natural disasters that occur. How could advance warnings of these help?

Fig 2 Wind farms generate electricity

51 Feeding relationships

In this unit you will learn the answers to these questions:

■ What are the feeding patterns in communities of plants and animals?
■ What happens to the energy taken into a community?

Fig 1 A small freshwater lake

The freshwater water lake shown in Fig 1 is a **community**. It will have a number of populations of different species living in it. The **plants and animals** present will be **interacting** with each other and their **environment** to form an **ecosystem**. One important interaction in any ecosystem is the one based on feeding.

A feeding relationship involves the transfer of **energy** from one organism to another. Energy enters an ecosystem as **light**. Light energy is used by **plants** in photosynthesis to make **glucose**. Plants then use glucose to make other organic substances (see Units 32 and 35). Plants are the only organisms which can make their own food in this way. This means that all other organisms must be dependent on green plants for their food and therefore their energy. As a result, plants are called the **producer** organisms of an ecosystem.

All non-photosynthetic organisms are dependent on the products of photosynthesis for survival. This will mean that bacteria, animal members of the Protoctista, fungi, animals and non-photosynthetic plants must get their food from the producers. Organisms which feed on others are called **consumers**.

There are basically three types of consumer. **Herbivores** are animals that feed on plants, **carnivores** feed on other animals, and **omnivores** eat both plants and animals.

The sequence of organisms in a feeding relationship forms what is known as a **food chain**. Fig 2 shows a simple food chain which could be drawn up for the lake shown in Fig 1.

plankton (producer)   water flea (primary consumer)   stickleback (secondary consumer)   heron (tertiary consumer)

Fig 2 A food chain, based on the lake in Fig 1

Food webs arise when one producer or consumer can be eaten by more than one consumer. Food webs are interconnected food chains. Each **level of feeding** in a food chain is described as a trophic level. The producer (plankton) will be at trophic level 1, a herbivore at trophic level 2 (water flea) and two carnivores at trophic levels 3 and 4 (the stickleback and the heron, respectively). **Decomposers** (see Units 52 and 53) will be at trophic level 5.

As energy is passed from one trophic level to the next, much of it is lost as heat during respiration. This means there will be less to pass on each time. There soon comes a point where there is not enough energy to pass on to keep a trophic level going. This usually limits the number of links in a food chain to four.

It is possible to study the size of populations at each trophic level in a food chain. Data from these studies can be represented graphically in a diagram called a **pyramid of numbers**. Fig 3 shows a pyramid of numbers for a freshwater food chain. Each trophic level is represented by a block. The block is scaled to represent the number of organisms at that trophic level.

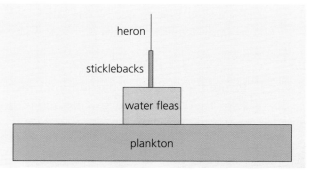

Fig 3 Pyramid of numbers for a freshwater food chain

Food chains often show this pyramidal shape. The producers are usually smaller and more numerous than the herbivores. The carnivores are usually fewer in number, but larger in size, than the herbivores. Sometimes, however, it differs. The difference is caused by the size of the individual organisms in the chain. This is particularly so where one large producer supports a large population of herbivores and carnivores (see Fig 4). In this case it is called an **inverted pyramid**.

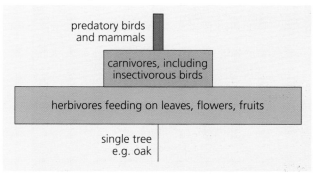

Fig 4 Inverted pyramid of numbers for a food chain based on a tree

A better picture of what is going on in a food chain is provided by a **pyramid of biomass**. This is not based on the number of individuals at a particular trophic level. It looks at the total dry mass of their bodies instead. (Dry mass is the mass remaining after all the water has been removed.)

Respiration uses up food reserves so the body mass decreases. Excretion of waste products, such as carbon dioxide and urea, also leads to a loss of mass, as does the egestion of faeces. Parts fall off plants. All of these will mean that less substance, less mass, gets passed along the food chain. A pyramid of biomass therefore always has the shape of a pyramid, only the slope of the sides can vary.

Q1 What is the difference between a food chain and a food web?

Q2 When is a pyramid of numbers not shaped like a pyramid?

Q3 Why is a pyramid of biomass always shaped like a pyramid?

52 Nutrient cycles – the carbon cycle

In this unit you will learn the answers to these questions:
- How is carbon recycled?
- Where are we going wrong?

Carbon is one of the Earth's most important elements. Much of the planet's carbon is **fixed** into compounds in the bodies of plants and animals. Some of it is **free** in the air in carbon dioxide gas, and some dissolved in the sea and freshwater as hydrogen carbonate.

Plants and animals need a constant supply of carbon to make organic compounds such as carbohydrates, fats and proteins to stay alive.

How is carbon fixed?

Plants absorb carbon dioxide from the air and water around them. **Photosynthesis** fixes the carbon into glucose molecules (see Unit 32). Plants make other carbon compounds from this sugar (see Unit 35). The bodies of plants, whole or in parts, are used by herbivores, and indirectly by carnivores, as **food** (see Units 9 and 51). The carbon which was fixed by photosynthesis is now part of an animal.

The waste materials which plants and animals produce contain carbon.

Fig 1 Getting rid of waste carbon

How is carbon released?

When an organism, or a part of an organism, dies the compounds it contains can be passed on to soil bacteria and fungi as their food. These organisms are called **decomposers** and carry out a process called **decomposition**.

Decomposers release carbon dioxide into the air when they respire. The minerals in their food are released into the soil (see Unit 53). Some of the energy from decomposition is released into the surroundings. You may have noticed that rotting (decomposing) organic material, e.g. compost heaps, get warm.

Plants and animals release carbon dioxide into the air when they respire (see Units 19 and 20).

In the past, large amounts of energy were trapped in fossil fuels such as coal, gas and oil. Today, the process still goes on, forming peat in bogs.

When fossil fuels are burned carbon dioxide is released into the air. The same is true for anything made from plant or animal remains. Wood and paper (made from plant cellulose) will give off carbon dioxide when they are burnt, as will fats and oils made from plant and animal material.

The way in which carbon is fixed and released is one example of the recycling of an element. This cycle is described as the **carbon cycle**. Fig 2 is a summary of the recycling which takes place.

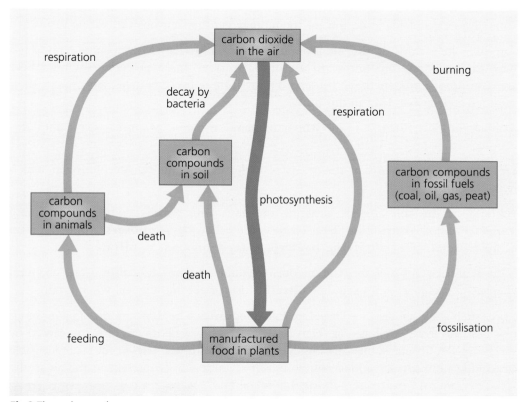

Fig 2 The carbon cycle

Carbon dioxide balance in the air

Scientists believe that for long periods of time in the past the carbon dioxide concentration in the Earth's atmosphere remained fairly constant. However, evidence is building up to suggest that carbon dioxide levels are currently increasing (see Unit 49).

In the match, 'Photosynthesis versus the Rest' (decomposition, respiration and combustion), the 'Rest' are beginning to win. Two human activities in particular which are seriously affecting the recycling of carbon are the burning of fossil fuels and the ploughing up and burning of tropical forests.

Q1 Which process(es) fix carbon dioxide?

Q2 Which process(es) release carbon dioxide?

53 Nutrient cycles – the nitrogen cycle

In this unit you will learn the answers to these questions:
- Which organisms are involved in the recycling of nitrogen?
- How do they do it?
- What has lightning got to do with it?
- How can we help?

How does nitrogen get back into the soil?

Nitrogen is essential for the manufacture of amino acids and, from them, proteins. Animals rely on plants to do this for them. They get their nitrogen by eating plants.

Approximately 80% of the air around plants is nitrogen. Most plants cannot use nitrogen gas. A few organisms can use nitrogen gas to make proteins. Amongst these are a group of nitrogen-fixing bacteria. The way these bacteria help plants to get their nitrogen is described later in this unit.

Animals produce urea, a waste which contains nitrogen. Mammals get rid of this dissolved in urine (see Unit 28).

Dead organisms, or parts of them, e.g. plant leaves, contain valuable nitrogen which living organisms need.

Bacteria in the soil convert proteins and urea into another nitrogen-containing substance called **ammonia**. These bacteria are called **decomposers**. Another group of soil bacteria, called **nitrifying bacteria**, convert ammonia to **nitrates**.

Nitrates are also put back into the soil during thunderstorms. **Lightning** causes chemical changes to take place in the air. The **nitrates** formed get into the soil when it rains.

Plants such as clover, peas and beans are called **legumes**. The root systems of leguminous plants usually have swellings on them (see Fig 1). The swellings are growths, caused by the presence of bacteria that form nodules in the root tissues. These bacteria are capable of making nitrogen-containing compounds from nitrogen gas present in the air in the

soil. They are called **nitrogen-fixing bacteria**. The bacteria do not kill the legume, but do take some organic substances from the plant to use as food. The legume benefits by taking some of the nitrogen-containing substances from the bacteria. This type of feeding relationship, involving 'give-and-take', is called **symbiosis**.

carbohydrate

legume, e.g. clover ⟶⟵ nitrogen-fixing bacteria

nitrogen compounds

Not all nitrogen-fixing bacteria take part in symbiosis. Some nitrogen is fixed by bacteria living free in the soil.

Fig 1 *The root system of a legume, showing root nodules*

How is nitrogen removed from the soil?

Plants absorb nitrates from the soil. Nitrates dissolve in the water in the soil. When water enters the root hairs of a plant, mineral ions, including nitrates, diffuse in too. Active transport is also involved, so high concentrations of nitrates can be absorbed by the roots. The root cells can then make amino acids and proteins.

There are other bacteria present in the soil which undo the beneficial work of nitrifying and nitrogen-fixing bacteria. This group breaks down nitrates to release nitrogen gas. They are called **denitrifying bacteria**.

How do farmers help to 'balance the nitrogen books'?

Farmers may play their part in the following ways:

1 grow leguminous crops, e.g. clover, in crop rotation as part of organic farming practice;

2 sow 'dressed seeds', coated with a culture of the symbiotic bacteria;

3 plough back plant remains, or turf, to provide 'green manure' for decay; and

4 provide additional nitrate by spreading artificial fertilisers (see Unit 34).

The way in which nitrogen is added and taken away from the soil is described as the **nitrogen cycle**. Fig 2 summarises the way this is achieved.

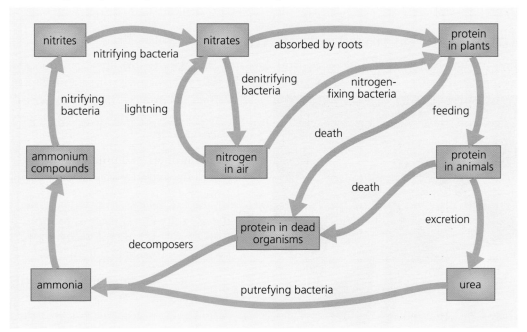

Fig 2 The nitrogen cycle

Q1 What do nitrifying bacteria do?

Q2 How is lightning involved in the nitrogen cycle?

54 Artificial ecosystems

In this unit you will learn the answers to these questions:
- How do farmers get the best yield from their land?
- How can we use low quality land such as moorland to the best advantage?

Unit 51 discussed briefly how the light energy trapped by plants passes along a food chain. By the time it reaches the carnivores, most of the energy has gone elsewhere. It follows therefore that an area of land can feed more people if it is used to grow plants rather than using it to support livestock (milk and meat). In terms of food energy, land would be more economically used if we were all vegetarians.

Intensive farming of plants

The crop yield from a given area of land can be increased by growing plants closer together. There are, however, two things that may reduce the yield which have to be taken into account. Firstly, growing plants closer together increases competition between the individuals in the crop. Secondly, the effect of weeds, insect pests and fungal diseases, which benefit from host plants being close together, will be increased.

Plants compete for light, mineral nutrients and water. There is not much that can be done about the amount of light for field crops, but those grown commercially under glass or in plastic tunnels can be provided with supplementary artificial light. Additional mineral nutrients can be supplied in artificial or natural fertilisers (see Unit 34). Crops may need to be watered.

The losses to insect pests and fungal disease organisms can be kept as low as possible by the use of pesticides (see Unit 49).

Intensive farming of animals

Free-range chickens and pigs need large areas of land. Given this, they can find the necessary amount of food to grow and remain healthy. Alternatively, these animals can be farmed intensively in 'battery units'. The advantages offered by the battery approach include:

1 large numbers of animals can be reared on a relatively small area of land; and

2 the quantity and quality of food, e.g. cereal, eaten by the animals can be better controlled.

The first of these does not necessarily free land for other use, however, because the cereals used to feed the flock or herd must be grown somewhere.

Fig 1 Battery farming of pigs

Hill farming

Mountainous and high moorland areas of Britain have a higher annual rainfall than the lowlands. The soils in these areas are often shallow, with the bedrock not far beneath the surface. Rainwater falling on soils like these dissolves the basic mineral nutrients. As a result they are washed out or '**leached**' from the soil. Mineral–rich water flows along streams to join rivers in the lowland valleys, where they may be deposited to form more fertile soils.

Upland soils tend to be **acidic** and **poor in nutrients**. This severely limits the type of plant which can survive there. Plants which can survive include moorland grasses and heathers. Moorlands are not much good for crop plants which humans eat, but the plants which grow there will support **grazing animals** such as sheep and deer. However, a large area of moorland is necessary to support even a single sheep or deer because of the low energy value of the plants on which they can feed (Fig 2).

Fig 2 *Upland grazing*

Hill farming occurs in some of the upland parts of Central and North Wales, Northern England and Scotland. Sheep are farmed there for meat and wool. Uplands are also used for **silviculture**, with vast areas of moorland being used to establish conifer plantations (Fig 3).

Q1 Give one reason why it would be better, in terms of energy, if more people ate a vegetarian diet.

Q2 Why does it take several acres of moorland to feed one sheep?

 ICT Extra!

Use the Web to explore farming practices used in different parts of the world.

Fig 3 *Conifer plantation*

Materials and their properties

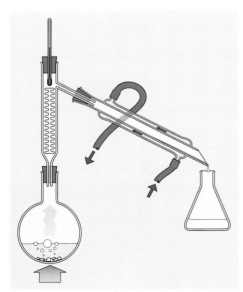

This part of the book covers aspects of Chemistry and Earth Science. It is divided into three sections. Each of these sections build upon topics you have studied at Key Stage 3. They will extend your knowledge and understanding of materials, properties and uses. You will be introduced to important ideas in Chemistry, including writing balanced symbol equations, chemical calculations and the Periodic Table.

Classifying materials extends your understanding of matter being made up of particles and the way particles are arranged in solids, liquids and gases. It also introduces you to a model of the structure of atoms involving protons, neutrons and electrons.

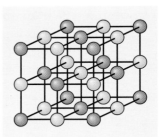

The section introduces the ways in which atoms are joined or bonded together. Ionic and covalent bonding are two important methods of bonding. Bonding in different ways can lead to different structures, including molecular and giant structures. Many properties of materials can be explained in terms of their atomic, ionic or molecular structures.

The second section is **Changing materials**. This includes many more examples of chemical reactions and the use of word and balanced symbol equations to summarise these reactions.

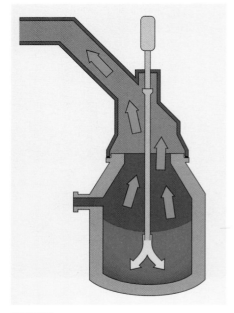

Crude oil is a valuable resource and this section extends your knowledge of how crude oil was formed in the Earth, how it is refined by fractional distillation, and how it is used to make many valuable materials including polymers (plastics).

Metal ores are also important resources in the Earth. This section deals with the methods used to extract metals from their ores, including electrolysis and reduction. The method used to extract a metal from its ores is related to the position of the metal in the reactivity series.

The atmosphere is dealt with in this section, including the composition of the atmosphere and how, by processes including photosynthesis, combustion and respiration, the composition of the atmosphere remains unchanged. Four-fifths of the atmosphere is nitrogen, and nitrogen is used to make ammonia by the Haber process. Most of the ammonia is then converted into nitrogen fertilisers.

This section extends your knowledge and understanding of rocks and how the three types of rocks – igneous, sedimentary and metamorphic – can be formed, and how one type of rock is converted into another. This explains many observations about the formation, deformation and recycling of rocks.

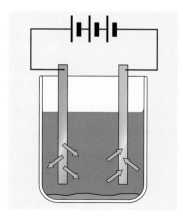

Underpinning this section is an introduction to aspects of quantitative chemistry – chemical calculations. These involve the introduction of the concept of the mole. Chemical calculations can be used to work out the formulae of compounds, the masses of chemicals which will react and be formed in a chemical reaction, and the percentage of nitrogen in, for example, a particular fertiliser.

The third section is **Patterns of behaviour**. In this section a systematic approach to Chemistry is introduced. Much of this section involves the Periodic Table (page 179). You should become used to using the Periodic Table, and a copy of it will be given to

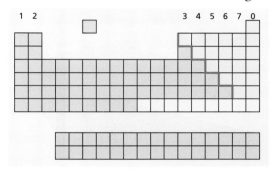

you to use in examinations. In the section you find out how the Periodic Table can be used for explaining the properties of elements. You will study families of similar elements including the alkali metals, the halogens, the noble gases and the transition metals. You will find out how the properties of elements are dependent on the position of the elements in the Periodic Table. You will be able to make simple predictions using the Periodic Table.

You will be aware that chemical reactions proceed at varying rates. In this section you will study factors which affect the rate of reaction. You will also attempt to use simple models to explain why rates of reaction are affected by temperature, concentration etc. You will study the effects of biological catalysts called enzymes and the conditions under which they will operate. Many important industrial processes, e.g. fermentation, are controlled by enzyme processes.

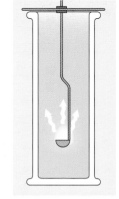

Most reactions convert reactants entirely into products. However, in some reactions 100% conversion is impossible because the products start to react to produce the reactants again. These are called reversible reactions. You will study reversible reactions and how they can lead to the setting up of an equilibrium. You will also study industrial processes where controlling equilibrium conditions is essential for the economic production of a chemical. These include the production of ammonia and sulphuric acid.

Finally in this section, you will look at the changes in energy in chemical reactions. You will be aware that reactions are often accompanied by changes in temperature. Reactions may be exothermic (energy given out to the surroundings) or endothermic (energy taken in from the surroundings). In this section energy changes are related to changes in bonding which occur during reactions.

55 Materials

In this unit you will learn the answers to these questions:
- What are materials?
- What is a property?
- How can materials be grouped according to properties?
- What is a composite material?

Raw materials

Fig 1 shows two houses – an old stone house and a modern brick house.

These houses have been built using a variety of **materials**. Some of these materials are naturally occurring and are called **raw materials**. Other parts of the houses are made using materials made from raw materials.

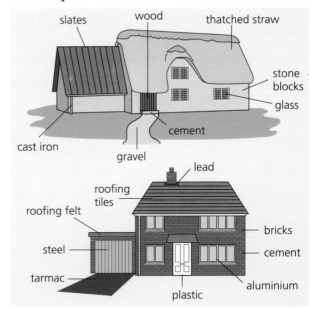

Fig 1 The building materials used in two different houses

Raw materials	Manufactured materials
thatched straw	cement
stone blocks	glass
wood	cast iron
slates	
gravel	

The table contains materials used to make the old stone house.

Q1 Which parts of the modern house are made of:
  a) raw materials
  b) materials manufactured from raw materials?

Q2 What do you notice about the materials used to make a modern house rather than an older house? Suggest a reason for the difference.

We use a particular material because it has an advantage over other possible materials. It is said to have a special **property**.

Properties of glass include:

- it is hard;
- it breaks easily (it is brittle);
- it has a high melting point;
- it does not react with chemicals.

None of these properties explain why glass is used for windows. The main reason is because it has the property of being transparent, i.e. light passes though it.

The properties of a material may make the material either suitable or unsuitable for a particular purpose.

Materials can be classed into five major groups according to their properties. These groups are:

metals   plastics   ceramics (pottery)   glasses   fibres

The table on the next page summarises the main properties of these five materials.

Material group	Example of material	Typical properties of group	Raw material used
metals	iron, steel, lead, copper, brass	hard, strong, high density, good conductors of heat and electricity, malleable (can be beaten into thin sheets), ductile (can be drawn into fine wires), usually burn on heating, high melting points	metal ores in Earth's crust
plastics	poly(ethene), polystyrene, rubber	flexible, low density, easily moulded, poor conductors of heat and electricity, often transparent, melt and often burn on heating	crude oil, sap of rubber trees
ceramics (pottery)	china, concrete, bricks, tiles	hard, brittle, medium density, very high melting point, non-conductors of heat and electricity, very unreactive, do not burn	clay, sand and other minerals
glasses	Pyrex, lead crystal, soft soda glass	same properties as ceramics, often transparent	sand, limestone and other minerals
fibres	cotton, wool, paper, nylon, polyester	flexible, low density, may burn on heating, long stringy strands	natural fibres from plants and animals, crude oil

Q3 The table shows some of the properties of glass, copper, aluminium and stainless steel. Use the properties of materials from above to complete the table. (Copper, aluminium and stainless steel are metals.)

Q4 Why is glass unsuitable for making a saucepan?

Q5 The handle of a saucepan is usually made of plastic or wood. Suggest one property of the material used for the handle which is important.

Property	Glass	Copper	Aluminium	Stainless steel
good conductor of heat				
high density	✓	✓	✗	✓
high melting point				
shiny	✗	✓	✗	✓
reacts with an alkali	✗	✗	✓	✗

When choosing a material for a particular purpose it is important to make sure it has the best properties. Properties can be:

1 **Physical properties**, e.g. hardness, strength, melting point, conductivity of heat and electricity, density, transparency.

2 **Chemical properties**, e.g. does it burn, react with water, corrode, etc.

The relative costs of materials must also be considered.

Composite materials

Often a material has some properties which make it suitable for a particular use but other properties which are not very suitable. Composite materials (or composites) are made of two or more materials which produce a material more suitable for the job than either of the materials separately.

For example, car windscreens can be made of toughened glass or plastic. However, toughened glass still shatters and plastic is too soft and scratches easily. Laminated glass consists of a 'sandwich' of plastic between two thin sheets of glass. It provides a material which does not easily shatter and does not scratch easily.

Other composites include fibreglass and carbon fibre.

56 Solids, liquids and gases

In this unit you will learn the answers to these questions:
- What are states of matter?
- How are particles arranged in solids, liquids and gases?
- How do particles move in solids, liquids and gases?
- What is diffusion?

States of matter

All substances can exist in three states of matter depending upon temperature and pressure. These three states of matter are:

solid   liquid   gas

Water, for example, can exist as:
- ice (solid) below 0°C;
- water (liquid) between 0°C and 100°C;
- steam (gas) above 100°C.

Property	Solid	Liquid	Gas
volume	definite	definite	fills the whole container
shape	definite	takes up the shape of the bottom of the container	takes up the shape of the whole container
density	high	medium	low
ease of flow	does not flow unless powdered	flows easily	flows easily
expansion on heating	low	medium	high
compression	very low	low	high
movement of particles	very slow	medium	fast-moving particles

The properties of solids, liquids and gases are summarised in the table.

Changes of state

When water is heated to 100°C it starts to **boil** and water (liquid) turns to a gas. When steam is cooled, it **condenses** and forms liquid water. When liquid water is cooled to 0°C, the water **freezes** and forms ice. When ice warms up it **melts** and forms liquid water. Steam (or water vapour) in the air can turn directly into solid ice. This happens in a freezer where rapid cooling of water vapour produces ice directly by a process of **sublimation**.

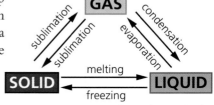

Fig 1 Changes in the state of matter

The changes of state of matter are summarised in Fig 1.

Substances are made up of particles

All solids, liquids and gases are made up of particles. Fig 2 shows simple representations of the arrangements of particles in solids, liquids and gases.

In a solid the particles are closely packed together. The arrangement of particles is usually regular. The particles are vibrating.

In a liquid the particles are not as closely packed as in a solid and the arrangement is not regular.

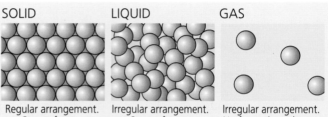

SOLID — Regular arrangement. Strong forces between particles. Particles only vibrate.

LIQUID — Irregular arrangement. Strong forces between particles. Particles move more than in solids.

GAS — Irregular arrangement. No forces (or only very weak forces) between particles. Rapid movement of particles but no pattern to the movement.

Fig 2 Arrangements of particles in solids, liquids and gases

In a gas the particles are not regularly arranged. They are widely spaced and are moving in all directions. This movement is called **random movement**. The particles in a gas collide with each other and also with the walls of the container. Fig 3 shows two samples of gas. In Fig 3a there are more particles than in Fig 3b. The particles in Fig 3a will make more collisions with the walls of the container, so this gas is said to be at a higher pressure than the gas in Fig 3b.

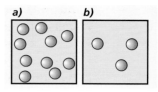

Fig 3 The gas in **a)** is at a higher pressure than the gas in **b)**

Diffusion

The smell of a perfume can spread very quickly through a room. The perfume is made up of millions of tiny particles and these spread out to fill the whole room. This process is called **diffusion**.

Diffusion is the movement of the particles of a gas to fill all of the available space. Diffusion can be demonstrated in the laboratory using bromine (Fig 4). A gas jar filled with air is placed above a gas jar filled with brown bromine vapour. After a few minutes the gases are thoroughly mixed and both gas jars look the same. The bromine particles have spread out to fill both gas jars.

Most examples of diffusion occur with gases. Diffusion does take place in liquids, but more slowly. This is because particles are moving much more slowly in liquids than in gases.

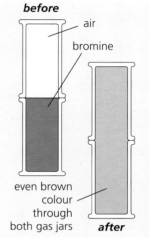

Fig 4 Diffusion of bromine in air

If a crystal of purple potassium manganate(VII) is placed in water, the crystal dissolves and the pink colour spreads evenly through the water (see Unit 4). Without stirring, this can take several hours.

Diffusion is possible in solids, but it is very slow indeed.

Comparing the rates of diffusion of gases

Fig 5 shows a horizontal glass tube which is completely dry. At the same time, pads of cotton wool soaked in concentrated hydrochloric acid and ammonia solution are placed at opposite ends of the tube. Ammonia and hydrogen chloride gases pass along the tube towards each other. When they meet, they form a white solid ring of ammonium chloride.

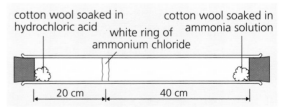

Fig 5 Comparing the rates of diffusion of ammonia and hydrogen chloride

ammonia + hydrogen chloride ➡ ammonium chloride
NH_3 (g) + HCl (g) ➡ NH_4Cl (s)

If the particles of the two gases move at the same speed, you would expect the ring to be formed exactly in the middle of the tube.

The particles are moving fast but the ring takes about five minutes to form.

Q1 What does the diagram tell us about the relative speeds of movement of ammonia and hydrogen chloride particles?

Q2 Why does the ring take five minutes to form?

57 Structure of the atom

In this unit you will learn the answers to these questions:

- ■ What are atoms made up from?
- ■ What is the difference between atomic number and mass number?
- ■ How many protons, neutrons and electrons are there in an atom?
- ■ What are isotopes?

Atoms

Every substance is made up from very tiny particles called **atoms**. Atoms are extremely small. A cube of iron ($2\,cm \times 2\,cm \times 2\,cm$) contains about 600 000 000 000 000 000 000 000 atoms of iron. Each atom has a diameter of about 0.000 000 1 mm and a mass of about 0.000 000 000 000 000 000 000 09 g.

> **Ideas and evidence** About 2500 years ago the Greek thinker Democritus proposed that Being (the physical world) consisted of a vacuum in which moved an infinite number of atoms. Atoms were eternal, indivisible and very small. In fact, these ideas may have existed even earlier. His proposal was not based upon scientific evidence. Aristotle, the most powerful and influential man of his day, strongly disagreed with the idea of atoms, so others did not take up the ideas.

Although the ideas were never completely forgotten, it was not until John Dalton introduced his atomic theory in 1803 that the idea of matter being made up of atoms became widely accepted. Dalton thought of atoms as being similar to snooker balls – hard, solid and impossible to divide. We now know that atoms can be subdivided.

Atoms cannot be seen through ordinary microscopes, which can only distinguish objects about 0.001 mm or larger. Powerful **electron microscopes** have now been developed which can magnify up to two million times. Using an electron microscope, it is possible to see groups of atoms or large single atoms.

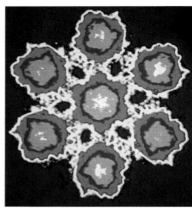

Fig 1 Electron micrograph of uranium atoms in a crystal

 ICT Extra!

Use the Internet to find out the history of development of the idea of atoms. Use atom, Democritus and Dalton as starting points in your search.

Protons, neutrons and electrons

All atoms are made up from three basic particles:

protons, neutrons and **electrons**

An iron atom is different from a copper atom because it contains different numbers of these particles.

All atoms are **neutral**, i.e. there is no overall positive or negative charge.

particle	charge	mass
proton (p)	+1	1 a.m.u.
neutron (n)	0	1 a.m.u.
electron (e)	−1	0

1 a.m.u. (atomic mass unit) is the mass of one twelfth of a carbon-12 atom. It is sometimes called 1 dalton.

Q1 What does this tell you about the numbers of protons and electrons in any atom?

When an atom gains or loses electrons it forms a charged **ion**. An ion does not contain equal numbers of protons and electrons. Note that it is electrons which are lost or gained because they are on the outside of the atom.

Atomic number (Z) and **mass number** (A) are two 'vital statistics' for any atom. The atomic number is the number of protons in an atom. It is also the number of electrons in an atom. The mass number is the total number of protons and neutrons in an atom.

A phosphorus atom has an atomic number of 15 and a mass number of 31. It can be represented as $^{31}_{15}P$. It contains 15 protons, 15 electrons and 16 neutrons. The number of neutrons is the difference between the mass number and the atomic number.

Q2 Lithium has an atomic number of 3 and a mass number of 7. How many protons, electrons and neutrons are there in a lithium atom?

Arrangement of protons, neutrons and electrons

In any atom the protons and neutrons are tightly packed together in the **nucleus** (Fig 2). The nucleus is positively charged.

The electrons move around the nucleus at high speeds in certain **shells** or **energy levels**. Each shell can only contain up to a fixed maximum number of electrons (Fig 3).

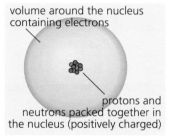

Fig 2 Arrangement of protons, neutrons and electrons in an atom

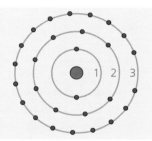

Fig 3 Maximum number of electrons in shells 1, 2 and 3

Fig 4 shows simple representations of some atoms.

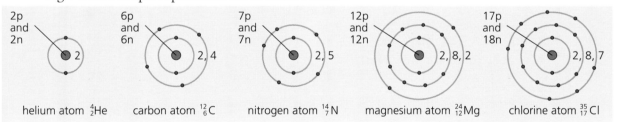

helium atom $^{4}_{2}He$ carbon atom $^{12}_{6}C$ nitrogen atom $^{14}_{7}N$ magnesium atom $^{24}_{12}Mg$ chlorine atom $^{35}_{17}Cl$

Fig 4 Simple diagrams of some atoms

Isotopes

Atoms of the same element containing different numbers of neutrons but, of course, the same number of protons and electrons are called **isotopes**. For example, there are three isotopes of hydrogen (Fig 5):

■ normal hydrogen atom, $^{1}_{1}H$ (1 proton, 1 electron, 0 neutrons);
■ heavy hydrogen atom (deuterium), $^{2}_{1}H$ (1 proton, 1 electron, 1 neutron);
■ radioactive hydrogen atom (tritium), $^{3}_{1}H$ (1 proton, 1 electron, 2 neutrons).

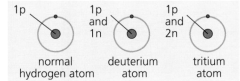

All three atoms are hydrogen atoms because they contain one proton and one electron. The three isotopes of hydrogen have the same chemical properties but slightly different physical properties.

Fig 5 The three isotopes of hydrogen

58 Ionic bonding

In this unit you will learn the answers to these questions:
- What is ionic bonding?
- What properties will ionic compounds have?

Ionic bonding is one way of joining atoms together. It usually involves the combining of a metal atom with a non-metal atom.

The common example of ionic bonding is sodium chloride. The arrangement of electrons in sodium and chlorine atoms is:

    Na   2, 8, 1   Cl   2, 8, 7

To understand how sodium and chlorine atoms bond, you must first understand a little about **noble gases** (see Unit 91). Noble gases have very stable electron arrangements, and atoms of other elements gain and lose electrons in order to achieve similar electron arrangements. (The noble gases are helium, neon, argon, krypton, xenon and radon.)

A sodium atom has one more electron than the noble gas neon. A chlorine atom has one less electron than the noble gas argon.

The sodium atom loses one electron and forms a sodium ion, Na^+, with an electron arrangement of 2, 8. The chlorine atom gains one electron and forms a chloride ion, Cl^-, with an electron arrangement of 2,8,8.

$$Na \atop atom \Rightarrow Na^+ + e^- \atop ion$$

$$Cl + e^- \atop atom \Rightarrow Cl^- \atop ion$$

The sodium and chloride ions are held together by strong electrostatic forces. This can be summarised by Fig 1.

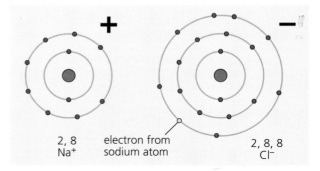

2, 8
Na^+ electron from sodium atom   2, 8, 8
Cl^-

Fig 1 *Electron arrangements of Na^+ and Cl^-*

Another example of ionic bonding is magnesium oxide. The electron arrangements of magnesium and oxygen atoms are:

    Mg 2, 8, 2   O   2, 6

Two electrons are lost by each magnesium atom and two electrons are gained by each oxygen atom.

$$Mg \Rightarrow Mg^{2+} + 2e^-$$
$$O + 2e^- \Rightarrow O^{2-}$$

Both magnesium ions and oxide ions have the same electron arrangement as neon, i.e. 2, 8 (with full outer electron shells). Again, strong electrostatic forces hold the ions together.

Properties of ionic compounds

Compounds containing ionic bonds usually have high melting and boiling points. At room temperature they are usually crystalline solids. The ions are held together in a **lattice**. Fig 2 shows a sodium chloride lattice. This is a cubic arrangement of sodium and chloride ions. Each sodium ion in the lattice is surrounded by six chloride ions and each chloride ion in the structure is surrounded by six sodium ions. The high melting point is due to the very strong electrostatic forces between these ions. Ionic compounds do not conduct electricity when solid but do conduct when molten or in aqueous solution.

Q1 Lithium and nitrogen form a compound Li$_3$N.
   a) What are the electron arrangements in lithium and nitrogen atoms?
   b) Assuming that the bonding is ionic, what changes take place when lithium and nitrogen combine?
   c) Why would you expect lithium nitride to have a different crystal lattice structure from sodium chloride or magnesium oxide?

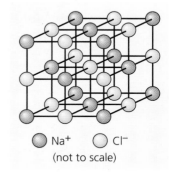

Na$^+$ Cl$^-$
(not to scale)

Fig 2 *Sodium chloride lattice*

Substances containing ionic bonding usually dissolve in water to form a solution which conducts electricity. These substances do not usually dissolve in organic solvents such as hexane or methylbenzene.

Q2 Why is the melting point of magnesium oxide much greater than the melting point of sodium chloride?

Crystal structure

The regular arrangement of ions in a lattice of sodium chloride will lead to the formation of a **crystal**. Crystalline structures are evidence of the regular arrangement of particles. There are seven basic crystal shapes. These are shown in Fig 3.

Q3 What are the crystal shapes of
   a) sugar
   b) salt (sodium chloride)?

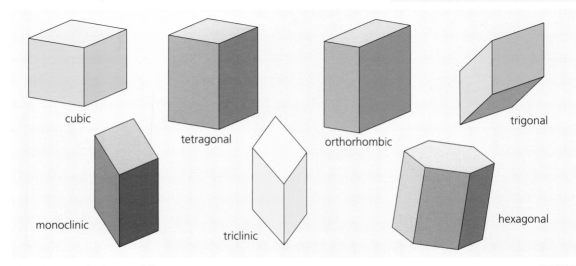

cubic

tetragonal

orthorhombic

trigonal

monoclinic

triclinic

hexagonal

Fig 3 *The seven basic crystal shapes*

59 Covalent bonding

In this unit you will learn the answers to these questions:
- ■ What is covalent bonding?
- ■ What properties do compounds containing covalent bonding have?

Covalent bonding is a way of joining atoms together which involves the **sharing of electrons** between two atoms. It is particularly used to join **non-metal atoms** together.

For example, two hydrogen atoms join together with a **single covalent bond**. Each hydrogen atom has a single electron. The two electrons, one from each atom, form an electron pair which joins the two hydrogen atoms together.

H_×H   H$_2$
electron pair

The electrons are shared so as to give each atom a full outer shell.

H–H

The electron pair is usually represented as a single bond by a single line.

Another example of covalent bonding is a chlorine molecule, where two chlorine atoms are bonded together by a single covalent bond. There are now eight electrons associated with each chlorine atom.

$\overset{x\;x}{\underset{x\;x}{×}}Cl\overset{•\;•}{\underset{•\;•}{×}}Cl\overset{•\;•}{\underset{•\;•}{:}}$ Cl–Cl   Cl$_2$

before bonding   after bonding   CH$_4$

Methane is a compound of carbon and hydrogen with each molecule containing four single covalent bonds. In each bond one electron comes from the carbon atom and one from the hydrogen atom. The pair of electrons is then shared.

Other examples of molecules containing single covalent bonds include:

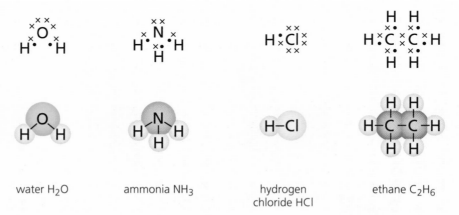

water H$_2$O   ammonia NH$_3$ hydrogen chloride HCl   ethane C$_2$H$_6$

Q1 Draw diagrams to show the arrangement of electrons in molecules of hydrogen bromide, HBr, and phosphorus trichloride, PCl$_3$. Use the Periodic Table on page 189 to help you.

Oxygen, O_2, is an example of covalent bonding containing a **double covalent bond**. Here each oxygen atom gives two electrons and two covalent bonds are formed, each containing two electrons.

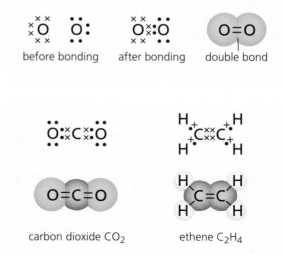

before bonding   after bonding   double bond

Other molecules containing double covalent bonds are carbon dioxide and ethene.

The double bond is represented by two lines.

carbon dioxide CO_2 ethene C_2H_4

before bonding   after bonding   triple bond

A nitrogen molecule contains two nitrogen atoms bonded together with a **triple covalent bond**. Each nitrogen atom gives three electrons and three covalent bonds are formed.

Another example of a compound containing a triple covalent bond is ethyne.

The triple bond is represented by three lines.

C_2H_2

Properties of substances containing covalent bonds

In all of the examples of covalent bonding, small, separate molecules are produced. It is possible for covalent bonding to produce large structures. These are considered in Unit 60.

Covalent bonds have a definite direction which give covalent molecules a definite shape. For example, water is a bent molecule with an angle of approximately 104° between the bonds and not a straight line as might be expected.

A compound consisting of small molecules containing covalent bonding will have a low melting point and a low boiling point. They are frequently gases or low boiling point liquids or solids. They are usually insoluble in water but soluble in organic solvents.

Q2 Using a simple particle model (Unit 56), explain why the boiling point of hydrogen, H_2, is much lower than the boiling point of oxygen, O_2.

60 **Structure**

In this unit you will learn the answers to these questions:
- ■ What are giant structures?
- ■ What is allotropy?
- ■ How are properties of substances related to structure?

Molecular structures and giant structures

The table shows some of the properties of iodine, silicon(IV) oxide, sodium chloride, and iron.

Substance	Melting point/°C	Boiling point/°C	Electrical conductivity when solid	Electrical conductivity when molten	Type of structure
iodine	114	183	none	none	molecular structure
silicon(IV) oxide	1610	2230	none	none	giant structure of atoms
sodium chloride	808	1465	none	good	giant structure of ions
iron	1540	3000	good	good	giant structure of atoms (metal structure)

When iodine crystals are heated they melt at a low temperature and form a dark-coloured liquid. On further heating the liquid boils and a purple vapour is produced. This consists of I_2 molecules. Iodine crystals (Fig 1) are in a **molecular structure** made up of iodine molecules regularly arranged and joined together by weak forces. Gentle heating breaks down the forces between the molecules without breaking the forces within the molecules.

● represents an iodine atom

— represents a strong covalent bond (2 shared electrons) between 2 iodine atoms

... represents weak attractive forces between iodine atoms

Fig 1 Iodine crystals

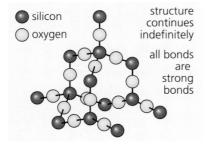

● silicon
○ oxygen

structure continues indefinitely

all bonds are strong bonds

Fig 2 Silicon(IV) oxide

In contrast, heating silicon(IV) oxide produces no change until a high temperature is reached. This is because the atoms of silicon and oxygen are all bonded together to form one large molecule or **giant structure**. This is shown in Fig 2. Molten silicon(IV) oxide does not conduct electricity.

Sodium chloride consists of a **giant structure of ions** (Fig 2, Unit 58). When solid, the ions are not free to move and so electricity is not conducted through the crystal. When heated to a high temperature, the molten sodium chloride conducts electricity because there are **free ions**. When an electric current passes, free ions move through the melt and carry the charge.

Iron consists of a closely packed **giant structure of atoms** with electrons free to move through the structure to give good electrical conductivity. Fig 3 shows a layer of close packed atoms in iron. The sea of free electrons carry the electrical charge through a metal.

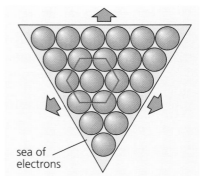

sea of electrons

Fig 3 Part of an iron layer

Forms of carbon

Diamond and **graphite** are two forms of carbon with different properties and different structures. Different forms of the same element, in the same physical state, are called **allotropes**. Fig 4 shows the arrangement of atoms in diamond and graphite.

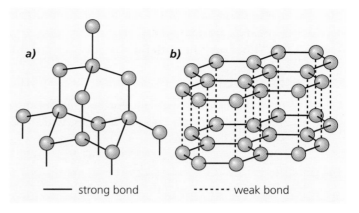

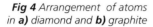
— strong bond   ------ weak bond

Fig 4 Arrangement of atoms in **a)** diamond and **b)** graphite

Diamonds were formed in the Earth when carbon was subjected to tremendous pressures as the Earth cooled. The arrangement of carbon atoms is tetrahedral. Each carbon atom is attached to four other carbon atoms. All of the bonds are strong so it is difficult to break up the structure.

Graphite has a layer structure. Although the bonds within each layer are very strong, the forces between the layers are very weak. Graphite is soft because the layers slide easily over each other. Graphite, unlike diamond, is a good conductor of electricity as electrons move easily though the structure.

A chance discovery in 1985 led to the identification of a new allotrope of carbon. In fact, a new family of closed carbon clusters has been identified and called **fullerenes**. Two fullerenes, C_{60} and C_{70}, can be prepared by electrically evaporating carbon electrodes in helium gas at low pressure. They dissolve in benzene to produce a red solution.

Q1 Why is it important to evaporate carbon in helium rather than air?

Q2 Refer to Unit 65. Suggest a method for separating the different fullerenes dissolved in benzene.

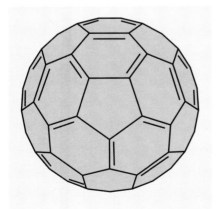

Fig 5 Buckminsterfullerene (C_{60})

Fig 5 shows C_{60} – sometimes called buckminsterfullerene after R. Buckminster Fuller, the American who designed the geodesic dome that resembles the structure of fullerene.

Carbon fibre is a new material which is stronger and less dense than steel. It can be used for golf clubs, tennis rackets and bicycle frames. Carbon fibre is formed by partial decomposition of fibres. The structure consists of graphite layers arranged along the fibre to give strength.

Fig 6 A carbon fibre tennis racket

In this unit you will learn the answers to these questions:
- **What are elements?**
- **What are the differences between mixtures and compounds?**

Elements

Pure substances which cannot be split up into simpler substances are called **elements**. There are over 100 known elements, with 92 occurring naturally. Each element can be represented by a **symbol**, e.g. O for oxygen, Ca for calcium, Fe for iron, Mg for magnesium.

Q1 Use the Periodic Table on page 189 to identify the elements represented by the following symbols.

H; S; Na; Cl; P; K; Sb; Mn; Pb; Au; Ag; Hg.

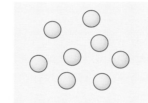

Most of the elements are metals. There are 22 non-metallic elements.

Elements are composed of **atoms**. All atoms of the same element contain the same number of protons. A lump of sulphur is made up from sulphur atoms and a lump of carbon is made up from carbon atoms. Fig 1 shows a simple representation of atoms in sulphur and in carbon.

Key ⬤ carbon ◯ sulphur

Fig 1 *Atoms in the elements carbon and sulphur*

Mixtures

Many substances exist as mixtures of other pure substances.

1 Air is a mixture of gases.

2 Universal Indicator is a mixture of simple indicators.

3 Sea water is a mixture of substances dissolved in water.

4 Crude oil is a mixture of hydrocarbons.

Fig 2 shows a simple representation of the atoms in two mixtures of carbon and sulphur.

You will notice that the atoms of carbon and sulphur are not joined and the proportions of the two elements in the two mixtures are different.

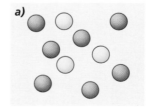
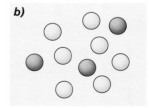

Fig 2 *Mixtures of carbon and sulphur atoms*

Q2 Which mixture *a)* or *b)* contains the greater proportion of carbon?

The properties of a mixture are always the same as the properties of the substances which make up the mixture. Sea water tastes salty because of the salt it contains.

A pure substance has a definite melting point. An impure substance (i.e. a mixture of substances) melts at a lower temperature and over a range of temperature. Butter is a mixture and it melts in a frying pan over a range of temperature.

Compounds

Compounds are pure substances made from two or more elements joined together. Some compounds may be split up or **decomposed** by heat (Fig 3) or electricity (Fig 4).

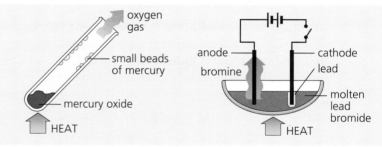

Fig 3 *Thermal decomposition: heating mercury oxide splits mercury oxide into mercury and oxygen*

Fig 4 *Electrolysis: molten lead bromide is split up into lead and bromine by electrolysis*

Joining elements together involves a **chemical reaction** called **synthesis**, e.g. heating a mixture of iron and sulphur forms a compound called iron sulphide. Fig 5 shows the change which occurs when iron sulphide is formed.

The composition of a compound is fixed. For example, iron sulphide contains 7 parts of iron and 4 parts of sulphur by mass. You will notice that one iron atom is combined with one sulphur atom. For this reason the **formula** of iron sulphide is written as FeS.

The table compares the properties of a mixture and a compound.

Mixture	Compound
Proportions of different elements can be altered	Different elements have to be present in fixed proportions
Elements can be separated by simple methods	Difficult to separate into its constituent elements
Properties of the mixture are the same as the properties of the elements making it up	Properties of the compound are different from the properties of the elements making it up
No energy change when a mixture is made	Energy is usually evolved or absorbed when a compound is formed

Ideas and evidence

John Dalton introduced symbols for elements and compounds. Some of these are shown in Fig 6. Some of his elements were not elements. Later it was found that they could be split up.

He understood that compounds were made when atoms of elements combined. He did not realise, however, that the ratio of each element was not always 1:1.

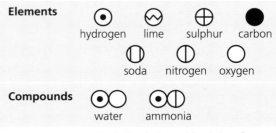

Fig 5 *The synthesis of iron sulphide*

Q3 Hydrogen and oxygen combine together to form water, H_2O. In both hydrogen gas and oxygen gas the atoms are in pairs, i.e. H_2 and O_2.

Draw diagrams to show particles in **a)** hydrogen gas; **b)** oxygen gas; **c)** a mixture of hydrogen and oxygen; **d)** steam.

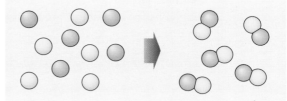

Fig 6 *Symbols used by Dalton for some elements and compounds*

Q4 Which of the elements Dalton listed are now known not to be elements? Use the Periodic Table on page 189 to help you.

Q5 Use modern symbols to represent the formulae of water and ammonia proposed by Dalton. Use Dalton's symbols to write the correct formulae for water and ammonia.

62 Separating mixtures – 1

In this unit you will learn the answers to these questions:
■ How does purity affect the price of chemicals?
■ How can sodium chloride be purified?
■ How can chemicals be purified using other solvents?

Purity

Separating mixtures of substances is very important in producing pure chemicals. Pure chemicals are essential for certain uses, e.g. medical uses, food production.

Below is information from a chemical catalogue about three grades of sodium chloride:

1 Technical grade,
2 General purpose reagent grade (GPR),
3 Analytical grade (Analar).

Sodium chloride technical	
3 kg	£5.50

Sodium chloride GPR	
Minimum purity	99.5%
Maximum limits of impurities	
Loss on drying at 105°C	1.0%
Sulphate	0.02%
Ammonia	0.002%
Iron	0.002%
Lead	0.0005%
Potassium	0.02%
1 kg	£4.10

Sodium chloride 'Analar'	
Minimum purity	99.8%
Maximum limits of impurities	
Water insoluble matter	0.003%
Bromide	0.005%
Ferrocyanide	0.00001%
Iodide	0.001%
Nitrogen compounds	0.0005%
Phosphate	0.0005%
Sulphate	0.002%
Barium	0.001%
Calcium	0.002%
Copper	0.0002%
Iron	0.0002%
Lead	0.0002%
Magnesium	0.002%
Potassium	0.005%
500 g	£3.40

Q1 Compare the prices of 3 kg of each grade of sodium chloride.

Q2 What is the minimum purity of GPR sodium chloride?

Q3 As the purity increases, the cost _____.

Uses of salt (sodium chloride)

The table gives some uses of sodium chloride.

Q4 Which of the uses in the table require pure sodium chloride?

Uses of sodium chloride
1 De-icing roads
2 Flavouring food
3 Preservative for butter, meat and fish
4 Making sodium carbonate industrially
5 Making sodium hydroxide, chlorine and hydrogen industrially
6 Salting out soap in the soapmaking process

Making pure sodium chloride

Sodium chloride is found in rock salt which consists of salt crystals mixed with insoluble materials such as sandstone. It can be mined as solid rock salt or mined by **solution mining** (Fig 2). A hole is drilled down to the salt deposits, cold water is pumped down to the deposits and salt solution (brine) is pumped back to the surface.

Fig 1 *Electron micrograph of pure sodium chloride*

Q5 Why can salt be mined by solution mining but coal cannot?

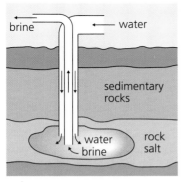

Fig 2 *Solution mining*

Salt can be purified by a series of processes. These are summarised in Fig 3.

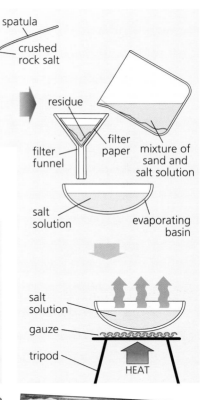

Fig 3 *Purification of rock salt*

The salt produced by these processes will not be completely pure as it may still contain some of the soluble impurities.

Q6 Give two ways in which the dissolving of sodium chloride is speeded up in this experiment.

Q7 In the evaporation of sodium chloride solution, the solution starts to spit. Suggest two ways of slowing down the rate of evaporation, apart from removing the flame or turning down the gas.

Q8 Using the data in the table from the chemical catalogue, suggest likely impurities in the salt produced from rock salt.

Although water is a very good solvent which dissolves a wide range of substances, other solvents may be used in the purification of substances. Ethanol (meths), propanone and hexane are three **organic solvents** which can be used to purify substances.

In many places in the world, salt is produced from sea water. The photograph shows salt being produced in Brazil.

Q9 What is the source of energy used in this process?

Q10 Why are large, shallow lakes better than small, deep lakes for producing salt in this way?

63 Separating mixtures – 2

In this unit you will learn the answers to these questions:
- **What is distillation?**
- **What are miscible and immiscible liquids?**
- **How would you separate miscible liquids?**

Separating a liquid from a solid

Water can be obtained from a solution of a solid in water by the process of **distillation**.

For example, water can be obtained from a salt solution by distillation. Fig 1 shows a simple distillation apparatus which can be used to obtain pure water from a salt solution.

The following points should be remembered about simple distillation.

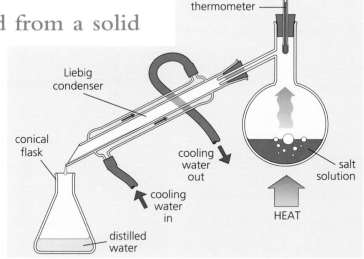

Fig 1 *Distillation apparatus*

1 Distillation consists of boiling followed by condensation.

2 Only steam leaves the flask. The solid salt remains in the flask.

3 The bulb of the thermometer should be alongside the exit to the condenser. The maximum temperature on the thermometer during the experiment should be 100°C – the boiling point of water.

4 The condenser is used for the efficient condensation of the steam. The cooling water should enter at the bottom of the condenser and leave at the top. The condenser must slope downward.

5 There should not be a stopper in the receiver, i.e the receiver should be open at the top.

6 The liquid collected in the receiver is called the **distillate**.

Separating mixtures of liquids

When two liquids are poured into the same container they may:

1 not mix but form two separate layers, **2** mix completely and form a single layer.

When the two liquids form separate layers they are said to be **immiscible** and when they mix completely and form a single layer they are said to be **miscible**.

An example of two immiscible liquids is glycerol and water. The table gives the densities of these two immiscible liquids.

Liquid	Density in g/cm³
water	1.00
glycerol	1.26

Fig 2 shows the two liquids, glycerol and water, in a beaker. There are two layers with glycerol, the denser liquid, forming the lower layer. Immiscible liquids are best separated with a separating funnel (see Fig 3).

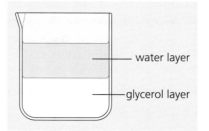

Fig 2 *Glycerol and water*

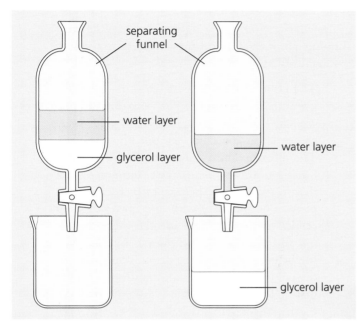

Fig 3 *Separating liquids with a separating funnel*

When two immiscible liquids are shaken together, an **emulsion** may be formed. An emulsion consists of small droplets of one liquid spread through the other liquid. Fig 4 shows an emulsion of oil–in–water viewed through a microscope. Droplets of oil are distributed through the water layer. Milk is an example of an oil–in–water emulsion.

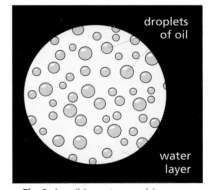

Fig 4 *An oil-in-water emulsion as seen through a microscope*

Q1 What would happen if a water-soluble dye was added to an oil-in-water emulsion?

Q2 Butter is a water-in-oil emulsion. What is a water-in-oil emulsion?

An **emulsifying agent** is added to an emulsion to stop the emulsion separating into two layers – an oil layer and a water layer.

Q3 Put the six statements below into the correct order so that they describe the method used to separate glycerol and water.

A Put a second beaker under the separating funnel.

B Put the mixture of water and glycerol into a separating funnel.

C Leave the liquids to settle out into two layers.

D Open the tap and allow the water to run into a beaker.

E Remove the stopper from the separating funnel.

F Open the tap and allow the glycerol to run into a beaker.

Miscible liquids can be separated by **fractional distillation** (see Unit 64).

64 Separating mixtures – 3

In this unit you will learn the answers to these questions:
- What is fractional distillation?
- What do petrol and whisky have in common?
- What is sublimation and how can it be used to separate substances?

Fractional distillation

Fractional distillation can be used to separate two or more liquids that have *different boiling points*. For example, hexane (boiling point 69°C) and methylbenzene (boiling point 111°C) can be separated by fractional distillation.

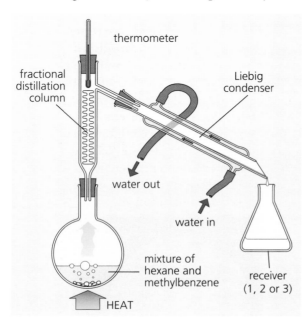

The apparatus in Fig 1 can be used for fractional distillation. The mixture to be separated is placed in the flask and small pieces of broken china are put into the flask. The broken china helps to ensure smooth boiling without the mixture 'bumping'. The flask is then slowly heated with receiver 1 in place. The hexane, with the lower boiling point, starts to boil first and the vapour passes up the fractional distillation column. Any methylbenzene that vaporises condenses in the column and the liquid drops back into the flask. The temperature shown by the thermometer remains below 69°C and only the hexane distils over. The liquid collected in the first receiver is called the **first fraction**. It consists almost entirely of hexane.

Fig 1 *Fractional distillation*

When the temperature reaches 70°C, receiver 2 is put in place. It is removed when the temperature rises to 110°C. The second fraction (liquid boiling between 70°C and 111°C) is collected. Receiver 3 is then put in place and a third fraction (liquid boiling above 111°C) is collected, which consists largely of methylbenzene.

Fractional distillation is used in the refining of crude oil (Unit 68).

Q1 Why are fractions 1 and 3 large, but fraction 2 very small?

Whisky production

Whisky is a spirit produced by the fractional distillation of a mixture of ethanol (boiling point 78°C) and water (boiling point 100°C).

Barley is malted by soaking the seeds in water and allowing them to germinate in a warm, damp atmosphere. When the barley has germinated, further growth is stopped by drying the barley in a peat-fired oven. The peat smoke gives much flavour to the whisky. The malt is then ground into a fine powder and the powder is mixed with warm water to produce a sugary solution called 'wort'. This process is called **mashing**.

The wort is mixed with yeast and **fermentation** takes place (see Unit 72). This turns the sugar into ethanol. The resulting mixture of ethanol and water is then distilled twice in copper fractional distillation vessels called **stills**. The stills are usually heated internally by steam-filled pipes. The resulting concentrated ethanol solution is stored in oak casks for years to mature. During the maturing process the whisky absorbs colouring and flavour from the casks.

Mashing

Fermentation

Maturation

Q2 During the fermentation froth is seen. What is produced to cause this froth?

 ICT Extra!

Use the Internet to find out more about how whisky is made. Start with (http://www.scotch-whisky.org.uk). Find out how Irish whisky and American rye whisky are made.

Sublimation

If a mixture of sodium chloride and ammonium chloride is heated in the apparatus in Fig 2, the sodium chloride remains in the evaporating basin and the ammonium chloride re-forms after **sublimation** on the cool walls of the funnel. Iodine can also be separated from mixtures by sublimation.

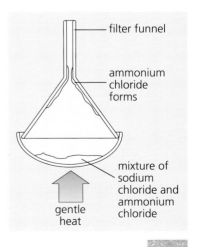

filter funnel

ammonium chloride forms

mixture of sodium chloride and ammonium chloride

gentle heat

Fig 2

65 Separating mixtures – 4

In this unit you will learn the answers to these questions:
■ What is chromatography?
■ How can chromatography be used to identify substances present in a mixture?

Chromatography

Chromatography is a method which can be used to separate mixtures of substances dissolved in a solvent. It was first carried out in 1903 by the Russian biologist Mikhail Tswett. He used a glass column packed with powdered chalk to separate plant pigments. A solution of plant pigments dissolved in petrol was poured through the column (Fig 1). The different dyes separated out and different bands were formed. These bands formed because the different dyes passed through the column at different rates.

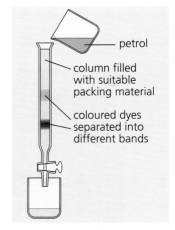

petrol

column filled with suitable packing material

coloured dyes separated into different bands

Fig 1 Column chromatography to separate plant dyes

Paper chromatography

In 1944 scientists showed that paper could be used to identify the components in a mixture and separate small quantities of these materials.

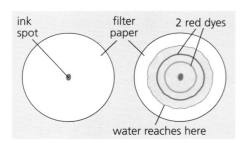

ink spot   filter paper   2 red dyes

water reaches here

Fig 2 Simple paper chromatography with red ink

The dyes that are present in a red ink can be separated by simple **paper chromatography**. A spot of the red ink is dropped onto the centre of a filter paper circle (Fig 2). The ink is left to dry. Drops of water are then dropped onto the centre of the ink spot using a teat pipette. If this is done slowly and carefully the ink blot gets larger. The different dyes present in the ink spread out at different rates. Each dye forms a separate ring. In Fig 2 it can be seen that the red ink contains two red dyes.

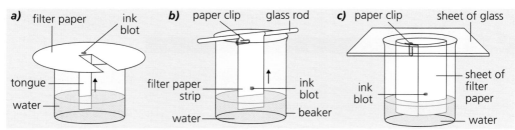

Fig 3 Three alternative ways of carrying out paper chromatography

Fig 3 shows three alternative ways of carrying out paper chromatography. In *a)* a filter paper is used with a small 'tongue' cut out. The 'tongue' dips into water in the beaker. The water slowly rises up the 'tongue', reaches the blot on the filter paper and the blot spreads out as before. In *b)* and *c)* the separation of dyes takes place on a strip or sheet of filter paper. In each case the water (or solvent) moves upwards and the dyes separate to form spots on the filter paper. Each dye present forms a separate spot. This type of chromatography is called ascending paper chromatography and the resulting strip or sheet of filter paper is called a **chromatogram**.

Identifying the dyes present in a sample

Fig 4 shows a chromatogram for a blue ink and also for three separate pure dyes – a pale blue dye, a dark blue dye and a purple dye. From these results we can conclude that:

1 the pale blue, dark blue and purple dyes are not split up as they each produce only a single spot on the chromatogram;

2 the blue ink is made up from a mixture of pale blue and purple dyes. The chromatogram for the blue ink shows two spots in the same positions on the chromatogram as the spots for pale blue and purple dyes.

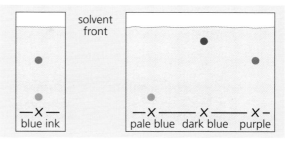

Fig 4 *Paper chromatography of blue ink and three dyes*

Q1 Fig 5 shows a chromatogram of the colour from orange squash and five possible dyes which could be used as colouring.

a) Why is the spot for A further up the paper than B, C or D?

b) Which dye or dyes are present in the colouring in the orange squash?

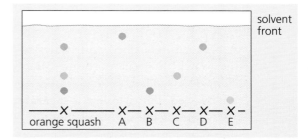

Fig 5 *Chromatography of orange squash*

Uses of paper chromatography

Paper chromatography is used to identify the colouring in coloured solutions, e.g. squashes, felt pens. In these cases the solvent is water.

2 Amino acids are colourless. Mixtures of amino acids can be separated by paper chromatography. The chromatogram is sprayed with a developing chemical called ninhydrin. The amino acids then show up as bluish spots.

3 A child suffering from phenylketonuria ('PKU') produces chemicals called ketones in its urine. Paper chromatography can be used to identify the presence of ketones in urine.

Q2 Ballpen ink is not soluble in water but is soluble in ethanol. How should you modify the method for paper chromatography if you wished to find the dyes present in a ballpen ink?

Q3 Fruit juices contain amino acids. It is illegal to add other amino acids to fruit juices to act as sweeteners. How would you try to show that amino acids had not been added?

Gas–liquid chromatography

Gas–liquid chromatography is a technique widely used in industry to identify substances present in a mixture. In 1952 Martin and James showed that this method was useful for separating small quantities of volatile materials. A small sample is injected into a stream of carrier gas. The different substances pass through the gas column at different rates.

66 Solubility

In this unit you will learn the answers to these questions:
- What is solubility?
- How can you find the solubility of a solute at a particular temperature?
- How does the solubility of a solute vary with temperature?
- What is a solubility curve?

We have seen that water is a good **solvent** because it dissolves a wide range of substances (called **solutes**). Some solutes dissolve more than others.

> **The solubility of a solute is the mass of the solute that dissolves in 100 g of solvent at a particular temperature.**

The solubility of sodium chloride

Fig 1 summarises the steps that should be taken to find the solubility of sodium chloride (salt) in water *at room temperature*.

A beaker is half filled with water at room temperature. Sodium chloride is added to the water in small portions. After each addition, the solution is stirred. Sodium chloride is added until no more sodium chloride will dissolve and some remains undissolved. This is called a **saturated solution**. A dry evaporating basin is weighed and some of the saturated solution, without sodium chloride crystals, is poured into the evaporating basin, which is then weighed again. The solution is carefully evaporated to dryness. After cooling the evaporating basin is weighed again.

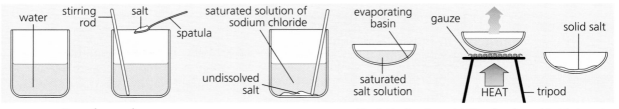

Fig 1 *Finding the solubility of sodium chloride in water*

Sample results:

1 Mass of evaporating basin $= 50.25\,\text{g}$

2 Mass of evaporating basin + sodium chloride solution $= 118.25\,\text{g}$

3 Mass of evaporating basin + solid sodium chloride $= 68.25\,\text{g}$

From these results:

Mass of sodium chloride solution $= \boxed{2} - \boxed{1} = 118.25\,\text{g} - 50.25\,\text{g} = 68.00\,\text{g}$

Mass of solid sodium chloride $= \boxed{3} - \boxed{1} = 68.25\,\text{g} - 50.25\,\text{g} = 18.00\,\text{g}$

Mass of water in solution $= \boxed{3} - \boxed{2} = 118.25\,\text{g} - 68.25\,\text{g} = 50.00\,\text{g}$

18.00 g of sodium chloride dissolved in 50.00 g of water at room temperature. Therefore, $\frac{18}{50} \times 100\,\text{g}$ of sodium chloride dissolved in 100 g of water at room temperature. The solubility of sodium chloride at room temperature is 36.0 g of sodium chloride per 100 g of water.

The solubility of potassium chlorate at different temperatures

A weighed mass of potassium chlorate is put into a dry test tube. A measured volume of water is added to the test tube and the test tube is heated until all the solid potassium chlorate has dissolved. The test tube is then allowed to cool and the solution is constantly stirred with a thermometer (Fig 2). The temperature when crystals first start to appear is noted. A known volume of water is added to the test tube and the test tube is reheated and cooled as before. A new temperature is recorded. If this is repeated, a series of volumes of water and temperatures are recorded. Sample results are shown in the table for an experiment using 2.0 g of potassium chlorate.

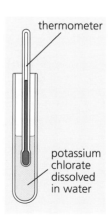

thermometer

potassium chlorate dissolved in water

Fig 2

Total volume of water/cm³	Total mass of water/g	Temperature at which crystals are first seen/°C	Solubility (calculated) in g per 100 g of water $\dfrac{\text{mass of potassium chlorate}}{\text{mass of water}} \times 100$
4	4	90	$2/4 \times 100 = 50.0$
6	6	74	$2/6 \times 100 = 33.3$
8	8	62	$2/8 \times 100 = 25.0$
12	12	48	$2/12 \times 100 = 16.7$
16	16	36	$2/16 \times 100 = 12.5$
20	20	27	$2/20 \times 100 = 10.0$

Note that the mass of 1 cm³ of water is 1 g.

Solubility curves

The experiment with sodium chloride at room temperature could be repeated using saturated solutions prepared at different temperatures. You would then be able to see how the solubility of a solute changes with temperature. This is best shown in a graph, called a **solubility curve**. This is a graph of solubility of a solute (on the vertical, or y, axis) against temperature (on the horizontal, or x, axis).

Fig 3 shows a solubility curve for potassium chlorate in water. You will notice that the solubility of potassium chlorate increases with increasing temperature. This is true with most solutes in water. Use the solubility curve for potassium chlorate to answer the following questions.

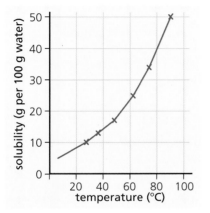

Q1 What is the solubility of potassium chlorate in water at 20°C?

Q2 What is the solubility of potassium chlorate in water at 80°C?

Q3 What mass of potassium chlorate would dissolve in 50 g of water at 40°C?

Q4 If a saturated solution of potassium chlorate containing 100 g of water at 80°C was cooled to 20°C, what mass of potassium chlorate would crystallise out?

Fig 3 *Solubility curve of potassium chlorate in water*

67 Change

In this unit you will learn the answers to these questions:
- What are temporary (physical) and permanent (chemical) changes?
- How does the mass change during a chemical reaction?
- What are the three types of decomposition?
- What are oxidation and reduction?

Physical and chemical change

Fig 1 shows two changes taking place. In *a)* a block of ice is melting to form a pool of water. This is a temporary or physical change. No chemical reaction has taken place. It is easy to reverse by putting the water back in the freezer. In *b)* wood is burning. This is a permanent or chemical change. It is accompanied by an energy change with energy being lost to the surroundings. It is impossible to reverse the change, i.e. get the wood back from the ashes.

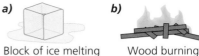

a)	b)
Block of ice melting	Wood burning

Fig 1 *Physical and chemical changes*

Are each of the following changes physical (no chemical reaction taking place) or chemical (chemical reaction taking place)?

Q1 A mixture of hydrogen and oxygen explodes.

Q2 Sugar is added to water and the mixture is stirred.

Q3 Water in a kettle is boiled and turned to steam.

Q4 A sparkler firework is lit.

Q5 A piece of iron rusts.

Q6 A sample of flour is sieved to remove lumps.

Q7 A cake mixture is cooked to produce a sponge cake

Burning magnesium in oxygen is another permanent change. There is an apparent increase in mass when magnesium burns.

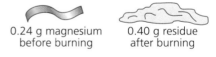

0.24 g magnesium before burning	0.40 g residue after burning

However, this is not the whole story. The apparent increase in mass is due to the oxygen which has combined with the magnesium. The sum of the mass of magnesium and the mass of oxygen is equal to the mass of magnesium oxide formed. This is true in all chemical reactions.

> **The sum of the masses of the reacting substances = the sum of the masses of the substances produced.**

Q8 Copy and complete the following: A physical or _____ change is one where _____ chemical _____ has taken place. A _____ change is one that cannot easily be _____ .

Decomposition

Decomposition is a chemical reaction that results in the breaking down of a substance into simpler substances. There are three types of decomposition.

1 **Thermal decomposition.** A substance is split up by heating, e.g. copper carbonate is split up on heating into copper oxide and carbon dioxide.

2 **Catalytic decomposition.** A substance is split up with the help of a catalyst, e.g. hydrogen peroxide is split into water and oxygen by manganese(IV) oxide.

3 **Electrolytic decomposition.** A substance, which is molten or dissolved in water, is split up by an electric current, e.g. molten lead bromide is split into lead and bromine.

> **Q9** Copy and complete the following: The splitting of a substance into simpler products is called _____ . This can be carried out by heating , using a _____ or by electrolysis.

Oxidation and reduction

A substance which combines with oxygen is said to be **oxidised**. The process is called **oxidation**. Any burning or combustion process is oxidation.

When a piece of magnesium is burned in oxygen, white magnesium oxide is formed.

magnesium + oxygen ➡ magnesium oxide

Magnesium has gained oxygen and is said to have been oxidised.

Oxidation can also be regarded as a reaction where hydrogen is lost.

Reduction is the opposite of oxidation. A substance is reduced (or reduction has taken place) when it loses oxygen or gains hydrogen.

For example, Joseph Priestley discovered oxygen by heating mercury oxide.

mercury oxide ➡ mercury + oxygen

The mercury oxide is reduced because it has lost oxygen.

When chlorine reacts with hydrogen, hydrogen chloride is formed.

hydrogen + chlorine ➡ hydrogen chloride

The chlorine has gained hydrogen and has been reduced.

Redox reactions

Oxidation and reduction reactions occur together. When one substance loses oxygen, another gains it. A reaction where both reduction and oxidation occur is called a **redox reaction**. For example, when hydrogen is passed over heated yellow lead oxide, lead and water are produced.

lead oxide + hydrogen ➡ lead + hydrogen oxide (water)

Lead oxide loses oxygen during this reaction and is reduced, while hydrogen gains oxygen and is oxidised.

The reduction of lead oxide to lead does not take place on its own. The presence of hydrogen is necessary if reduction is to take place. Hydrogen is called a **reducing agent**. The change of hydrogen to hydrogen oxide uses oxygen from the lead oxide. Lead oxide is called the **oxidising agent**. The overall reaction between hydrogen and lead oxide is a redox reaction.

68 Crude oil and its refining

In this unit you will learn the answers to these questions:
- What makes up crude oil?
- How was crude oil formed in the Earth?
- How is crude oil trapped in the Earth?
- How is crude oil refined?
- What are alkanes?

What is crude oil?

Crude oil (sometimes called petroleum) is an important source of energy and chemicals. It is a source of **organic compounds**, i.e. compounds containing carbon. It is a complex mixture of hydrocarbons (compounds of carbon and hydrogen only). When it comes out of the ground it is a black, treacle-like liquid with an unpleasant smell. Until it could be refined it was of little economic importance. It was used in ancient Babylon to make mortar to stick bricks together. Sir Walter Raleigh (1552–1618) used it to make his wooden ships watertight. Over 100 years ago farmers in Texas used to burn it off when they found it on the surface of their land.

Q1 Which two elements are combined in the compounds which make up crude oil?

How crude oil was formed

Crude oil was formed in the Earth millions of years ago. A larger area of the Earth was covered with sea then and the sea was full of all types of animal life. This included tiny sea creatures called plankton.

When these creatures died they sank to the sea bed and were mixed with mud. Over millions of years this layer was compressed by the rocks above and partial decomposition of the remains produced crude oil and the natural gas associated with it.

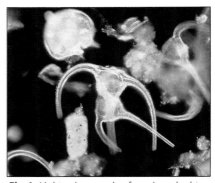
Fig 1 Light micrograph of marine plankton

The layers of sedimentary rocks bent and deposits of crude oil became trapped between layers of impermeable rocks. The crude oil remained trapped until oil explorers drilled down to the deposits. Then the crude oil is forced to the surface under pressure with the natural gas. Fig 2 summarises the processes which produce crude oil.

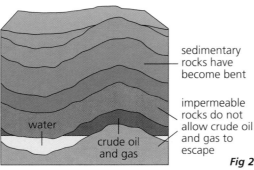

sedimentary rocks have become bent

impermeable rocks do not allow crude oil and gas to escape

water

crude oil and gas

Scientists use a variety of techniques to find underground deposits of crude oil. These include:

1 a geological study of the rocks present;

2 seismic studies – shockwaves are sent through the rock layers and measuring instruments on the surface record the echoes from rock layers;

3 studying fossils from different rocks, which then gives an idea of the age of rocks.

Fig 2 Processes which produce crude oil

Refining of crude oil

Crude oil is separated into useful saleable fractions by the process of fractional distillation (Unit 64). The fractional distillation separates the crude oil into different fractions. Each fraction has a range of boiling points and contains all of the carbon compounds boiling within the temperature range.

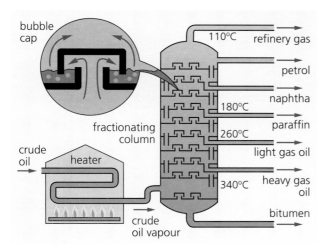

The crude oil is heated in a furnace and the vapour is passed into the bottom of the fractionating column (Fig 3). The hot vapours pass up the column. When each fraction reaches the tray where the temperature is just below its own boiling point it condenses and changes back into a liquid. In this way the different fractions are separated and drawn off separately.

Q2 How do we know that crude oil is a mixture of substances rather than one pure substance?

Fig 3 Fractional distillation of crude oil

The fractions which come off from the top of the column are called **light fractions**. They have low boiling points and are clear, light-coloured, runny liquids which burn readily. Those that condense near the bottom of the column are **heavy fractions**. They are darker in colour, viscous (thick and difficult to pour) and catch alight less easily.

The table contains the properties and uses of the fractions produced by the fractional distillation of crude oil.

Fraction	Boiling point range/°C	Number of carbon atoms in molecules	Uses
refinery gas	up to 40	1 – 4	gases for gas cookers, liquified petroleum gas (LPG)
petrol	40 – 140	5 – 10	fuel for vehicles, chemicals
naphtha	140 – 180	8 – 12	raw material for chemicals and plastics
paraffin	180 – 250	10 – 16	aircraft fuel, heating and raw material for chemicals
light gas oil	250 – 300	14 – 20	fuel for trains and lorries, raw materials for chemicals, plastics
heavy gas oil	300 – 340	20 – 30	fuel for ships, factories, central heating
bitumen	above 340	more than 25	for roads and roofing

Q3 Which fraction boils off first?

Q4 Write down four properties of the petrol fraction.

Q5 Why does the boiling point increase as the number of carbon atoms per molecule increases

The fractions produced contain hydro-carbons called **alkanes**. Alkanes all fit a general formula C_nH_{2n+2}, e.g hexane is C_6H_{14}. The light fractions contain small alkane molecules and heavy fractions contain large alkane molecules.

69 Uses of alkanes

In this unit you will learn the answers to these questions:
- Why do alkanes make such good fuels?
- What are the products of combustion of alkanes?
- How can methane be made?

Alkanes

The table shows some information about the first six members of the alkane family. Alkanes are **saturated hydrocarbons**, i.e. all of the bonds between the carbon atoms are single covalent bonds.

Alkane	Formula	Structure	Melting point/°C	Boiling point/°C	Mass of 1 mole/g	State at room temperature and pressure
methane	CH_4		−182	−161	16	gas
ethane	C_2H_6		−183	−89	30	gas
propane	C_3H_8		−188	−42	44	gas
butane	C_4H_{10}		−138	0	58	gas
pentane	C_5H_{12}		−130	36	72	liquid
hexane	C_6H_{14}		−95	68	86	liquid

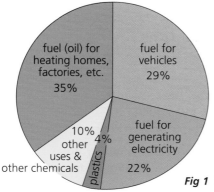

Fig 1 Uses of crude oil

Pie chart values: fuel (oil) for heating homes, factories, etc. 35%; fuel for vehicles 29%; fuel for generating electricity 22%; plastics 4%; 10% other uses & other chemicals

Reactions of hydrocarbons

The hydrocarbons called alkanes are fairly unreactive. Petrol, for example, does not react with sulphuric acid (an acid), sodium hydroxide (an alkali), sodium (metal and strong reducing agent) or potassium manganate(VII) (strong oxidising agent). However, alkanes do burn well to produce energy. Most of the uses of alkanes rely on exothermic reactions when they burn. Fig 1 shows a pie diagram which shows that most crude oil (86%) is used for fuel purposes.

Burning or **combustion** of hydrocarbons, including alkanes, requires oxygen from the air. Providing there is a *plentiful* supply of oxygen, the products are water vapour and carbon dioxide. The apparatus in Fig 2 can be used to show that carbon dioxide and water are produced when methane burns.

The table summarises the results of the experiment.

Test with	Before experiment	After experiment	Conclusion
cobalt chloride paper	blue	pink	water produced
limewater	solution clear	solution white and cloudy	carbon dioxide produced

If hydrocarbons, including alkanes, burn in a *limited* supply of oxygen, water vapour is still produced but the poisonous gas carbon monoxide, CO, can be produced.

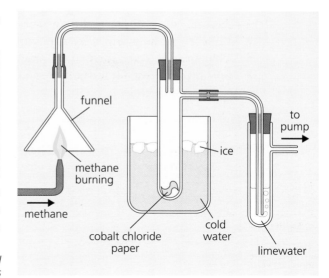

Fig 2 *Carbon dioxide and water are produced when methane burns*

Q1 Complete these word equations for the burning of methane:
plentiful supply of air   methane + oxygen ➡ _____ + _____
limited supply of air   methane + oxygen ➡ _____ + _____

Q2 Write balanced symbolic equations for the combustion of methane.

Methane from refuse and animal dung

When rubbish is tipped in landfill sites and covered with soil, bacteria break down the rubbish to form methane gas. In Birkenhead, near Liverpool, gas produced in a landfill site is being used to provide energy for a local factory where sweets and biscuits are made.

Q3 Before biodigesters were developed, cow dung and straw were mixed together and dried. These were then used as fuel. What are the advantages of methane produced from biodigesters?

Q4 What is the waste remaining from the biodigester used for?

In countries such as India where fossil fuels such as coal are very expensive, methane made from animal dung can be used to provide energy. In a biodigester animal dung is broken down by bacteria to produce a gas containing 60% methane.

Making hydrogen from methane

Hydrogen is produced from methane (natural gas) by **steam reforming**. Methane is mixed with steam and passed over a nickel catalyst at a high temperature and pressure.

methane + steam ➡ hydrogen + carbon monoxide
$CH_4(g)$ + $H_2O(g)$ ➡ $3H_2(g)$ + $CO(g)$

The gases are then mixed with more steam and passed over an iron(III) oxide catalyst.

carbon monoxide + steam ➡ carbon dioxide + hydrogen
$CO(g)$ + $H_2O(g)$ ➡ $CO_2(g)$ + $H_2(g)$

The carbon dioxide is removed by dissolving it under pressure in water.

70 Cracking hydrocarbons

In this unit you will learn the answers to these questions:
- What is cracking and why is it important economically?
- What products are formed by cracking alkanes?
- How do you test for unsaturated compounds?
- What are alkenes?

The products of fractional distillation

Fraction	Percentage produced by refining	Percentage demand for finished products
refinery gas	2	4
petrol	8	22
naphtha	10	5
paraffin	14	8
light gas oil	21	23
heavy gas oil	45	38

The table shows the percentage of each fraction produced by the refining of crude oil and the demand for the finished products.

The lighter fractions (e.g. petrol and gas) are in greater demand than the heavier ones (naphtha and paraffin). These large molecules can be broken down into smaller ones. This is called **cracking**.

Cracking alkanes

Alkanes are **saturated** hydrocarbons. They contain only single carbon–carbon and carbon–hydrogen bonds.

E.g. propane

Cracking is a process which breaks down long-chain alkanes into smaller molecules. For example, the breakdown of a decane molecule produces smaller molecules, including some that are **unsaturated**, i.e. they contain one or more carbon–carbon double bonds.

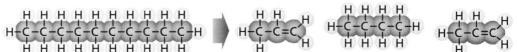

Cracking takes place when alkane vapour is passed over a catalyst at high temperature and pressure. Fig 1 shows how cracking is carried out in industry. The catalyst which is used becomes spent and has to be regenerated for reuse.

It is also possible to change the shape of hydrocarbon molecules by processes of **reforming**.

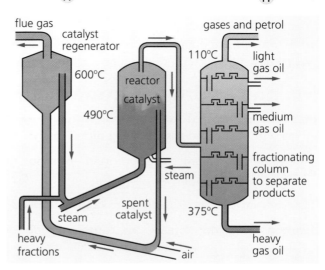

Fig 1 *Industrial cracking process*

Cracking liquid paraffin in the laboratory

Liquid paraffin is a mixture of alkanes with about 12 carbon atoms. If liquid paraffin vapour is passed over strongly heated broken china, the vapour is cracked to produce a colourless gas which is insoluble in water and can be collected over water. The apparatus in Fig 2 can be used for cracking liquid paraffin vapour.

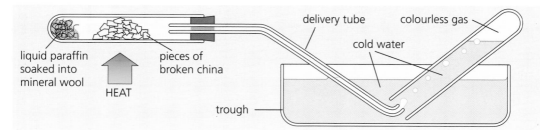

liquid paraffin soaked into mineral wool

HEAT

pieces of broken china

delivery tube

colourless gas

cold water

trough

Fig 2 *Cracking liquid paraffin vapour*

The table summarises the properties of liquid paraffin and the gas which is produced by cracking liquid paraffin.

Property	Liquid paraffin	Gas produced by cracking liquid paraffin
colour	colourless	colourless
state	liquid	gas
smell	no smell	sweet smell
flammable	burns well after heating	burns well with a yellow flame
test with bromine	red colour remains	turns colourless

The colourless gas collected is an alkene called ethene.

The structure of ethene is

Alkenes can be distinguished from alkanes by the **addition** reaction with bromine. Bromine is red in colour. When it reacts with ethene it produces a colourless product called 1,2-dibromoethane. The solution is therefore decolorised.

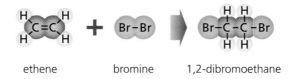

ethene　　　　　bromine　　　1,2-dibromoethane

This test with bromine is used to show if a hydrocarbon is unsaturated. Alkanes contain only single bonds and do not decolorise bromine.

> **Q1** An oily liquid collects on the surface of the water in the trough. What is this liquid and how is it formed?
>
> **Q2** During the experiment water from the trough sometimes enters the delivery tube. Why does this happen?

71 Addition polymerisation

In this unit you will learn the answers to these questions:
- What are addition polymers and how are they made?
- What are addition polymers used for?
- What is a copolymer?

Materials we commonly call plastics are more correctly called **polymers**. They are made by a process of **polymerisation** by joining together small molecules called **monomers**. The process is summarised by:

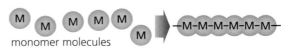

monomer molecules

The most common polymer is poly(ethene), which is made from joining together many ethene molecules to form long poly(ethene) chains.

The polymer is formed by a series of **addition** reactions and is therefore called an **addition polymer**. You will notice that the monomer molecules contain a carbon–carbon double bond but the polymer does **not** contain double bonds.

The conditions used to produce poly(ethene) can vary and the properties of the final polymer will depend upon the reaction conditions.

1 If ethene is heated at high temperatures and high pressures in the presence of a catalyst, **low density poly(ethene)** is produced.

2 If ethene is bubbled through an organic solvent containing complex catalysts, **high density poly(ethene)** is formed.

Both contain poly(ethene) chains.

Q1 In which form of poly(ethene) are the chains more closely packed together?

Q2 The average relative molecular mass of a poly(ethene) chain is 140 000. The relative molecular mass of an ethene molecule is 28. How many ethene molecules are there in an average poly(ethene) chain?

Polymers made from crude oil

The process of cracking (Unit 70) produces unsaturated alkenes from long-chain alkanes. These alkenes can be used to make a wide range of polymers. The table gives information about some common addition polymers.

Polymer	Structure of polymer	Monomer	Uses of polymer
poly(styrene) or poly(phenylethene)	$\begin{bmatrix} C_6H_5 & H \\ -C-C- \\ H & H \end{bmatrix}_n$	styrene or phenylethene C_6H_5 $C=C$ H	flowerpots, yoghurt cartons, plastic model kits, ceiling tiles
poly(vinyl chloride) or PVC or poly(chloroethene)	$\begin{bmatrix} Cl & H \\ -C-C- \\ H & H \end{bmatrix}_n$	vinyl chloride or chloroethene Cl $C=C$ H	artificial leather for furniture, luggage cases, clothes
poly(tetrafluoro-ethene) or PTFE	$\begin{bmatrix} F & F \\ -C-C- \\ F & F \end{bmatrix}_n$	tetrafluoroethene F $C=C$ F	non-stick coatings in saucepans

Q3 Propene, C_3H_6, has a structure of

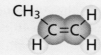

Draw the structure of part of a poly(propene) chain.

Uses of polymers

Polymers have become increasingly useful in recent years for several reasons.

1 There is a wider range of different polymers around now and each polymer has its own properties.

2 Traditional materials such as wood and metals have become less available and more expensive.

3 The density of polymers is much less than metals.

4 The reactivity of polymers is very low and so, unlike metals, there are no corrosion problems.

Factors which may affect the properties of a polymer

The properties of a polymer can be altered by changing its structure either during its making or by treatment afterwards.

1 Chain length

The average chain length of a polymer can be altered by the conditions used when polymerisation takes place.

The longer the chain length the higher will be the melting point of the polymer. Many polymers melt over a range of temperature and soften first before melting.

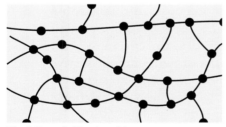

Fig 1 Cross-linking in rubber

2 Cross-linking

Natural rubber is an addition polymer formed from the latex of the rubber tree.

Before natural rubber can be used for car tyres it has to be hardened by a process called vulcanisation. The rubber is mixed with sulphur and cross-linking takes place between the polymer chains (Fig 1).

3 Degree of crystallisation

Fig 2 shows the chains in two polymers. In **a)** the chains are more regularly arranged than in **b)**. The polymer in **a)** is more crystalline.

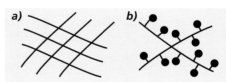

Fig 2 Degree of crystallisation

Copolymers

A polymer such as poly(ethene) contains one unit repeated over and over again. In practice, a more suitable polymer is often produced using two monomers polymerised together. For example, there is a copolymer of chloroethene and dichloroethene which has a trade name of Saran. It is used for making food wrappings.

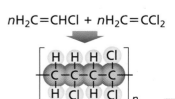

$$n\mathrm{H_2C=CHCl} + n\mathrm{H_2C=CCl_2}$$

72 Ethanol

In this unit you will learn the answers to these questions:

- How can ethanol be prepared from sugar and from ethene?
- What is produced when ethanol burns?
- What are the uses of ethanol?
- What effects can ethanol have on the human body?

Ethanol is a compound with the formula C_2H_5OH, commonly called alcohol. Its structural formula is:

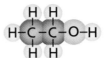

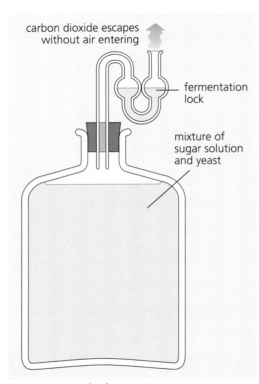

carbon dioxide escapes without air entering

fermentation lock

mixture of sugar solution and yeast

Fig 1 *Apparatus for fermentation*

It can be prepared by the process of **fermentation**. This involves the action of enzymes in yeast on sugar or carbohydrate solution. The apparatus in Fig 1 can be used to produce a solution of ethanol in water by fermentation. The valve in the neck of the jar allows the escape of carbon dioxide gas, produced during the fermentation, without allowing air into the jar.

Q1 What may happen if air is allowed to enter during the fermentation?

Q2 What precaution is taken with the fermenting equipment before using it to produce wine?

Fermentation is an example of **anaerobic respiration** (respiration without oxygen) (see Unit 21). Fermentation stops when the ethanol content reaches about 14% as the enzymes cannot survive in high ethanol concentrations. More concentrated ethanol solutions can be produced by fractional distillation (see whisky production, Unit 64).

The overall equation for fermentation is:

sugar (glucose) ⟹ ethanol + carbon dioxide + energy
$C_6H_{12}O_6$ (aq) ⟹ $2C_2H_5OH$ (aq) + $2CO_2$ (g) + 84 kJ

This is an example of an **exothermic** reaction.

Q3 How does the equation tell you that the reaction is exothermic?

Manufacture of ethanol from ethene

Ethene, produced by cracking fractions from crude oil, undergoes an addition reaction with steam at 300°C and very high pressure to produce ethanol.

$C_2H_4 + H_2O$ ⟹ C_2H_5OH

Uses of ethanol

Ethanol has four important uses.

1 **As a solvent**. Ethanol is a very good solvent, dissolving a wide range of different substances. It is very volatile, i.e. it evaporates easily. It is used as a solvent in paints, varnishes and perfumes. Ethanol evaporates quickly, causing the product to dry rapidly.

2 **As a fuel**. Ethanol burns with a clean, non-smoky flame. It is used for spirit burners. It is sold in the form of methylated spirits (meths) for this purpose with substances added to make it unsuitable for drinking.

Fig 2 An ethanol and petrol pump in Brazil

Ethanol burns in a plentiful supply of air to produce carbon dioxide and water.

ethanol + oxygen ➡ carbon dioxide + water
C_2H_5OH + $3O_2$ ➡ $2CO_2$ + $3H_2O$

In Brazil motorists use a mixture of ethanol and petrol as the fuel in motor cars. Ethanol is made from fermentation of sugar for this purpose.

Q4 Why has ethanol been developed as a fuel in Brazil but not in Western Europe?

3 **In alcoholic drinks** (see Unit 31).

4 **A useful reactant in the chemical industry**. Ethanol is used widely to make other chemicals. Ethanol reacts with ethanoic acid to form an **ester**, called ethyl ethanoate.

ethanoic acid + ethanol ⇌ ethyl ethanoate + water
CH_3COOH + C_2H_5OH ⇌ $CH_3COOC_2H_5$ + H_2O

Ethyl ethanoate is used to make nail-varnish remover. Esters are important compounds which are responsible for the fragrant odours of fruits and flowers. Synthetic esters are used in the food industry as flavouring agents.

Q5 Methyl butanoate is present in pineapples and gives the smell and flavour to the fruit. The structure of methyl butanoate is:
$$CH_3CH_2CH_2\overset{\displaystyle O}{\overset{\displaystyle \|}{C}}OCH_3$$
Write down the acid and the alcohol which can be used to make methyl butanoate.

Esters occur naturally in fats and oils. They are split up by hydrolysis into acid and alcohol. This process, using sodium hydroxide solution, is called **saponification**. The word saponification comes from the Latin word *sapo*, which means soap. Soap is produced when animal fat is hydrolysed by an alkali.

animal fat + sodium hydroxide (alkali) ➡ soap + alcohol (glycerol)

$$\begin{array}{l} CH_2OCOR \\ | \\ CHOCOR \\ | \\ CH_2OCOR \end{array} + \quad 3NaOH \quad ➡ \quad 3RCOONa \quad + \quad \begin{array}{l} CH_2OH \\ | \\ CHOH \\ | \\ CH_2OH \end{array}$$

R represents carbon chains of between 12 and 18 carbon atoms, e.g. $C_{12}H_{25}$.

In this unit you will learn the answers to these questions:
■ How do different metals react with air, water and dilute hydrochloric acid?
■ How can metals be arranged in order of reactivity using reactions with air, water and dilute acid?
■ What are displacement reactions and when will they take place?

Reactions of metals

There is a wide variety in the way metals react with air, water and dilute hydrochloric acid. The table compares the reactivity of some metals.

Metal	Reaction with air	Reaction with water	Reaction with dilute hydrochloric acid
potassium	burn in air or oxygen to form an oxide	reacts violently with cold water to produce hydrogen; hydrogen burns with a lilac flame	violent reaction to produce hydrogen (dangerous)
sodium		reacts quickly with cold water to produce hydrogen; hydrogen does not ignite	
calcium		reacts slowly with cold water to produce hydrogen	
magnesium		reacts very slowly with cold water; violent reaction with steam	react with acid to produce a metal chloride and hydrogen; react more slowly down list
zinc		fairly fast with steam	
iron		reacts only reversibly with steam	
lead	converted to the oxide by heating in air or oxygen but do not burn	no reaction with water	exceedingly slow reaction to produce hydrogen
copper			hydrogen not produced; no reaction with dilute hydrochloric acid
silver	not affected by oxygen or air		

In the table the metals have been arranged in order of reactivity. The most reactive metals are at the top of the list and the least reactive metals at the bottom. This order of metals is called the **reactivity series**. Other metals can be included in the series, as shown here. This reactivity series can be used to explain many reactions which take place.

The same order of metals can be obtained by measuring the voltages of simple cells. Two pieces of metal rod or foil are dipped into a beaker containing salt solution (Fig 1). The voltage produced is measured on a voltmeter.

most reactive
potassium
sodium
calcium
magnesium
aluminium
zinc
iron
lead
copper
silver
gold
least reactive

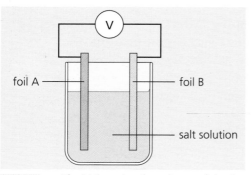

Fig 1 *Measuring the voltages of simple cells*

The results of a series of experiments are shown in the table.

When the voltages are arranged in descending order, the metals are in the same order as the reactivity series.

Foil A	Foil B	Voltage measured /V
magnesium	copper	1.0
zinc	copper	0.6
iron	copper	0.3
lead	copper	0.02
copper	copper	0.0
silver	copper	−0.05

Displacement reactions of metals

A displacement reaction is a reaction where one metal replaces another during a chemical reaction. For example, if an iron nail is put into blue copper(II) sulphate solution, a displacement reaction takes place.

iron + copper(II) sulphate ➡ iron(II) sulphate + copper
$Fe (s) +$ $CuSO_4 (aq)$ ➡ $FeSO_4 (aq)$ $+$ $Cu (s)$

The blue colour of copper(II) sulphate solution fades and a brown deposit of copper forms on the nail. The reaction takes place because iron is more reactive than copper. Iron is higher in the reactivity series than copper.

No reaction takes place when zinc is added to magnesium sulphate. Zinc is less reactive than magnesium (zinc is below magnesium in the reactivity series).

Q1 Write a word equation for the reaction which takes place when zinc is added to silver nitrate solution.

Displacement reactions can take place when a metal is added to an aqueous solution of a metal compound. They can also take place when a mixture of a powdered metal and a powdered metal oxide is heated.

One industrial application of a displacement reaction is the Thermit reaction used to weld lengths of railway track together (Fig 2). If a mixture of aluminium powder and iron(III) oxide is heated, a very violent reaction takes place. Aluminium, being more reactive than iron, replaces iron in iron(III) oxide.

Fig 2 *A Thermit reaction used to weld rail tracks*

aluminium + iron(III) oxide ➡ aluminium oxide + iron
$2Al (s)$ $+$ $Fe_2O_3(s)$ ➡ $Al_2O_3 (s)$ $+ 2Fe (l)$

Q2 Suggest a metal which could be used instead of aluminium for this reaction.

157

74 Stability of compounds

In this unit you will learn the answers to these questions:
- How is the stability of metal compounds related to the position of the metal in the reactivity series?
- How does the method used for extracting metals from their ores depend on the position of the metal in the reactivity series?

In Unit 73 we arranged metals in order of reactivity according to reactions with air, water and dilute hydrochloric acid. We called the list of metals the reactivity series. We used the reactivity series to predict displacement reactions.

We can also use the reactivity series to predict the stability of compounds. That is, we can predict how easily compounds will be split up on heating.

The reactivity series and the stability of compounds

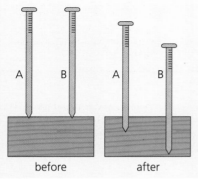

Fig 1 Hitting nails into a piece of wood. Nail B is hit harder than nail A and so goes further into the wood

Consider the analogy of hitting nails into a piece of wood. In Fig 1 there are two identical nails.

Nail A is hit gently with a hammer but nail B is hit with a hard blow by the hammer. You will see that nail A does not go as far into the wood as nail B. When it comes to removing the nails, the reverse process to hammering them in, nail A is easier to pull out than nail B.

If we react magnesium with oxygen, a very exothermic reaction takes place and a large quantity of energy is lost to the surroundings. If copper is reacted with oxygen, copper oxide is formed but there is no significant energy loss to the surroundings.

When it comes to splitting up magnesium oxide and copper oxide, much more energy is required to produce magnesium and oxygen from magnesium oxide than to produce copper and oxygen from copper oxide.

Metals high in the reactivity series are most reactive. This means that when they react to form compounds, they produce the largest energy losses (Fig 2).

Compounds of metals high in the reactivity series are difficult to split up. The energy lost on compound formation must be returned if the compound is to be split up.

Q1 Which one of the following oxides decomposes on heating: sodium oxide, silver oxide, calcium oxide, iron(III) oxide?

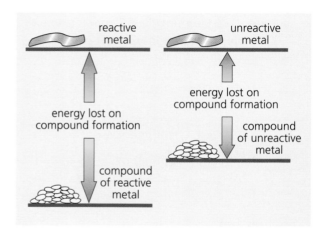

Fig 2 Metals higher in the reactivity series lose more energy when forming compounds

Stability of metal carbonates

The table shows what is observed when metal carbonates are heated. The stability decreases as you move down the reactivity series.

Q2 Which gas is produced when all carbonates (except sodium and potassium) are heated?

Metal carbonate	Action of heat
potassium carbonate	not decomposed even at very high temperatures
sodium carbonate	
calcium carbonate	decomposed on heating into the oxide and carbon dioxide; ease of decomposition increases as you move down the list
magnesium carbonate	
zinc carbonate	
iron carbonate	
lead carbonate	
copper carbonate	
silver carbonate	unstable – does not exist at room temperature

Stability of metal nitrates

This table shows what is observed when metal nitrates are heated. Again the stability decreases as you move down the reactivity series. The same sort of pattern is seen if other metal compounds are considered.

Q3 Which gas is produced when *all* nitrates are decomposed by heating?

Q4 Why is potassium nitrate used in gunpowder?

The stability of compounds is important when considering the methods used to extract metals from their ores.

Metal nitrate	Action of heat
potassium nitrate	on heating, oxygen is lost at high temperatures; a nitrite remains; no nitrogen dioxide is produced
sodium nitrate	
calcium nitrate	decomposed on heating producing the oxide of the metal, nitrogen dioxide and oxygen gas
magnesium nitrate	
zinc nitrate	
iron nitrate	
lead nitrate	
copper nitrate	
silver nitrate	decomposed producing the metal, oxygen and nitrogen dioxide

Extracting metals from their ores

The table summarises the methods used to extract metals from their ores.

The table shows that if there is a metal high in the reactivity series present in a compound which is difficult to split up, it can be extracted by electrolysis. This method requires a large amount of energy.

Metals in the middle of the reactivity series are extracted by reduction – usually with carbon.

Metals low in the reactivity series are present in compounds which are unstable. The metal can be extracted just by heating.

Metal extracted	Method of extraction
potassium	electrolysis of fused chloride
sodium	
calcium	
magnesium	
aluminium	electrolysis of oxide dissolved in molten electrolyte
zinc	reduction with carbon or other reducing agent
iron	
lead	
copper	
silver	heating
mercury	

75 Extraction of metals – 1

In this unit you will learn the answers to these questions:
- How do metals exist in the earth?
- How can sodium and aluminium be extracted from their ores?

In Unit 74 it was shown that the method of extraction of a metal depends on the position of the metal in the reactivity series. Metals at the top of the reactivity series form stable compounds and require electrolysis to extract them. Metals in the middle of the reactivity series are extracted by reduction, often with carbon. Metals at the bottom of the reactivity series are usually extracted by heating alone.

Metal	Common ore	Chief chemical constituent of ore	Formula of chief constituent
sodium	rock salt	sodium chloride	NaCl
mercury	cinnabar	mercury sulphide	HgS
copper	copper pyrites	copper sulphide and iron sulphide	$CuFeS_2$
aluminium	bauxite	aluminium oxide	Al_2O_3
zinc	zinc blende	zinc sulphide	ZnS
iron	haematite	iron(III) oxide	Fe_2O_3
calcium	limestone	calcium carbonate	$CaCO_3$
lead	galena	lead sulphide	PbS
potassium	carnallite	potassium magnesium chloride	$KMgCl_3.6H_2O$
magnesium	carnallite	potassium magnesium chloride	$KMgCl_3.6H_2O$
	dolomite	magnesium calcium carbonate	$MgCO_3.CaCO_3$

Q1 Is there any link between the position of a metal in the reactivity series and the type of compound present in the ore – chloride, carbonate, sulphide?

Metal ores

Few metals are found uncombined in the Earth. Most metals are usually present in the Earth as **ores**. An ore is a rock containing a mixture of substances including a compound of the metal that is to be extracted. The aluminium ore bauxite, for example, consists of about 40% aluminium oxide (a compound of aluminium and oxygen) with iron oxide, sand and titanium dioxide.

The table gives the names and chemical constituents of common ores.

Ideas and evidence

In 1886 Charles Hall and Paul Heroult independently found a way of producing aluminium by electrolysis. Heroult used a small, power-driven dynamo from his father's tannery and Hall used batteries he made himself. Both found out that molten cryolite could be used as the solvent for aluminium oxide. Fifteen years of legal action followed as to who owned the rights to the process.

Extraction of sodium

Sodium is extracted from molten sodium chloride by electrolysis in the Downs cell (Fig 1). Calcium chloride is added to the sodium chloride to lower the melting point of the electrolyte from about 800°C to 600°C. At the cathode (negative electrode), sodium is formed and, because of its low density, it floats upward and is collected in an 'upside down' trough. It can be tapped off from here. A little calcium is also produced at

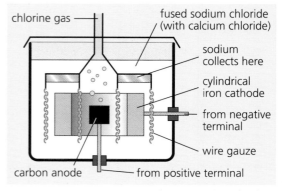

Fig 1 Extraction of sodium

the cathode but this crystallises and can be removed. Chlorine is produced at the anode (positive electrode) and then escapes through the hood. The chlorine produced is a useful by-product.

The cell reactions are :

cathode sodium ions + electrons ➡ sodium atoms
$$Na^+ \ + \ e^- \ \Rightarrow \ Na$$
anode chloride ions ➡ chlorine molecules + electrons
$$2Cl^- \ \Rightarrow \ Cl_2 \ + \ 2e^-$$

Q2 What is the economic advantage of adding calcium chloride to the sodium chloride in the cell?

Q3 Why is it important to keep the sodium and chlorine apart?

Extraction of aluminium

Although aluminium is present in small quantities in almost every handful of soil, it is extracted from bauxite.

Q4 Why is it not economic to use soil which would not have to be transported?

Bauxite is found mainly in tropical and subtropical parts of the world – Australia, Guinea, Jamaica, Indonesia, India and Brazil.

Q5 How is the bauxite obtained from the ground?

Fig 2 Open cast mining of bauxite in Australia

Removing the ore in this way leaves ugly scars on the landscape (Fig 2).

Purification of the bauxite takes place at the mining site. During the purification, the ore is treated with strong alkali. The main impurity is red iron oxide which forms a red mud which is pumped into huge ponds and left. These also spoil the landscape.

Q6 What are the advantages of purifying the bauxite and producing pure aluminium oxide at the mining site?

The extraction of aluminium is carried out by electrolysis of molten aluminium oxide dissolved in molten cryolite (sodium aluminium fluoride). Electrolysis takes place in carbon-lined steel tanks called pots. The carbon lining acts as a cathode and carbon anodes are used (Fig 3).

The products of electrolysis are aluminium (produced at the cathode) and oxygen (produced at the anode).

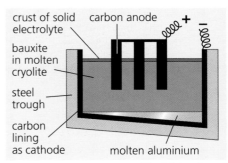

Fig 3 Extraction of aluminium

cathode aluminium ions + electrons ➡ aluminium atoms
$$Al^{3+} \ + \ 3e^- \ \Rightarrow \ Al$$
anode oxide ions ➡ oxygen molecules + electrons
$$2O^{2-} \ \Rightarrow \ O_2 \ + \ 4e^-$$

The aluminium collects at the bottom of the pot and can be removed. The carbon anodes burn in the oxygen produced and have to be replaced from time to time. The exhaust gases from the pots are bubbled through water to remove soluble gases.

76 Extraction of metals – 2

In this unit you will learn the answers to these questions:
- How is iron extracted from iron ore?
- How is steel produced from iron?
- How is copper purified by electrolysis?
- What affects the price of a metal?

Extraction of iron

Ores containing large amounts of iron (called 'rich' ores) include haematite and magnetite (both oxides of iron). These are often mixed with 'poorer' ores for extraction.

Iron is produced in a blast furnace (Fig 1). A furnace is about 70 metres high, made of steel and lined with fireproof bricks. The raw materials are iron ore, coke (carbon) and limestone. They are loaded from time to time through the top of the furnace.

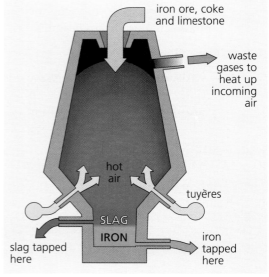

Fig 1 *Extraction of iron in a blast furnace*

Q1 What are the three solid materials added to the blast furnace?

Q2 What is the reducing agent in the furnace?

Hot air is blown into the base of the furnace through a series of pipes called **tuyères**. Burning the coke produces sufficient heat to raise the temperature inside the furnace to 1900°C, sufficient to melt the contents of the furnace. Carbon monoxide is produced in the furnace. This acts as the reducing agent which reduces the iron oxide to iron.

The limestone (calcium carbonate) added to the furnace removes the impurities, especially the sand, forming slag – calcium silicate.

The hot waste gases escaping from the blast furnace contain carbon monoxide.

Q3 What can the waste gases be used for?

Q4 What are the two liquids tapped off the furnace?

The main reactions in the blast furnace are:

carbon	+	oxygen	⇨	carbon dioxide	
C (s)	+	O_2 (g)	⇨	CO_2 (g)	

calcium carbonate	⇨	calcium oxide	+	carbon dioxide
$CaCO_3$ (s)	⇨	CaO (s)	+	CO_2 (g)

carbon dioxide	+	carbon	⇨	carbon monoxide
CO_2 (g)	+	C (s)	⇨	2CO (g)

iron(III) oxide	+ carbon monoxide	⇨	iron	+ carbon dioxide
Fe_2O_3 (s)	+ 3CO (g)	⇨	2Fe (l)	+ 3CO_2 (g)

calcium oxide	+	silicon dioxide	⇨	calcium silicate
CaO (s)	+	SiO_2 (s)	⇨	$CaSiO_3$ (l)

Q5 Give two reasons why limestone is added to the blast furnace.

The iron obtained is impure, containing carbon, phosphorus and silicon. Most of the iron produced is immediately turned into steel. The steel-making furnace (Fig 2) is tilted and loaded with 30% scrap iron and 70% molten iron from the blast furnace. A water-cooled lance is lowered into the upright furnace and pure oxygen is blown, under high pressure, onto the surface of the molten iron. The oxides of carbon and phosphorus escape as gases. Limestone is added to remove other impurities as slag. Finally, any additional substances are added for the grade of steel being produced.

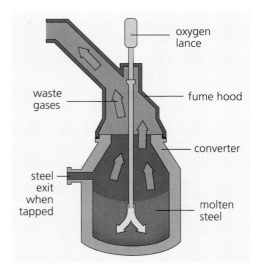

Fig 2 Steel-making furnace

Purification of copper by electrolysis

Copper is extracted by reduction but for many purposes, e.g. electrical wiring, is required in a high state of purity. Copper is purified by electrolysis (Fig 3) with the anode made of an impure copper plate and the cathode a pure copper plate. The electrolyte is copper(II) sulphate solution.

During the electrolysis the anode dissolves and pure copper is deposited on the cathode.

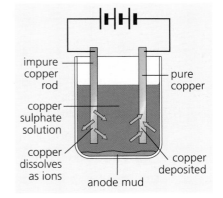

Anode   copper atoms ➡ copper ions + electrons
$$Cu \implies Cu^{2+} + 2e^-$$

Cathode   copper ions + electrons ➡ copper atoms
$$Cu^{2+} + 2e^- \implies Cu$$

Fig 3 Purification of copper by electrolysis

The impurities that were in the impure plate collect at the bottom of the cell as 'anode mud'. This can be refined to produce precious metals such as silver, gold and platinum.

Factors affecting the price of a metal

The price of a metal depends upon a number of factors. These include:

1. the amount of the metal available in ores in the Earth;
2. where the ores are;
3. the ease of extraction;
4. the quantity of metal re-cycled;
5. the demand for the metal by industry.

Fig 4 Steel production: a worker taking the slag from a blast furnace

163

77 Types of rock

In this unit you will learn the answers to these questions:
- What are sedimentary, igneous and metamorphic rocks?
- How are these different rock types formed?
- What tests do geologists use to identify minerals in rocks?

What is a rock?

A rock is a solid part of the Earth's crust. Although some rocks are almost pure substances, most rocks are usually made up of a mixture of chemicals called **minerals**. The properties of a rock will depend upon:

1 the type of minerals;   **2** the concentration of the minerals in the rock;

3 how the minerals are held together.

Identifying the minerals in rocks

A **geologist** identifies the particular minerals in a rock by carrying out a series of tests. These include:

1 **Colour** There can be considerable variations in the colours of minerals. Many minerals can have a variety of colours, so using colour as the only way of identifying a mineral can lead to wrong conclusions.

2 **Streak test** The colour of the mineral in a powdered form is helpful in identification. The simplest way of doing this is a streak test where the mineral is scratched across an unglazed ceramic tile called a **streak plate**. Different materials produce different colours.

3 **Lustre** Look at the mineral – is it shiny, glassy, dull, etc.?

4 **Hardness** Hardness is measured on Moh's scale. This is a scale of hardness from 1 to 10 using certain standard materials. If a mineral can be scratched with a fingernail it has a hardness of about 2. A 2p coin has a hardness of about 3.5 and a steel penknife about 6. These tests give a geologist a guide to the hardness of a mineral.

5 **Density** The density can give a guide to identifying the minerals present. For example, galena (lead sulphide) has a very high density.

6 **Testing with acid** When dilute acid is added to a carbonate mineral such as calcite (a form of calcium carbonate), fizzing will be seen as carbon dioxide is produced.

7 **Crystal shape** This can also be useful in identifying minerals present in a rock (see Unit 58).

Moh's scale	Mineral
1	talc
2	gypsum
3	calcite
4	fluorite
5	apatite
6	feldspar
7	quartz
8	topaz
9	corundum
10	diamond

Rocks can be divided into three groups according to the way they are formed. These three groups are **sedimentary rocks**, **igneous rocks** and **metamorphic rocks**.

Sedimentary rocks

A sedimentary rock is formed when a layer of mud, sand or other natural debris is compressed. This process is called **consolidation**. The sedimentary rocks are laid

Fig 1 *A cliff of sedimentary rocks, showing the layered structure*

down in layers, called **beds**, and the joins between layers are called **bedding planes** (Fig 1). New rocks are deposited on existing rocks and so the older the rocks are, the lower they are in the Earth's crust. After being deposited, these layers can tilt and twist. Examples of sedimentary rocks are shown in Fig 2.

Fig 2 *Examples of sedimentary rocks*

limestone

sandstone

conglomerate

Igneous rocks

Igneous rocks are hard rocks formed when the molten magma inside the Earth's crust crystallises. These rocks are composed of crystals of different minerals. The crystals are not packed together in any pattern. The sizes of the crystals are determined by the rate of cooling of the magma. If the crystallisation is slow, large crystals are formed, while rapid cooling produces small crystals. There are two types of igneous rock – **intrusive** and **extrusive**. Intrusive rocks solidify within the Earth's crust and are found at the Earth's surface only when overlying rocks are worn away. Because they are formed on slow cooling, they usually contain larger crystals. Granite is an example of an intrusive igneous rock. Extrusive rocks solidify on the surface of the Earth when liquid magma reaches the Earth's surface. Basalt is an example of an extrusive rock. Some igneous rocks contain tiny bubbles formed because molten magma contains gases. Examples of igneous rocks are shown in Fig 3.

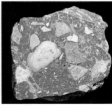

granite

basalt

Fig 3 *Examples of igneous rocks*

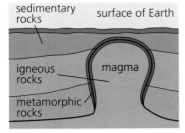

Fig 4 *An intrusion*

Magma from deep inside the Earth can push its way close to the surface. These 'upwellings' of magma are called **intrusions** (Fig 4). They cool to form igneous rocks.

Q1 Why are the crystals of extrusive rocks generally smaller than the crystals of intrusive rocks?

Metamorphic rocks

Metamorphic rocks are also hard rocks formed when high temperatures and high pressures act on other rocks. For example, the action of high temperatures and high pressures on the sedimentary rock limestone produces marble. Around a magma intrusion, the high temperatures and high pressures cause rocks to change to metamorphic rocks.

Fossils, the remains of plants and animals from millions of years ago (see Unit 46), are commonly found in sedimentary rocks and less commonly in metamorphic rocks. An example of a metamorphic rock is shown in Fig 5.

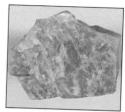

marble

Fig 5 *Example of a metamorphic rock*

Q2 Why are fossils not found in igneous rocks?

78 **Uses of rocks**

In this unit you will learn the answers to these questions:
- What are natural rocks used for?
- What factory-made materials can be used as substitutes for rocks?

Stone for buildings

Fig 1 shows the two houses we used in Unit 55.

The old cottage is made of limestone blocks and has a roof made of slate. Limestone is a sedimentary rock and slate is a metamorphic rock produced by the action of high temperatures and high pressures on mud. These traditional materials have properties which make them suitable for use in house-building.

Fig 1 An old stone cottage and a modern brick house

> **Q1** Write down the properties of
> **a)** limestone
> **b)** slate
> which make them suitable for house-building.

Fig 2 A slate mine in North Wales showing the slates in sheets

However, with the growth in the number of houses built in this century, these materials have become expensive and alternatives have been developed. The walls of a modern house are often made of bricks and the roof made of ceramic tiles. Both of these are made from clay and the clay is baked in an oven. The formation of bricks and tiles resembles the formation of metamorphic rock. The change taking place is permanent and the resulting products are hard and brittle.

> **Q2** In areas of natural beauty, there are often restrictions on the types of building materials which can be used. Fig 3 shows a village in the Peak District in Derbyshire. What sort of building materials would you recommend and what sort of building materials would you not recommend?
>
> *Fig 3 A village in the Peak District*

Using stone for statues

Igneous and metamorphic rocks are frequently used for statues. They are generally harder than sedimentary rocks.

Action of acid rain on rocks

Rainwater has a pH of about 5.5, but often the pH is much lower due to dissolved chemicals such as sulphur dioxide and oxides of nitrogen. Fig 4 shows a limestone carving on a cathedral. The detail of the carving has been eaten away by the acid rain.

Fig 4 A limestone carving badly eroded by acid rain

Cement and concrete

Cement is a very useful material produced by heating limestone powder with clay. When water is added to cement, a chemical reaction takes place which causes the cement to harden.

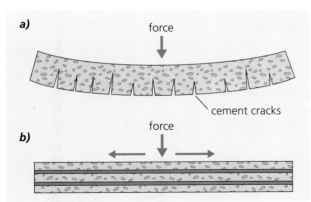

a)

force

cement cracks

b)

force

Fig 5 **a)** The vertical force causes the concrete to break
b) The reinforcing steel rods transfer the force sideways

Usually cement is mixed with water, sand and gravel to produce concrete. Concrete is a very useful building material. It is poured into moulds to produce concrete railway sleepers, beams, lamp-posts, etc. However, concrete is not a strong material unless it is reinforced. In Fig 5 it can be seen that a vertical force will cause the beam to bend and break. Reinforcing the concrete with steel rods transfers the forces sideways and makes the beam stronger.

Fig 6 shows the reconstructed Library of Celsus in Ephesus, Turkey. In the reconstruction, missing parts of the structure were made using reinforced concrete mixed with chippings of marble. This gives it an appearance similar to the original marble.

Fig 6 The Library of Celsus in Ephesus, Turkey

79 The rock cycle

In this unit you will learn the answers to these questions:
- What is weathering or erosion of rocks?
- What is the rock cycle?

Breaking down of rocks

The rocks in the Earth's crust are constantly being broken down by **weathering** or **erosion**. These processes are caused by the action of wind and rain, water and ice.

Water attacks certain minerals as it passes through rocks. In granite areas, minerals called feldspars in granite are attacked and turned into soft clay minerals. This causes the granite to crumble and the other minerals present – quartz and mica – then fall loose and are carried away as sand.

Rainwater is naturally acidic due to dissolved carbon dioxide. It can be called carbonic acid and has a pH of about 5.5. Rainwater attacks limestone, which is almost entirely made up of the mineral calcite. Calcite reacts with dilute acids.

$$CaCO_3 \text{ (s)} + H_2O \text{ (l)} + CO_2 \text{ (g)} \rightleftharpoons Ca(HCO_3)_2 \text{ (aq)}$$

limestone + water + carbon dioxide $\rightleftharpoons$ calcium hydrogencarbonate

The action of rainwater on limestone produces large underground caverns (Fig 1). The stalactites and stalagmites are formed when the calcium hydrogencarbonate decomposes and re-forms calcite.

Q1 Stalactites and stalagmites are made of solid calcium carbonate in the form of calcite. In Fig 1, which ones are stalactites and which ones are stalagmites?

Q2 How is the calcium carbonate formed in stalactites and stalagmites?

Q3 Some stalactites and stalagmites are stained brown. What causes the brown stain?

Fig 1 A limestone cavern

Rocks can be broken down by repeated freezing and thawing (Fig 2). When water freezes it expands considerably, forcing rocks apart. This process occurs over and over again, eventually breaking down the rock.

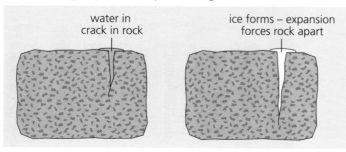

water in crack in rock

ice forms – expansion forces rock apart

Fig 2 Repeated freezing and thawing breaks down rocks

Rocks break down even in the absence of water. Rocks in a dry desert area can be broken down by the wind. The wind picks up sand particles and hurls them at exposed rocks. This natural 'sandblasting' produces more sand, which

Fig 3 *The Sphinx, Egypt, eroded by 'sandblasting'*

continues the process. The erosion of the Sphinx in Egypt by sand is a good example of this type of weathering (Fig 3).

The rock fragments produced by these forms of weathering often get washed into rivers. As the fragments get carried along in rivers they become more rounded, losing sharp edges. As the speed of the river slows, the fragments drop and are deposited on the river bed. Heavy fragments drop first and fine fragments are carried further.

Conglomerate is a rock containing large fragments (see Unit 77). This will be deposited close to where the river enters the sea (Fig 4). Shale is made of very fine particles and is formed away from the entry of the river into the sea.

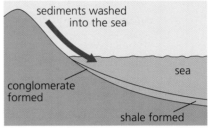

Fig 4 *Formation of conglomerate and shale*

The rock cycle

Rocks are being constantly broken down and new rocks are being formed. Molten rocks in the magma are crystallised to form igneous rocks. Weathering and erosion of rocks produces sediments which are deposited to produce sedimentary rocks. Metamorphic rocks can be produced from sedimentary rocks. Rocks returning to the magma complete the cycle. The rock cycle is summarised in Fig 5.

The rock cycle is driven by two energy processes. On the surface, processes are powered by the Sun's energy. Within the Earth, energy is provided by radioactive decay.

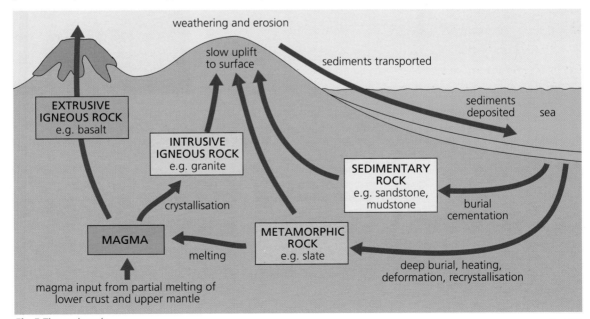

Fig 5 *The rock cycle*

80 The rock record

In this unit you will learn the answers to these questions:
- What happens to the layers of rock when movement of tectonic plates takes place?
- What are fossils and how can they be used to date rocks?

The rock record

The rock record represents the evidence that is left behind from events in the past that have led to the formation and distortion of layers of rocks.

William Smith, in his First Law, recognised that a layer of sedimentary rock was older than the layer above it.

Rock layers may be faulted, folded or contain fossils. All of these may provide evidence to help date rocks and suggest what may have happened to them in the past.

Ideas and evidence

William Smith is now called the Father of English Geology. He was born about 250 years ago. He had little formal education and worked for much of his life in rural Somerset. He produced detailed geological maps and fossil studies. His work was not recognised until he was over 60 years old.

Suggest why the importance of his work was not recognised for so long.

Faults

When large plates of the Earth move, great stresses will be placed on the rocks. They may crack and shift. This leads to a **fault**.

> A fault is a crack in rock along which movement has taken place.

When two plates are moving apart, a block of rock can drop down (Fig 1).
This forms a **tension fault**. The African rift valley is an example of a tension fault.

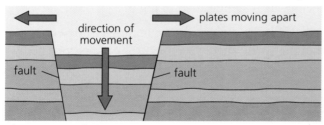

Fig 1 A tension fault

Fig 2 The African rift valley

When two plates are moving together, one block is pushed above the other (Fig 3). This forms a **compression fault**. A fault also occurs when plates slide past each other (Fig 4)

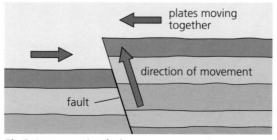

Fig 3 A compression fault

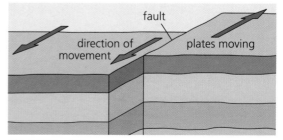

Fig 4 Plates sliding past each other

At any fault there is a build up of energy and this may be released in **earthquakes**.

Folds

When rocks are pushed together they may deform without faulting. This is called **folding**. Fig 5 shows the folding of sedimentary rocks. The peaks and troughs are called **anticlines** and **synclines**.

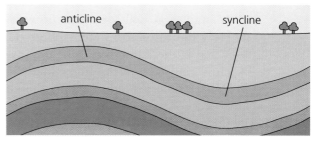

Fig 5 Folding of rocks

Geologists can use information about faults and folds to work out the order in which events happen.

Fig 6 shows a section through the some rocks.

Q1 Which rock is **a)** the oldest sedimentary rock; **b)** an intrusive igneous rock; **c)** a layer in which marble may form?

Q2 What evidence is there that the granite was formed before the clay layer was deposited?

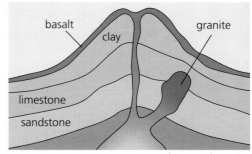

Fig 6 Rock section

Q3 Fig 7 shows a rock succession with a fault and a fold. Which came first, the fault or the fold? Explain your answer.

Q4 Fig 8 shows a rock succession where there is a great deal of folding taking place. Why can this type of folding, called **overfolding**, lead to mistakes in deciding on the age of a layer of rocks?

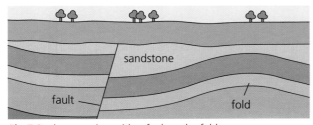

Fig 7 Rock succession with a fault and a fold

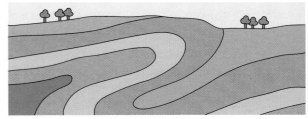

Fig 8 Overfolding

Fig 9 A fossil

Fossils

A fossil is the remains of a plant or animal that has remained trapped in sediments. These may be either:

- the actual parts of a creature, e.g. a tooth or a bone, or
- replicas of the original formed when it decays and the remaining cast fills up with deposited salts. A hard solid remains.

If scientists know approximately when a species lived, they can use this information to date the rock in which the fossils are found. Fossils used to date rocks are called **zone fossils**.

Q5 A fossil called didmograptus is found in shale rocks in North Wales that are 500 million years old. The same fossils are found in similar rocks in central Wales. What does this suggest about the age of these rocks?

81 Composition of the atmosphere

In this unit you will learn the answers to these questions:
- How did the Earth's atmosphere develop?
- What is the composition of the present atmosphere?
- How can we find the percentage of oxygen in the atmosphere?
- What processes help to keep the composition of the atmosphere constant?

How the Earth's atmosphere was formed

- The first atmosphere around the Earth probably consisted of hydrogen and helium – the same gases as make up the Sun. This was a time of intense volcanic activity when vast amounts of gas escaped into the atmosphere. This gas was mostly carbon dioxide and water vapour, but also contained smaller quantities of methane, sulphur dioxide and ammonia.

- When the Earth cooled the water vapour condensed. At this stage the atmosphere was mainly carbon dioxide and there was little or no oxygen.

- About 3500 million years ago the first primitive life was formed. The action of lightning on dissolved compounds in hot pools produced amino acids, which in turn formed proteins. The first simple living things were bacteria.

- Ammonia in the atmosphere was converted into nitrates by nitrifying bacteria and the nitrates were turned into gaseous nitrogen by denitrifying bacteria.

- Much of the carbon dioxide became trapped in carbonate rocks.

- When green plants started to grow, about 2200 million years ago, they turned carbon dioxide into oxygen by the process of photosynthesis. Burning methane and other fossil fuels put more carbon dioxide into the atmosphere.

- In the upper atmosphere the effect of uv light from the Sun produced ozone and the ozone layer developed. About 600 million years ago there was enough oxygen and protective ozone to allow simple animals to live.

Q1 The Earth's atmosphere has developed over millions of years. The present atmosphere of Mars and Venus resembles the atmosphere of the Earth billions of years ago. Is it possible that the atmospheres of Mars and Venus could at some time in the future resemble the Earth's?

Composition of the Earth's atmosphere today

Air is a mixture of gases. Its composition can vary from place to place.

The typical composition of a sample of dry air is:

Gas	Percentage
Nitrogen	78%
Oxygen	21%
Argon (and other noble gases)	1%
Carbon dioxide	0.04%

Ideas and evidence

At the end of the nineteenth century scientists thought that air was a single substance rather than a mixture of substances. Lavoisier, a French scientist, heated mercury in air. He found that with different samples of air only one-fifth of the air was used up and a red powder was formed. He realised that one gas, which he named oxygen, was used up.

Q2 What is the name of the red solid formed in Lavoisier's experiments?

Q3 How might the composition of the air be different in the centre of a city and in the country?

Finding the percentage of oxygen in the atmosphere

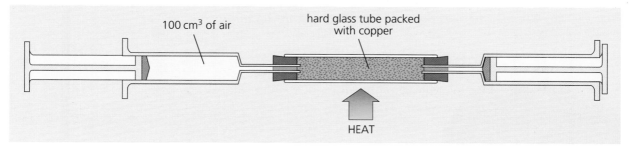

The apparatus in Fig 2 can be used to find the percentage of oxygen (the active gas) in air.

A sample of air is passed backwards and forwards over heated copper. The oxygen in the air is removed. Black **copper(II) oxide** is formed.

$$2Cu + O_2 \rightarrow 2\,CuO$$

The percentage of oxygen in the air can be calculated by measuring the volume remaining when the apparatus has cooled to room temperature.

Fig 2 Apparatus used to find percentage of oxygen in air

Q4 Why is it important that the apparatus cools back to room temperature before volume measurements are made?

Processes which help to keep the composition of the atmosphere constant

Oxygen is the reactive gas in the air. It is the gas that can easily be removed by processes of **combustion**, **respiration** and **rusting**.

Combustion and respiration produce carbon dioxide.

Oxygen does not run out because it is replaced by **photosynthesis**.

The **nitrogen cycle** (Unit 53) helps to keep the nitrogen concentration in the atmosphere constant

Fig 3 shows the way the percentage of carbon dioxide has changed over the period from 1960–1980.

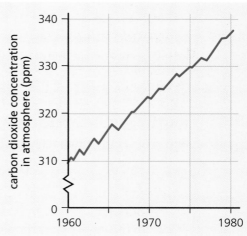

Fig 3 Graph showing how percentage of carbon dioxide has changed

Q5 Suggest why the percentage of carbon dioxide increased between 1960 and 1980.

Q6 What could be the effects of this trend continuing?

Q7 The Kyoto protocol was drawn up for world leaders to sign to pledge to reduce carbon dioxide emissions. Why is it essential that all countries sign up?

82 The oceans

In this unit you will learn the answers to these questions:
■ How were the oceans formed?
■ What processes add ions to sea water and remove them?
■ What is the function of phytoplankton in the oceans?

The formation of the oceans

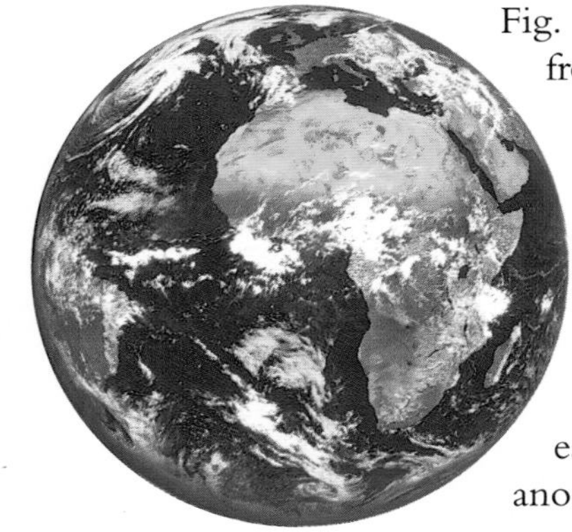

Fig 1 A view of the Earth from space

Fig. 1 shows a view of the Earth from space. The large expanse of the oceans can be seen. Over two-thirds of the Earth's surface is covered with oceans. All of the oceans are linked and, although the composition does vary from place to place, the ratio of each ion with respect to another is fairly constant.

Ion	Concentration of ion in g/1000 g of sea water
Chloride Cl⁻	19.2
Sodium Na⁺	10.7
Sulphate SO_4^{2-}	2.7
Magnesium Mg^{2+}	1.4
Calcium Ca^{2+}	0.4
Potassium K⁺	0.38
Hydrogencarbonate HCO_3^-	0.14
Bromide Br⁻	0.07

The table shows the typical composition of sea water.

Q1 Which positive ion and which negative ion are present in the largest quantities in sea water?

Q2 Sea water contains other ions in smaller quantities. It has been estimated that 1 cubic mile of sea water contains £100 000 000 worth of gold. This is dissolved in the sea water. Why is it not economic to extract gold from sea water?

Oceans were formed when the Earth cooled down and the condensed water settled in the lowest points on the Earth's surface.

Water is a very good solvent and started to dissolve substances from the rocks of the Earth. These were washed into rivers and then into the oceans.

Rocks such as halite (NaCl) and gypsum ($CaSO_4$) dissolve in rain water and get washed into rivers. Other minerals, e.g. limestone ($CaCO_3$) dissolve appreciably in rain water.

$$H_2O\,(l) \quad + \quad CO_2\,(g) \quad \rightleftharpoons \quad H_2CO_3\,(aq)$$
$$\text{Water} \quad + \text{ carbonic acid} \quad \rightleftharpoons \quad \text{carbonic acid}$$

$$CaCO_3\,(s) \quad + \quad H_2CO_3\,(aq) \quad \rightleftharpoons \quad Ca(HCO_3)_2\,(aq)$$
$$\text{Calcium carbonate} \quad + \text{ carbonic acid} \quad \rightleftharpoons \quad \text{calcium hydrogencarbonate}$$

Processes removing ions from sea water

There are three ways these ions in sea water are removed.

1 If the concentrations of the ions becomes too great, ions will **precipitate**, e.g. if the concentrations of calcium and sulphate ions becomes too great, calcium sulphate is precipitated.

$$Ca^{2+}\,(aq) \;+\; SO_4^{2-}\,(aq) \;\Rightarrow\; CaSO_4\,(s)$$

2 Marine animals called molluscs have shells made of calcium carbonate. These shells are formed by taking calcium and carbonate ions from the water.

$$Ca^{2+}(aq) + CO_3^{2-}(aq) \Rightarrow CaCO_3$$

3 In some countries sea water is evaporated to produce sea salt which is then marketed. Magnesium and bromine are also extracted from sea water.

Ions are constantly added to the oceans from rivers and removed by the three processes above.

> There is a balance in the oceans keeping the concentrations of dissolved ions approximately constant.

ICT Extra!

The Dead Sea between Israel and Jordan is a small inland sea. Use ENCARTA or other electronic encyclopaedia to find out the composition of dissolved ions in the Dead Sea and why the composition is so different from the oceans.

Balance of oxygen and carbon dioxide in the oceans

Fig 2 Phytoplankton

The oceans are important for keeping the balance of oxygen and carbon dioxide in the atmosphere. About 40% of the carbon dioxide we produce is absorbed by sea water and oxygen released. The oceans are just as important as rain forests in maintaining this balance.

The key to the process is the tiny algae called **phytoplankton** which live close to the surface of the oceans. They contain green chloroplasts that convert carbon dioxide into starches and oxygen.

When phytoplankton die, the protective casings of calcium carbonate sink to the bottom of the oceans and form a sediment. This eventually leads to the formation of limestone.

Q3 With global warming, it is suggested that more phytoplankton will be present in the ocean. What effect might this have on the carbon dioxide–oxygen balance in the atmosphere?

Q4 Waste materials are often discharged into the sea. What problem could this cause?

Ideas and evidence

We can exploit the oceans in the future as sources of minerals but this is expensive. There are rich deposits of metals in lumps on the sea bed. Which countries own the oceans and how should the research be developed and funded for the benefit of all?

Q5 Explain why the composition of the oceans remains unchanged.

Q6 The table gives the solubilities of some metal salts in water at 20°C. Explain why, although the rocks of the Earth are rich in calcium compounds, the concentration of calcium ions is relatively low.

substance	Solubility in g/100g of water
calcium chloride	65
calcium sulphate	0.2
magnesium chloride	54
magnesium sulphate	54
sodium chloride	36
sodium sulphate	20

83 Chemical equations

KS4

In this unit you will learn the answers to these questions:
- How do you write chemical formulae?
- What are chemical equations and how do you write them?
- What are ionic equations?

In a chemical reaction new substances are formed. The substances that react are called **reactants** and the new substances made are called **products**.

A chemical reaction can be represented by a **chemical equation** which summarises, in words or symbols, the change taking place. Substances which remain unchanged during the reaction are not shown in the equation. For example, the burning of magnesium in oxygen has the equation:

$$\text{magnesium} + \text{oxygen} \Rightarrow \text{magnesium oxide}$$
$$2Mg + O_2 \Rightarrow 2MgO$$
$$\textit{reactants} \qquad\qquad \textit{product}$$

In a chemical reaction the reactants are on the left-hand side and the products are on the right-hand side.

Chemical formulae

Correct chemical formulae are needed in order to write correct symbol equations. Chemical formulae can be obtained by carrying out experiments (Unit 83). They are determined by finding the masses of the different elements which combine in the compound. Magnesium oxide is written as MgO rather than MgO_2 or Mg_2O because one atom of magnesium combines with one atom of oxygen.

Q1 Write the correct chemical formulae of iron oxides using the information given. The symbols of iron and oxygen are Fe and O.

a) 1 atom of iron combines with 1 atom of oxygen.

b) 2 atoms of iron combine with 3 atoms of oxygen.

c) 3 atoms of iron combine with 4 atoms of oxygen.

You can write correct chemical formulae using the ions with the correct charges.

The correct formulae of compounds in the table are obtained by ensuring that **the number of positive and negative charges are the same**.

	Cl^-	O^{2-}	OH^-	NO_3^-	SO_4^{2-}	CO_3^{2-}
Na^+	NaCl					Na_2CO_3
Mg^{2+}						
Al^{3+}		Al_2O_3				

Q2 Now copy out the table and complete it.

sodium chloride Na^+ Cl^-
    number of positive charges = number of negative charges
so write **NaCl** (ignoring charges).

sodium carbonate Na^+ CO_3^{2-}
    number of positive charges = half the number of negative charges
To get equal numbers of positive and negative charges you need to have two Na^+, so write Na_2CO_3.

aluminium oxide Al^{3+} O^{2-}

To get equal numbers of positive and negative charges you need two Al^{3+}
and three O^{2-}, so write Al_2O_3.

Diatomic gases

Common gases such as oxygen, nitrogen and chlorine are composed of molecules
each containing two atoms. These are called diatomic gases. In equations, therefore, we
write O_2, H_2, N_2 and Cl_2.

Writing symbol equations

1 Calcium carbonate decomposes on heating to produce calcium oxide and carbon
dioxide. We can write a word equation.

    calcium carbonate ➡ calcium oxide + carbon dioxide

Then we can write the symbol equation.

    $CaCO_3$ ➡ CaO + CO_2

This equation is already **balanced**. There is the same number of each type of
atom on both the right-hand side and left-hand side of the equation.

    $Ca = 1, C = 1, O = 3$

Finally, state symbols can be added.

    $CaCO_3$ (s) ➡ CaO (s) + CO_2 (g)

| (s) = solid |
| (g) = gas |
| (l) = liquid |
| (aq) = aqueous (in solution) |

2 Calcium burns in oxygen to form calcium oxide.

    calcium + oxygen ➡ calcium oxide

Now, writing in the correct symbols and formulae:

    Ca + O_2 ➡ CaO

This equation then has to be balanced and state symbols added.

    LHS: $Ca = 1, O = 2$;   RHS: $Ca = 1, O = 1$

    $2Ca$ (s) + O_2 (g) ➡ $2CaO$ (s)

Ionic equations

Ionic equations are useful because they emphasise the important changes taking place
in a chemical reaction. For example, the equation for the neutralisation reaction
between sodium hydroxide and hydrochloric acid is:

    sodium hydroxide + hydrochloric acid ➡ sodium chloride + water
    $NaOH$ (aq)   + HCl (aq)   ➡ $NaCl$ (aq)   + H_2O (l)

Since all of the reactants and products (except water) are composed of ions, this
equation could be written:

    Na^+ (aq) OH^- (aq) + H^+ (aq) Cl^- (aq) ➡ Na^+ (aq) Cl^- (aq) + H_2O (l)

An equation should show change and therefore anything present before and after
the reaction can be deleted. The simplest ionic equation, deleting Na^+ (aq) and
Cl^- (aq), is therefore:

    OH^- (aq)   + H^+ (aq)   ➡ H_2O (l)

84 The mole

In this unit you will learn the answers to these questions:
■ What is a mole?
■ How can we use relative atomic masses, obtained from the Periodic Table, to calculate the mass of 1 mole of different substances?

Atoms are very small and it is impossible to weigh and measure individual atoms in the school laboratory. It is helpful to consider atoms in larger numbers.

■ A magnesium atom weighs 24 times as much as a hydrogen atom.
■ Ten magnesium atoms weigh 24 times as much as ten hydrogen atoms.
■ x magnesium atoms weigh 24 times as much as x hydrogen atoms.

Chemists usually use a very large number called Avogadro's number (L). Avogadro's number is approximately 6×10^{23} or 600 000 000 000 000 000 000 000. To give you some idea of the size of this number, if the whole population of the world wished to count up to this number between them and they worked without any breaks, twenty-four hours each day, it would take six million years to finish. Alternatively, a line 6×10^{23} mm long would stretch from the Earth to the Sun and back two million times.

■ 1 mole of hydrogen atoms weighs 1 g.
■ 1 mole of magnesium atoms weighs 24 g.
■ 1 mole of sulphur atoms weighs 32 g.
■ A mole of magnesium atoms weighs 24 times as much as a mole of hydrogen atoms.

> **The amount of a substance which contains Avogadro's number of particles is called 1 mole.**

Look at the Periodic Table on page 189.

Ideas and evidence

Amedeo Avogradro

Avogadro was an Italian physicist who worked at he beginning of the nineteenth century. He published his work on the relationship between atomic weights and properties of gases in a French Journal, *Journal de Physique*, in 1811. This would have been of great help to Dalton, but Dalton did not have access to it.

Avogadro's work was ignored for 50 years because:

1 he failed to recognise clearly the difference between atom and molecule;
2 his work seemed to suggest that atoms were divisible, when current scientific ideas were that atoms were indivisible;
3 he offered little experimental evidence to support his ideas.

He died a very disillusioned man in 1856. Shortly after his death Cannizzaro put forward a system of atomic weight determination based upon Avogadro's work and the real value of his work was realised.

Q1 What is the significance of the **mass** of 1 mole of hydrogen atoms, 1 mole of magnesium atoms and 1 mole of sulphur atoms?

Q2 A sample of magnesium weighs 6 g. What mass of sulphur contains the same number of atoms as 6 g of magnesium?

Q3 Use the Periodic Table to help you work out the mass of:
a) 1 mole of sodium atoms, Na;
b) 1 mole of oxygen atoms, O;
c) 1 mole of oxygen molecules, O_2 (each oxygen molecule contains two oxygen atoms);
d) 0.5 moles of bromine atoms, Br;
e) 0.1 moles of chlorine molecules, Cl_2;
f) 2 moles of calcium atoms, Ca;
g) 3 moles of helium atoms, He;
h) 0.25 moles of carbon atoms, C;
i) 0.5 moles of nitrogen atoms, N;
j) 0.5 moles of nitrogen molecules, N_2.

Because the mass of electrons is negligible compared to other particles in an atom, the mass of 1 mole of magnesium atoms, for example, is the same as the mass of 1 mole of magnesium ions.

Q4 Work out the mass of:
    a) 1 mole of chloride ions, Cl^-;   **b)** 1 mole of aluminium ions, Al^{3+};
    c) 0.1 moles of calcium ions, Ca^{2+};   **d)** 0.25 moles of sulphide ions, S^{2-};
    e) 1 mole of hydroxide ions, OH^-;   **f)** 1 mole of oxide ions, O^{2-};
    g) 0.25 moles of magnesium ions, Mg^{2+}; **h)** 0.25 moles of copper ions, Cu^{2+}.

The mass of one mole of compounds can be calculated using the correct formula.

1 **calcium carbonate $CaCO_3$**

The masses of 1 mole of calcium, carbon and oxygen are 40, 12 and 16, respectively.

The mass of 1 mole of calcium carbonate
    $= 40 + 12 + (3 \times 16)$
    $= 100\,g$

2 **calcium hydroxide $Ca(OH)_2$**

The mass of 1 mole of calcium hydroxide
    $= 40 + 2(16 + 1)$
    $= 74\,g$

3 **calcium nitrate $Ca(NO_3)_2$**

The mass of 1 mole of calcium nitrate
    $= 40 + 2[14 + (3 \times 16)]$
    $= 164\,g$

4 **hydrated copper(II) sulphate $CuSO_4.5H_2O$**

The mass of 1 mole of hydrated copper(II) sulphate
    $= 64 + 32 + (4 \times 16) + 5[(2 \times 1) + 16]$
    $= 250\,g$

Q5 Work out the mass of 1 mole of:
    a) calcium oxide, CaO;   **b)** magnesium chloride, $MgCl_2$;
    c) barium hydroxide, $Ba(OH)_2$;   **d)** chromium(III) sulphate, $Cr_2(SO_4)_3$;
    e) magnesium sulphate, $MgSO_4.7H_2O$; **f)** calcium hydrogencarbonate, $Ca(HCO_3)_2$;
    g) iron(III) sulphate, $Fe_2(SO_4)_3$;   **h)** iron(II) sulphate, $FeSO_4$;
    i) aluminium sulphate, $Al_2(SO_4)_3$;   **j)** sodium carbonate, $Na_2CO_3.10H_2O$.

Q6 Work out the mass of:
    a) 0.5 moles of calcium hydroxide, $Ca(OH)_2$;
    b) 0.1 moles of sodium hydroxide, $NaOH$;
    c) 0.1 moles of sulphuric acid, H_2SO_4;
    d) 0.5 moles of nitric acid, HNO_3;
    e) 2 moles of hydrochloric acid, HCl.

$$\text{number of moles} = \frac{\text{mass in g}}{\text{mass of 1 mole in g}}$$

85 Chemical formulae by experiment

In this unit you will learn the answer to this question:
■ How can the formula of a compound be found by experiment?

Every chemical formula can theoretically be found as a result of a chemical experiment.

Formula of magnesium oxide

A weighed mass of magnesium is burned in air and the mass of magnesium oxide formed is found.

a Mass of crucible and lid   =   25.15 g
b Mass of crucible, lid and magnesium   =   25.27 g
  Mass of magnesium **b** − **a**   =   0.12 g
c Mass of crucible, lid and magnesium oxide   =   25.35 g
  Mass of magnesium oxide **c** − **a**   =   0.20 g

From these results:

■ 0.12 g of magnesium combines with $(0.20 - 0.12)$ g of oxygen to form 0.20 g of magnesium oxide.

■ 0.12 g of magnesium combines with 0.08 g of oxygen.

■ In Unit 82 it was shown that
$$\text{number of moles} = \frac{\text{mass in g}}{\text{mass of 1 mole in g}}$$
Therefore $\frac{0.12}{24}$ moles of magnesium combines with $\frac{0.08}{16}$ moles of oxygen atoms.

■ 0.005 moles of magnesium combines with 0.005 moles of oxygen atoms.

The simplest formula of magnesium oxide is, therefore, MgO.

ICT Extra!

Put the results of different groups in the class into a spreadsheet.
Produce a graph which would enable the mass of oxygen combined with any given mass of magnesium to be found.

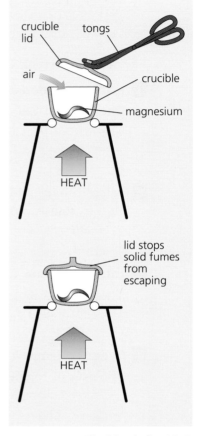

Fig 1 Producing MgO

Formula of silicon chloride

Silicon chloride is a liquid produced when dry chlorine is passed over a heated sample of silicon.

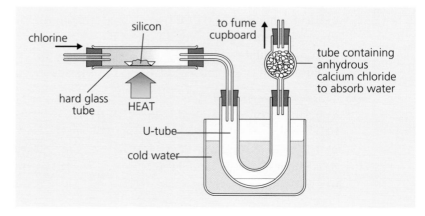

Fig 2 Producing silicon chloride

The silicon and the hard glass tube are weighed before and after heating to find the mass of silicon used. The mass of silicon chloride is found by weighing the U-tube before and after the experiment.

a Mass of hard glass tube and silicon before heating · = 38.86 g
b Mass of hard glass tube and silicon after heating = 38.30 g
   Mass of silicon used **a** − **b** = 0.56 g
c Mass of U-tube before experiment = 145.40 g
d Mass of U-tube after experiment = 148.80 g
   Mass of silicon chloride formed **d** − **c** = 3.40 g

From these results:

■ 0.56 g of silicon combines with 2.84 g of chlorine to produce 3.40 g of silicon chloride.

■ $\frac{0.56}{28}$ moles of silicon atoms combines with $\frac{2.84}{35.5}$ moles of chlorine atoms.

■ 0.02 moles of silicon atoms combines with 0.08 moles of chlorine atoms.

There are four times as many chlorine atoms as silicon atoms. The formula is, therefore, $SiCl_4$.

Formulae of copper oxides

There are two copper oxides – black copper oxide and red copper oxide. The formulae of the two oxides can be found by reducing the metal oxides to copper using hydrogen as the reducing agent.

copper oxide + hydrogen ➡ copper + water

Q1 The following results were obtained. Work out the formulae of the two oxides.

	Black copper oxide	Red copper oxide
mass of copper oxide	0.80 g	0.72 g
mass of copper	0.64 g	0.64 g

Ideas and evidence

The phlogiston theory
Over two hundred years ago scientists had a different way of explaining combustion. They believed that when a substance burns it loses a substance called phlogiston. Lavoisier showed, however, that when substances burn their mass increases. This was possible because, for the first time, accurate balances were available. The immediate reaction was to modify the theory by suggesting that phlogiston had a negative mass and this would explain an increase in mass on combustion. It took a lot of work by Lavoisier and others to get a new theory established. We now know that the increase in mass when, for example, magnesium burns is because it has gained oxygen form the air. Although the phlogiston theory was wrong, it was the first time that chemists had tried to establish a theory.

86 Calculations from equations

In this unit you will learn the answer to this question:

■ How can calculations of masses of reactants and products be carried out using a balanced chemical equation?

Balanced symbol equations summarise the reactants and products in a chemical reaction. They also enable us to work out the masses of substances that react and the masses of the products formed. This is vital, for example, for a chemical manufacturer who is then able to work out the costs of making a given mass of a chemical and so calculate the price that must be charged to make a profit.

Working out masses from a chemical equation

The equation for the reaction between calcium carbonate and dilute hydrochloric acid is

calcium carbonate + hydrochloric acid ➡ calcium chloride + water + carbon dioxide

$$CaCO_3 (s) + 2HCl (aq) \rightarrow CaCl_2 (aq) + H_2O (l) + CO_2 (g)$$

Mass of 1 mole of calcium carbonate $= 40 + 12 + (3 \times 16) = 100\,g$
Mass of 2 moles of hydrochloric acid $= 2 (1 + 35.5) = 73\,g$
Mass of 1 mole of calcium chloride $= 40 + (35.5 \times 2) = 111\,g$
Mass of 1 mole of water $= (2 \times 1) + 16 = 18\,g$
Mass of 1 mole of carbon dioxide $= 12 + (2 \times 16) = 44\,g$

If you add up the sum of the masses of the reactants it should always equal the sum of the masses of the products. Checking at this point will prevent arithmetical errors.

Calculate the mass of calcium chloride produced when 50 g of calcium carbonate reacts with excess hydrochloric acid

From the equation:

■ 100 g of calcium carbonate reacts to produce 111 g of calcium chloride.
■ 1 g of calcium carbonate reacts to produce $\frac{111}{100}$ g of calcium chloride.
■ 50 g of calcium carbonate reacts to produce $50 \times \frac{111}{100}$ g = 55.5 g of calcium chloride.

Calculate the mass of carbon dioxide produced when 4 g of calcium carbonate reacts with excess hydrochloric acid

From the equation:

■ 100 g of calcium carbonate reacts to produce 44 g of carbon dioxide.
■ 1 g of calcium carbonate reacts to produce $\frac{44}{100}$ g of carbon dioxide.
■ 4 g of calcium carbonate reacts to produce $4 \times \frac{44}{100}$ g = 1.76 g of carbon dioxide.

Volumes of gases used up or produced

When dealing with reactants or products that are gases it is often better to use volumes rather than masses. For example:

hydrogen + chlorine ➡ hydrogen chloride

$$H_2 (g) + Cl_2 (g) \rightarrow 2HCl (g)$$

1 mole of hydrogen molecules reacts with 1 mole of chlorine molecules to form 2 moles of hydrogen chloride molecules.

2 g of hydrogen reacts with 71 g of chlorine to produce 73 g of hydrogen chloride.

The volume of a fixed mass of gas changes with changes in pressure and temperature. At room temperature and atmospheric pressure, one mole of any gas has a volume of 24 dm³. So, in this example, 24 dm³ of hydrogen reacts with 24 dm³ of chlorine to produce 48 dm³ of hydrogen chloride.

Calculate the volume of hydrogen chloride produced when 10 dm³ of hydrogen reacts with 10 dm³ of chlorine

From the equation:

- 1 mole of hydrogen reacts with 1 mole of chlorine to produce 2 moles of hydrogen chloride.
- Volume of hydrogen chloride produced, at room temperature and atmospheric pressure = 20 dm³.

Calculate the volume of carbon dioxide, at room temperature and atmospheric pressure, produced when 4 g of calcium carbonate reacts with excess hydrochloric acid

$$CaCO_3 \text{ (s)} + 2HCl \text{ (aq)} \Rightarrow CaCl_2 \text{ (aq)} + H_2O \text{ (l)} + CO_2 \text{ (g)}$$

- 100 g of calcium carbonate reacts to produce 24 dm³ of carbon dioxide.
- 1 g of calcium carbonate reacts to produce $\frac{24}{100}$ dm³ of carbon dioxide.
- 4 g of calcium carbonate reacts to produce $4 \times \frac{24}{100}$ dm³ = 0.96 dm³ of carbon dioxide.

Unlike the masses, the volume of the reactants and products are not always the same. For example:

$$2NH_3 \text{ (g)} \Rightarrow N_2 \text{ (g)} + 3H_2 \text{ (g)}$$

Volume of reactants at room temperature and atmospheric pressure = 48 dm³.

Volume of products at room temperature and atmospheric pressure:
$$24 + (3 \times 24) \text{ dm}^3 = 96 \text{ dm}^3.$$

Percentage yield

So far in these calculations we have assumed that all of the reactants are turned into products, i.e. the yield is said to be 100% and there is no waste. This is usually not the case, especially in some reactions involving organic chemicals when the percentage yield is often between 50% and 80%.

Q1 The equation of methane burning in excess oxygen is

$$CH_4 \text{ (g)} + 2O_2 \text{ (g)} \Rightarrow CO_2 \text{ (g)} + 2H_2O \text{ (l)}$$

a) What volume of carbon dioxide is formed when 1 dm³ of methane is burned in excess oxygen?

b) What volume of water is formed when 1 dm³ of methane is burned in excess oxygen?

Q2 The equation for the decomposition of calcium carbonate is

$$CaCO_3 \Rightarrow CaO + CO_2$$

When 1 tonne of calcium carbonate was heated 0.5 tonnes of calcium oxide were produced. What was the percentage yield?

If the equation indicates that 10 g of product can be produced and 6 g is actually obtained, the percentage yield is $\frac{6}{10} \times 100 = 60\%$.

87 Concentration calculations

In this unit you will learn the answers to these questions:
- How do we work out the concentration of a solution?
- What is the advantage of using molar concentrations?

Molar concentrations

Concentrations of solutions can be expressed in different ways. One way is mass of solute per unit volume of liquid, for example g per dm^3 or g/dm^3.

For example, if 4 g of sodium hydroxide is dissolved in 100 g of water, the concentration of the solution is 40 g per dm^3.

> **Q1** Calculate the concentration, in g per dm^3, of a solution containing 2 g of sodium chloride in 25 g of water.

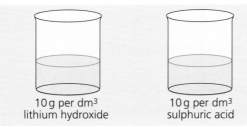

10 g per dm^3
lithium hydroxide

10 g per dm^3
sulphuric acid

Fig 1 Two solutions with the same concentration, but different numbers of particles

Fig 1 shows two solutions with the same concentration. However, there is no easy comparison of the number of particles. As the particles have different masses, the number of particles in each solution will be different.

If **concentrations in moles per dm^3** are used, we can make a direct comparison of the number of particles present.

> The concentration in moles per dm^3 can be calculated by dividing the mass in $1\,dm^3$ by the mass of 1 mole of the solute:
>
> $$\text{concentration in moles per } dm^3 = \frac{\text{mass in } 1\,dm^3 \text{ of solution}}{\text{mass of 1 mole}}$$

Compare the number of particles present in 10 g per dm^3 lithium hydroxide and 10 g per dm^3 nitric acid

10 g per dm^3 lithium hydroxide, LiOH
The mass of 1 mole of lithium hydroxide = 7 + 16 + 1 = 24 g
Molar concentration = $\frac{10}{24}$ = 0.42 moles per dm^3

10 g per dm^3 nitric acid, HNO_3
The mass of 1 mole of nitric acid = 1 + 14 + (3 × 16) = 63 g
Molar concentration = $\frac{10}{63}$ = 0.16 moles per dm^3

Because the mass of 1 mole of nitric acid is approximately $2\frac{1}{2}$ times the mass of 1 mole of lithium hydroxide, this disguises the difference in the number of particles present. There are approximately $2\frac{1}{2}$ times as many particles of lithium hydroxide as particles of nitric acid.

Sometimes a solution with a molar concentration of 2 moles per dm^3 is written as 2M.

> **Q2** Calculate the molar concentrations of the following solutions. (Refer to the Periodic Table on page 179 for the relative atomic masses you will need.)
> a) 10.6 g of sodium carbonate, Na_2CO_3, dissolved to make $1\,dm^3$ of solution.
> b) 73 g of hydrogen chloride, HCl, dissolved to make $500\,cm^3$ of solution.
> c) 117 g of sodium chloride, NaCl, dissolved to make $2\,dm^3$ of solution.

Q3 What do these three solutions have in common?

100 cm³
1 mole per dm³

10 cm³
10 moles per dm³

50 cm³
2 moles per dm³

Reacting volumes of solutions

In Unit 84 we saw that calculations can be made using masses of reacting substances and masses of products. We can extend this to include reactions between solutions of known concentrations. For example, the reaction of sodium hydroxide and sulphuric acid:

$$2NaOH\ (aq)\ +\ H_2SO_4\ (aq)\ \Rightarrow\ Na_2SO_4\ (aq)\ +\ 2H_2O\ (l)$$

From the equation, 2 moles of sodium hydroxide react with 1 mole of sulphuric acid to form 1 mole of sodium sulphate and 2 moles of water.

How many moles of sodium hydroxide, NaOH, are present in 50 cm³ of solution of molar concentration 2 mole per dm³?

1 dm³ of solution (2 mole per dm³) contains 2 moles of NaOH.
50 cm³ is $\frac{50}{1000}$ of 1 dm³ (i.e. $\frac{1}{20}$).
Number of moles of NaOH = $2 \times \frac{1}{20}$ = 0.1 moles.

How many moles of sulphuric acid would react with 50 cm³ of solution of NaOH of molar concentration 2 mole per dm³?

Because 2 moles of sodium hydroxide react with 1 mole of sulphuric acid, the number of moles of sulphuric acid reacting with 0.1 moles of NaOH = 0.05.

What volume of sulphuric acid (2 mole per dm³) reacts completely with 50 cm³ of solution of NaOH of molar concentration 2 mole per dm³?

A solution of sulphuric acid with a molar concentration of 1 mole per dm³ contains 1 mole of H_2SO_4 in each dm³ (1000 cm³). The volume of this solution containing 0.05 moles of H_2SO_4 is:

$$0.05 \times \frac{1000}{2} = 25\ cm^3.$$

Titrations

The reaction between sodium hydroxide and sulphuric acid is an example of a reaction producing a soluble salt (Unit 102). Fig 2 shows how this experiment could be carried out to find the volume of 2M sulphuric acid (2 mole per dm³) which reacts with 50 cm³ of sodium hydroxide solution (2 mole per dm³) can be carried out.

This is called a **titration**.

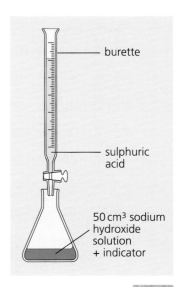

burette

sulphuric acid

50 cm³ sodium hydroxide solution + indicator

Fig 2 Apparatus to find the volume of sulphuric acid which reacts with sodium hydroxide solution

In this unit you will learn the answers to these questions:

■ What is the Periodic Table?
■ How can it help us to organise our knowledge of Chemistry?
■ How are the properties of elements related to their position in the Periodic Table?
■ What are periodic graphs?

In the middle of the nineteenth century chemists were discovering a large number of new elements. They were also able to determine atomic weights of the elements (now called atomic masses) accurately.

Attempts were made by chemists, including Johann Dobereiner, John Newlands and Lothar Meyer, to produce a system to classify the elements.

John Newlands, in 1865, arranged the known elements in order of increasing atomic weight. He realised that every eighth element in the series was similar.

H **Li** Be B C N O F **Na** Mg Al Si P S Cl **K**

He likened this to music and called it the Law of Octaves. It fell down, however, because some of the atomic weights were inaccurate and there were elements that had not been discovered.

Fig 1 *Mendeleev (1834–1907)*

но въ ней, мнѣ кажется, уже ясно выражается примѣнимость вы ставляемаго мною начала ко всей совокупности элементовъ, пай которыхъ извѣстенъ съ достовѣрностію. На этотъ разъ я и желалъ преимущественно найдти общую систему элементовъ. Вотъ этотъ опытъ:

			Ti=50	Zr=90	?=180.
			V=51	Nb=94	Ta=182.
			Cr=52	Mo=96	W=186.
			Mn=55	Rh=104,4	Pt=197,4
			Fe=56	Ru=104,4	Ir=198.
		Ni=Co=59	Pl=106,6	Os=199.
H=1			Cu=63,4	Ag=108	Hg=200.
	Be=9,4	Mg=24	Zn=65,2	Cd=112	
	B=11	Al=27,4	?=68	Ur=116	Au=197?
	C=12	Si=28	?=70	Sn=118	
	N=14	P=31	As=75	Sb=122	Bi=210
	O=16	S=32	Se=79,4	Te=128?	
	F=19	Cl=35,5	Br=80	I=127	
Li=7	Na=23	K=39	Rb=85,4	Cs=133	Tl=204
		Ca=40	Sr=87,6	Ba=137	Pb=207.
		?=45	Ce=92		
		?Er=56	La=94		
		?Yt=60	Di=95		
		?In=75,6	Th=118?		

Q1 How many elements did Mendeleev include in his table?

Q2 How did Mendeleev represent elements which had not been discovered?

Ideas and evidence

In 1869, the Russian chemist Dmitri Mendeleev produced a classification of the elements which has survived in the form of the modern Periodic Table (page 189). Mendeleev arranged the known elements in order of increasing atomic weight, but in such a way that elements with similar properties were in the same vertical column. He called these vertical columns **groups** and the horizontal rows **periods**.

Mendeleev's great contribution was to look at the evidence in a slightly different way. He realised that there were some elements that existed but had not been discovered. He left gaps for them and predicted their properties. He even changed the order slightly in places where elements were obviously misplaced.

Fig 2 *Mendeleev's Periodic Table*

Fig 2 shows a copy of Mendeleev's original table. Although the notes are in Russian, it is possible to make out the symbols of the elements. In this table, elements with similar properties are in the same row, e.g. Li, Na, K, Rb, Cs.

Q3 Look at each of the following sets of elements.
a) F Cl Br I   **b)** Ca Sr Ba Pb   **c)** N P As Sb Bi   **d)** Be Mg Zn Cd
In which of these sets are **all** of the elements in the same column in the
modern Periodic Table (page 179)?

Relating the electronic arrangement to the position in the Periodic Table

The electron arrangement in a sodium atom is
2, 8, 1. Sodium has three electron shells and is
therefore in period 3.

The table shows the number of electrons in the
outer shell for the first three elements. Finish this
table for the first 20 elements. Use the Periodic
Table on page 189 to complete it.

Element	Order of increasing atomic weight (atomic mass)	Number of electrons in outer energy level
hydrogen	1	1
helium	2	2
lithium	3	1

You should notice that the number of electrons in the outer energy level is the same as
the group number in the Periodic Table, except for the noble gases in group 0.

Q4 Copy and complete the bar
graph of number of
electrons in the outer energy
level against the order of the
elements in the table above.

Q5 Look carefully at the
elements potassium and
argon in the bar graph. Why
would they fit better if they
were changed round?

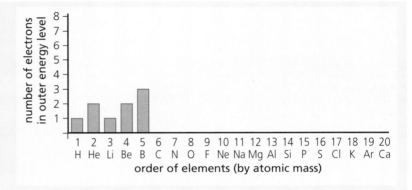

You will notice that the graph consists
of a series of peaks and troughs which
repeat. This is called a **repeating** or
periodic pattern.

Lothar Meyer saw similar periodic
graphs when he plotted physical
properties against atomic weight.

ICT Extra!

Find out all about the elements in the
Periodic Table using the Interactive Periodic
Table (http://www.shef.ac.uk/chemistry/
webelements). You can plot physical properties
such as melting point against atomic number.

Q6 a) Write down the name of the element which is
at the top of each peak in your graph. Use the
modern Periodic Table on page 179 to predict
which element would be at the top of the next
peak.
b) Write down the name of the element which is
at the bottom of each trough in your graph.
Use the modern Periodic Table on page 179
to predict which element would be at the
bottom of the next trough.

Q7 Use the Periodic Table to identify the elements
whose atoms have the following electron
arrangements.
a) 2, 8, 18, 5   **b)** 2, 8, 18, 8, 2   **c)** 2, 8, 18, 18, 7

89 Structure of the Periodic Table

In this unit you will learn the answer to this question:
- How can the Periodic Table be used in lessons and examinations? (You will have a copy of it with you in the examination.)

The modern Periodic Table is a way of classifying the elements. The elements are arranged in order of increasing **atomic number** to avoid any elements out of order when atomic masses are used. The Periodic Table can help you to make predictions about elements you have not yet met. Fig 1 shows the main parts of the Periodic Table. The **main block** of the Periodic Table consists of eight chemical families (i.e. groups 1–7 and group 0). Between groups 2 and 3 are three rows of **transition metals**.

Elements are classified as metals and non-metals. The bold red line which goes down through the main block elements in steps separates metals on the left-hand side of it from non-metals on the right-hand side of it.

In Unit 88 we saw that there were repeating patterns in physical properties. There are also repeating patterns in the main block of the Periodic Table in the formulae of compounds formed by these elements. The table shows the chemical formulae of the chlorides of some of the elements in the main block.

Q1 Are there more metals or more non-metals in the Periodic Table?

Q2 What change occurs across period 2 from lithium to neon?

Q3 What change occurs down group 4 from carbon to lead?

Group	1	2	3	4	5	6	7	0
period 2	LiCl	$BeCl_2$	BCl_3	CCl_4	NCl_3	OCl_2	FCl	no chlorides
period 3	NaCl	$MgCl_2$	$AlCl_3$	$SiCl_4$	PCl_3	SCl_2	–	no chlorides
period 4	KCl	$CaCl_2$	$GaCl_3$	$GeCl_4$	$AsCl_3$	$SeCl_2$	BrCl	no chlorides

You should be able to see patterns in these formulae. Elements in the same group form chlorides with a similar formula, e.g. LiCl and NaCl. The number of chlorine atoms combined with one of the atoms of the element is the same as the group number or the group number subtracted from eight. For example:

$AlCl_3$ three chlorine atoms combined with one aluminium atom
PCl_3 8 − 5 chlorine atoms combined with one phosphorus atom

Q4 Use the modern Periodic Table to write the formulae of:
   a) caesium chloride **b)** barium chloride **c)** tellurium chloride **d)** iodine chloride.

Similar patterns can be seen with oxides.

Group	1	2	3	4	5	6	7	0
period 2	Li_2O	BeO	B_2O_3	CO_2	N_2O_3	–	F_2O	no oxides
period 3	Na_2O	MgO	Al_2O_3	SiO_2	P_2O_3	SO_2	Cl_2O	no oxides
period 4	K_2O	CaO	Ga_2O_3	GeO_2	As_2O_3	SeO_2	Br_2O	no oxides

Q5 Use the modern Periodic Table to write the formulae of:
   a) caesium oxide **b)** barium oxide **c)** tellurium oxide.

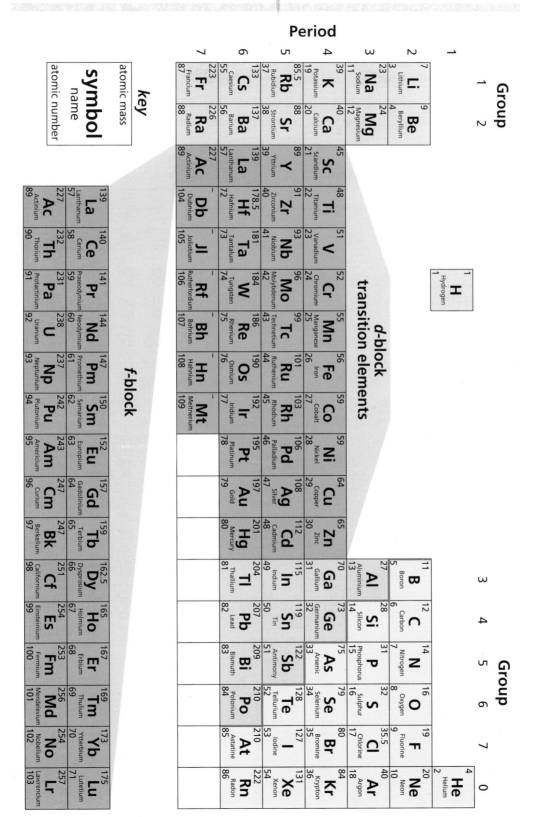

Fig 1 The Periodic Table of elements

90 The alkali metals

In this unit you will learn the answers to these questions:
- What are the alkali metals and where are they placed in the Periodic Table?
- How does the reactivity of alkali metals change down the group?

The elements in group 1 of the Periodic Table include lithium, sodium, potassium, rubidium and caesium. These form a family of elements called **alkali metals**. The table gives some information about these elements.

Element	Symbol	Atomic number	Melting point (°C)	Boiling point (°C)	Density (g per cm³)	Date of discovery
lithium	Li	3	181	1331	0.54	1817
sodium	Na	11	98	890	0.97	1807
potassium	K	19	63	766	0.86	1807
rubidium	Rb	37	39	701	1.53	1861
caesium	Cs	55	29	685	1.87	1861

There are similarities between the elements and certain trends down the group.

Fig 1 *Sir Humphrey Davy (1778 – 1829): he discovered potassium and sodium by electrolysis*

1 All of the elements are reactive metals. They are stored under paraffin oil to prevent reaction with air and water.

2 All of the elements are soft metals that can be easily cut with a knife. The softness increases down the group.

3 The melting points and boiling points decrease down the group.

4 The alkali metals are generally less strong than other metals but have better heat and electrical conductivities.

5 The densities generally increase down the group.

Because of the great stability of the compounds of alkali metals, they were undiscovered at the start of the nineteenth century. They were all discovered by the electrolysis of molten materials.

Q1 When an alkali metal is cut, a shiny surface is produced. This quickly turns dull. Suggest why this is so.

Reactions of alkali metals with oxygen (air)

All alkali metals burn in oxygen to form solid oxides. For example:

sodium + oxygen ➡ sodium oxide

$$4Na\ (s)\ +\ O_2\ (g)\ \implies\ 2Na_2O\ (s)$$

The solid oxides are alkaline, hence the name alkali metals.

Reactions of alkali metals with cold water

All alkali metals react with cold water to form a soluble alkaline hydroxide and hydrogen gas. For example:

sodium + water ➡ sodium hydroxide + hydrogen

$$2Na\ (s)\ +\ 2H_2O\ (l)\ \implies\ 2NaOH\ (aq)\ +\ H_2\ (g)$$

All reactions of alkali metals with cold water are exothermic. The table compares the reactivity of some of the alkali metals with cold water.

Alkali metal	Reaction with cold water
lithium	Lithium floats on water, gently fizzing and producing a colourless gas. The gas burns with a squeaky pop (hydrogen). Remaining solution is alkaline.
sodium	Sodium floats on water, fizzing rapidly and producing a colourless gas. The gas burns with a squeaky pop (hydrogen). Remaining solution is alkaline.
potassium	Potassium floats on water, fizzing violently and producing a colourless gas. From time to time hydrogen ignites and burns with a lilac-pink flame. Remaining solution is alkaline.
rubidium	Rubidium sinks (denser than water). Very violent reaction over in a fraction of a second. Remaining solution is alkaline.

It can be seen that the reactivity of alkali metals increases down the group. In all reactions of alkali metals, atoms lose one electron to form a single, positively charged ion. For example:

$$Na \rightarrow Na^+ + e^-$$

The metals become **more reactive** down the group because the outer electron is lost more easily as the group is descended.

least reactive
Li
Na
K
Rb
most reactive

Reactions of alkali metals with chlorine

All of the alkali metals burn in chlorine gas to form a salt. For example:

lithium + chlorine $\rightarrow$ lithium chloride
$2Li (s) + Cl_2 (g) \rightarrow 2LiCl (s)$

sodium + chlorine $\rightarrow$ sodium chloride
$2Na (s) + Cl_2 (g) \rightarrow 2NaCl (s)$

potassium + chlorine $\rightarrow$ potassium chloride
$2K (s) + Cl_2 (g) \rightarrow 2KCl (s)$

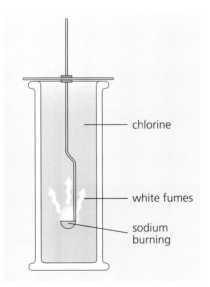

chlorine

white fumes

sodium burning

A small piece of alkali metal is heated in the bowl of a combustion spoon until it starts to burn. The spoon is then lowered into a gas jar of chlorine (Fig 2). As the alkali metal continues to burn, it combines with the chlorine gas to produce white fumes of sodium chloride that settle as a solid on the cool sides of the gas jar.

Fig 2 *Apparatus to show the reaction of an alkali metal (sodium) with chlorine*

Uses of alkali metals

There are few uses of alkali metals because of their great reactivities. There are, however, many uses of alkali metal compounds. A small quantity of metallic sodium is used in sodium street lights, which have a characteristic orange colour. Sodium is used as a coolant in some nuclear power stations. It is a good conductor of heat and removes heat from the reactor.

91 Noble gases

In this unit you will learn the answer to this question:
- What are noble gases and what are they used for?

The noble gases are a family of unreactive gases placed in group 0 of the Periodic Table.

These gases were not known in 1869 when Mendeleev devised the Periodic Table (Unit 88) and had to be added later. These gases occur in the atmosphere, sometimes, as in the case of argon, in fairly large amounts. The reason they were not discovered earlier was their great unreactivity.

helium	He
neon	Ne
argon	Ar
krypton	Kr
xenon	Xe
radon	Rn

Ideas and evidence

History of the discovery of the noble gases

In 1894, Lord Rayleigh was accurately measuring the densities of common gases. He produced several samples of nitrogen from different chemicals and, within the limits of experimental error, obtained a value for the density of nitrogen of 1.2505 g per dm³ at 0°C and atmospheric pressure.

Fig 1 Lord Rayleigh (1842 – 1919)

However, he also prepared samples of nitrogen from the air by removing oxygen, water vapour and carbon dioxide. The density of nitrogen prepared in this way was always 1.2575 g per dm³ under the same conditions.

In order to solve this mystery, Lord Rayleigh enlisted the help of William Ramsay. Ramsay was a young Professor of Chemistry at University College London. Ramsay believed that the reason for the difference in density was the presence of a heavier gas in the nitrogen obtained from the air, and within a few months he had proved this to be correct.

Fig 2 William Ramsay (1852 – 1916)

Nitrogen is an unreactive gas but it will react with burning magnesium to form solid magnesium nitride:

$$3Mg\ (s)\ +\ N_2\ (g)\ \Rightarrow\ Mg_3N_2\ (s)$$

Magnesium was used to remove the nitrogen from a sample of nitrogen made from the air. The gas that resulted did not react with magnesium and produced an entirely different spectrum from nitrogen. This, together with experiments carried out by Rayleigh, confirmed the presence of a new element called argon in 1894.

Fig 3 The spectrum of the Sun, analysis of which led to the discovery of helium

In another experiment, a gas was obtained from heating certain uranium minerals, and this was also, like argon, very inert. It was found to be identical to the element helium, first discovered in spectroscopic examination of light from the Sun (Fig 3). Later other noble gases were obtained by careful fractional distillation of liquid air by M. W. Travers.

Ramsay's discoveries brought him international fame. In 1904 he was awarded the Nobel prize for Chemistry. In the same year Rayleigh received the Nobel prize for Physics.

Reactions of noble gases

Until about forty years ago it was believed that noble gases did not react with other chemicals under any conditions. However, it is now possible to form a number of noble gas compounds. The first one, xenon tetrafluoride, XeF_4, was discovered by accident. A mixture of xenon and fluorine was passed through a heated nickel tube. When the resulting gases were cooled, white crystals of xenon tetrafluoride were formed.

$$Xe \text{ (g)} + 2F_2 \text{ (g)} \Rightarrow XeF_4 \text{ (s)}$$

Q1 Why is a compound between xenon and fluorine more likely than compounds between neon and fluorine or xenon and iodine?

Uses of noble gases

Helium is used for filling weather balloons and airships. It is denser than hydrogen and therefore is not as good as hydrogen for lifting balloons. Its main advantage is that it is not flammable and can be used safely without fire risks.

Nitrogen dissolved in the blood under pressure can cause a severe condition called diver's bends when a diver comes back to the surface. To avoid this, nitrogen is not used in a diver's breathing apparatus. A diver's breathing apparatus contains a mixture of helium and oxygen.

Neon is used to fill light tubes for advertising signs. The tubes are filled with neon at low pressure and an electric spark is passed through the tube.

Argon and argon/nitrogen mixtures are used to fill electric light bulbs. The tungsten filament is heated by an electric current until it glows. Oxygen must not be inside the bulb or the filament will burn out.

Krypton and xenon are used in special bulbs for lighthouses and projectors.

Radon is a radioactive gas and is used in the treatment of cancers.

Fig 4 Neon is used to fill the light tubes for advertising signs

Fig 5 Lighthouses use special bulbs which contain krypton and xenon

KS4 92 The halogens – 1

In this unit you will learn the answers to these questions:

■ What are the halogen elements and where can they be found in the Periodic Table?
■ How do the physical properties such as melting and boiling point change down group VII?
■ How does the reactivity of halogens decrease down group VII?

fluorine	F
chlorine	Cl
bromine	Br
iodine	I
astatine	At

The halogens are a family of reactive non-metallic elements placed in group 7 of the Periodic Table.

The table contains information about the halogens.

Element	Atomic number	Melting point (°C)	Boiling point (°C)	Density at room temperature and atmospheric pressure/g per dm³	Appearance at room temperature and atmospheric pressure
fluorine F	9	−220	−188	1.58	colourless gas
chlorine Cl	17	−101	−34	2.99	greenish-yellow gas
bromine Br	35	−7	58	3.12	dark red liquid
iodine I	53	114	183	4.94	black shiny solid
astatine At	85				

Although the halogens show similarities to one another in physical and chemical properties, there is a gradual change down the group. All of the halogens have simple molecular structures with diatomic molecules, i.e. Cl_2, Br_2, I_2. The covalent bonds are strong but the bonds between separate molecules are weak. The molecules are therefore easily separated and so their boiling points are relatively low.

Q1 Use the table to predict the physical properties of astatine.

As we move down the group, the halogen molecules get heavier and larger. Therefore, from fluorine to iodine, they are gradually more difficult to melt and vaporise. This is shown by their increasing melting and boiling points.

Reactions of halogens with water

The table summarises the reactions of halogens with cold water.

Halogen	Reaction with cold water
fluorine	Violent reaction with cold water forming oxygen and hydrogen fluoride gases. $2F_2 + 2H_2O \rightarrow 4HF + O_2$
chlorine	Forms a mixture of hydrochloric acid and hypochlorous acid. The solution is strongly acidic and a strong bleach. $Cl_2 + H_2O \rightarrow HCl + HOCl$
bromine	Forms a solution of hydrobromic acid and hypobromous acid. The solution is acidic and a bleach.
iodine	Only reacts slightly with water. Very slightly acidic and a mild bleach.

These reactions clearly show a decrease in reactivity down the group.

Q2 Suggest how astatine would react with cold water.

194

Reactions of halogens with metals

The word 'halogen' means salt-producer. All halogens react with metals to produce salts. For example, sodium burns in chlorine to form sodium chloride (see Unit 90):

$$sodium + chlorine \Rightarrow sodium\ chloride$$
$$2Na\ (s) + Cl_2\ (g) \Rightarrow 2NaCl\ (s)$$

In similar reactions, fluorine forms fluorides, bromine forms bromides and iodine forms iodides. The table shows the reactivity of halogens with hot iron.

Halogen	Reaction with hot iron
chlorine	reacts rapidly to form iron(III) chloride iron + chlorine $\Rightarrow$ iron(III) chloride $2Fe\ (s) + 3Cl_2\ (g) \Rightarrow 2FeCl_3\ (s)$
bromine	reacts slowly iron + bromine $\Rightarrow$ iron(III) bromide $2Fe\ (s) + 3Br_2\ (g) \Rightarrow 2FeBr_3\ (s)$
iodine	reacts very slowly iron + iodine $\Rightarrow$ iron(III) iodide $2Fe\ (s) + 3I_2\ (g) \Rightarrow 2FeI_3\ (s)$

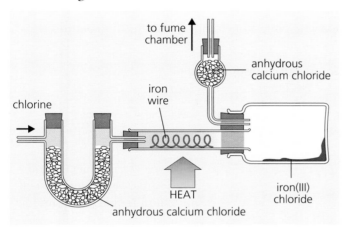

Fig 1 shows apparatus which can be used to produce iron(III) chloride from iron and dry chlorine.

Fig 1 Preparation of iron(III) chloride

Q3 Write a word and symbol equation for the reaction of aluminium and chlorine to produce aluminium chloride, $AlCl_3$.

Reactions of halogens with hydrogen

The reactions of halogens with hydrogen clearly show the differences in reactivity of the halogens.

Mixtures of fluorine and hydrogen react explosively to produce hydrogen fluoride.

$$hydrogen + fluorine \Rightarrow hydrogen\ fluoride$$
$$H_2\ (g) + F_2\ (g) \Rightarrow 2HF\ (g)$$

Chlorine and hydrogen can be mixed together without reaction providing they are kept in the dark. In sunlight they react together explosively.

$$hydrogen + chlorine \Rightarrow hydrogen\ chloride$$
$$H_2\ (g) + Cl_2\ (g) \Rightarrow 2HCl\ (g)$$

Mixtures of bromine and hydrogen react together on heating to produce hydrogen bromide.

$$hydrogen + bromine \Rightarrow hydrogen\ bromide$$
$$H_2\ (g) + Br_2\ (g) \Rightarrow 2HBr\ (g)$$

Iodine and hydrogen only react partially when they are heated.

$$hydrogen + iodine \rightleftharpoons hydrogen\ iodide$$
$$H_2\ (g) + I_2\ (g) \rightleftharpoons 2HI\ (g)$$

From these reactions the order of reactivity can be established.

most reactive
fluorine
chlorine
bromine
iodine
least reactive

93 The halogens – 2

In this unit you will learn the answers to these questions:
- What are displacement reactions?
- How can hydrochloric acid be produced from sodium chloride?
- What are the uses of fluorine, chlorine, bromine and iodine?

In Unit 90 we saw that the order of reactivity of the halogens is:

This was established by the reactivity of halogens with hydrogen, water and metals. The order can be confirmed by looking at displacement reactions of halogens.

most reactive
fluorine
chlorine
bromine
iodine
least reactive

Displacement reactions of halogens

If chlorine gas is passed through colourless potassium iodide solution, the solution turns brown as free iodine forms.

potassium iodide + chlorine ➡ potassium chloride + iodine
$2KI \, (aq)$ + $Cl_2 \, (g)$ ➡ $2KCl \, (aq)$ + $I_2 \, (aq)$

This reaction occurs because chlorine is more reactive than iodine and replaces it in the potassium iodide. Iodine is displaced.

A similar reaction takes place when chlorine is bubbled through potassium bromide solution. A red solution containing bromine is produced.

$2KBr \, (aq) + Cl_2 \, (g)$ ➡ $2KCl \, (aq) + Br_2 \, (aq)$

Q1 What are the products of the reaction between bromine and potassium iodide solution?

No reaction occurs when chlorine is bubbled through potassium fluoride solution as chlorine is less reactive than fluorine.

A displacement reaction is important in the extraction of bromine from sea water. Chlorine is bubbled through a concentrated sea water solution, rich in bromide. A displacement reaction takes place to produce bromine.

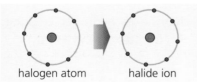
halogen atom   halide ion

The high reactivity of halogens compared to many other elements can be related to electronic structure. All halogens, in group VII of the Periodic Table, have seven electrons in their outer shell. This is one electron less than the stable electron arrangements of noble gases. Therefore all halogens gain one electron to form an ion with a single negative charge (e.g. F^-, Cl^-, Br^-).

As we go down the group the atoms become larger and less able to attract electrons. The reactivity therefore decreases.

| Halogen | Electron arrangement in | | |
	Atom	Ion	
fluorine	2, 7	2, 8	$F + e^- ➡ F^-$
chlorine	2, 8, 7	2, 8, 8	$Cl + e^- ➡ Cl^-$
bromine	2, 8, 18, 7	2, 8, 18, 8	$Br + e^- ➡ Br^-$

Hydrogen halides

When concentrated sulphuric acid is added to sodium chloride a colourless, steamy gas is produced, as shown on the next page.

sodium chloride	+	conc. sulphuric acid	➡	sodium hydrogensulphate	+	hydrogen chloride
$NaCl\ (s)$	+	$H_2SO_4\ (l)$	➡	$NaHSO_4\ (s)$	+	$HCl\ (g)$

This gas turns damp blue litmus paper red. The gas dissolves well in water to form a colourless solution.

This apparatus can be used to produce a solution of the gas in water.

The table shows the properties of the aqueous solution.

Test	Observations	Conclusions
Test pH with Universal Indicator	Red	pH 1
Add magnesium ribbon	Fizzes. Colourless gas burns with a squeaky pop	Gas is hydrogen
Add sodium carbonate	Fizzes. Colourless gas turns limewater milky	Carbon dioxide gas
Test conductivity of solution	Solution conducts electricity	Solution contains ions
Test for chloride ions – acidify with dilute nitric acid and add silver nitrate solution	White precipitate	Chloride present

The results of these tests confirm that the aqueous solution produced is hydrochloric acid.

Q2 A solution of dry hydrogen chloride in dry methylbenzene turns Universal Indicator green and gives no gas with magnesium ribbon or sodium carbonate. Suggest a reason for these observations.

Testing for chlorides, bromides and iodides

A solution suspected of containing chloride, bromide or iodide is acidified with dilute nitric acid, and silver nitrate solution is added. If a chloride is present a *white* precipitate of silver chloride is formed, e.g.

$$Ag^+\ (aq)\ +\ Cl^-\ (aq)\ ➡\ AgCl\ (s)\ \text{(white)}$$

If bromide is present, a *cream* precipitate of silver bromide is formed. If an iodide is present, a *yellow* precipitate of silver iodide is formed.

Q3 Write ionic equations for the tests for bromide and iodide.

Uses of halogens

- **Fluorine** is used in the form of fluorides in toothpastes and drinking water, as it hardens the enamel on teeth and reduces tooth decay. Fluorine is used to make PTFE (Unit 71) for non-stick coatings on saucepans.
- **Chlorine** is used in making household bleaches. It is used to kill bacteria and viruses in drinking water and swimming pools. Chlorine is also used to make PVC (Unit 71) which is used in furniture etc.
- **Bromine** is used in making fire-retardant materials, disinfectants and medicines.
- **Iodine** is used in medicines, disinfectants and photographic chemicals. Radioactive iodine is used as a medical tracer.

94 Rates of chemical reactions – 1

In this unit you will learn the answers to these questions:
- What is meant by rate of reaction?
- What is the relationship between rate and time?
- How does increasing surface area (decreasing particle size) affect the rate of a reaction?

Chemical reactions can take place at different speeds. An explosion, such as the reaction of hydrogen and oxygen together to produce water vapour, is a very fast reaction – it is over in a tiny fraction of a second. The rusting of iron and the souring of milk are slow reactions.

A reaction which is over in a fraction of a second is a very fast reaction. We say it has a **high rate of reaction**. As the time taken for the reaction to be completed increases, the rate of reaction decreases. That is:

$$\text{rate of reaction} \propto \frac{1}{\text{time}}$$

Altering the rate of reaction

From everyday experience we know that changing the conditions can alter the time a reaction takes. For example, cooling milk in a refrigerator slows down the souring process. It is difficult to study very fast reactions or very slow reactions. It is better to study reactions which progress steadily and where changes in rate of reaction can be clearly seen. Then it is possible to identify factors which alter the rate of reaction and possibly try to explain why.

Effect of particle size on the rate of reaction

Calcium carbonate reacts with dilute hydrochloric acid as follows:

calcium carbonate	+	hydrochloric acid	⇒	calcium chloride	+	water	+	carbon dioxide
$CaCO_3$ (s)	+	$2HCl$ (aq)	⇒	$CaCl_2$ (aq)	+	H_2O (l)	+	CO_2 (g)

Fig 1 shows a flask containing calcium carbonate and dilute hydrochloric acid. The progress of the reaction can be followed in several ways, including:

1 measuring the volume of carbon dioxide produced at regular intervals;

2 measuring the total mass of the container, calcium carbonate and hydrochloric acid at intervals. Remember that the carbon dioxide escapes from the container during the reaction.

Fig 2a shows how the gas can be collected in a gas syringe and its volume measured at intervals. Fig 2b shows how the loss of mass can be measured using a top-pan balance.

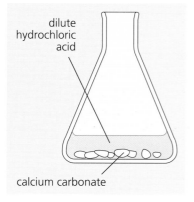

dilute hydrochloric acid

calcium carbonate

Fig 1 *Calcium carbonate and dilute hydrochloric acid*

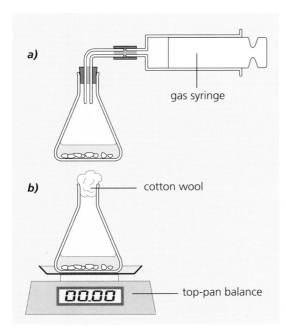

Fig 2 *Measuring* **a)** *the volume,* **b)** *the mass*

ICT Extra!

Link the top-pan balance directly to a computer.
This enables the data on mass loss at different times to be directly displayed as a graph.

Q1 What is the job of the cotton wool in Fig 2b?

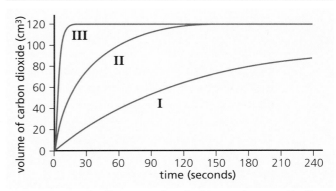

Fig 3 *Reactions of different samples of calcium carbonate with dilute hydrochloric acid*

Fig 3 shows graphs which were obtained when three samples of calcium carbonate reacted with the same volume of dilute hydrochloric acid of the same concentration and the same temperature. All possible variables were kept constant apart from the surface area. The three samples of calcium carbonate used were:

  I 1.00 g of large lumps of marble (calcium carbonate);
  II 1.00 g of small lumps of marble (calcium carbonate);
  III 1.00 g of powdered calcium carbonate.

Powdered calcium carbonate has a much larger surface area than the small lumps which, in turn, have a much larger surface area than the large lumps.

Although lumps of coal do not react with oxygen in the air without heating, mixtures of coal dust and air can be explosive.

Q2 At the end of each experiment some calcium carbonate remains in the flask. What does this tell you about the contents of the flask at the end of the experiment?

Q3 Use Fig 3. After how many seconds is the reaction with small lumps complete?

Why decreasing particle size speeds up a reaction

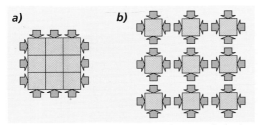

Fig 4 *The effect of particle size on the rate of reaction*

Fig 4 shows the effect of particle size on the rate of the reaction. In Fig 4a the square represents a large lump of marble. In Fig 4b the small squares represent the same mass of marble in smaller pieces. There is a larger surface area with small lumps so the hydrochloric acid can come into contact with the marble more easily.

95 Rates of chemical reactions – 2

In this unit you will learn the answers to these questions:
■ How is the rate of reaction affected by increasing the concentration of a reactant?
■ How does increasing the pressure of reactant gases affect the rate of reaction?
■ How does light affect some reactions?

Effect of concentration

The effect of increasing concentration on the rate of reaction is relatively easy to predict qualitatively. From the simple experiment between magnesium ribbon and hydrochloric acid in Fig 1 it can be seen that increasing the concentration of acid from 1 mole per dm³ to 2 moles per dm³, while keeping all other variables constant, causes more bubbles of hydrogen to be formed, i.e. increases the rate of reaction.

It is not possible to be sure of a quantitative relationship without carrying out experimental studies. In some cases, doubling the concentration of one of the reactants doubles the rate of reaction. However, it is possible to find reactions where increasing the concentration of one of the reactants has no effect at all on the rate of the reaction.

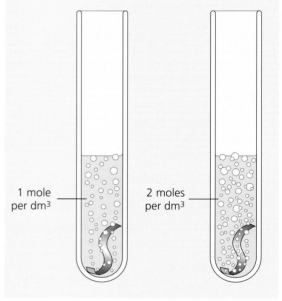

Fig 1 *Increasing the concentration of acid causes more hydrogen to be formed*

The reaction of magnesium and hydrochloric acid proceeds according to the equation:

$$\text{magnesium} + \text{hydrochloric acid} \Rightarrow \text{magnesium chloride} + \text{hydrogen}$$
$$\text{Mg (s)} + \text{2HCl (aq)} \Rightarrow \text{MgCl}_2\text{ (aq)} + \text{H}_2\text{ (g)}$$

Equal lengths of magnesium ribbon, ensuring that equal masses were used, were added to 40 cm³ hydrochloric acid of different concentrations. The length of time was measured for the magnesium to react with the hydrochloric acid and disappear. This is the end of the reaction because one of the reactants has been used up. The results are shown in the table.

Experiment	Concentration of acid/mole per dm³	Time/ seconds
A	0.5	500
B	0.7	250
C	0.8	160
D	1.0	100
E	1.5	30

Clearly, increasing the concentration of hydrochloric acid speeds up the reaction, i.e. increases the rate of reaction.

 ICT Extra!

Use modelling software to examine the effect on the rate of reaction of altering the concentration of the acid.

Effect of pressure

Fig 2a shows a diagram of particles of two gases mixed together. They are going to react. The collisions between ● and ○ may lead to a reaction to form molecules ●○. Not all of the collisions will lead to a reaction, as only a fraction of the collisions will have sufficient energy. There will also be collisions between ○ and ○, and between ● and ●. Neither of these will lead to a reaction.

In Fig 2b there are more particles of the two gases, i.e. there is a greater concentration, and, as a result, there will be more collisions per second. With the same fraction of collisions leading to a reaction, the reaction between ● and ○ will be faster.

In the case of gases only, concentration and pressure are two ways of expressing similar things. When a gas is at a high pressure the molecules are close together, i.e. the concentration is high.

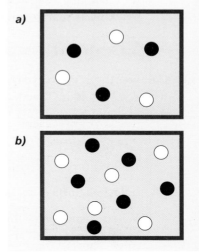

Fig 2 Effect of pressure on the rate of reaction

Effect of light

Some reactions are speeded up by light. For example, the reaction of hydrogen and chlorine is explosive in sunlight but only slow in the dark. In the case of this reaction, the sunlight breaks some of the chlorine molecules into **free atoms** and these react with hydrogen molecules. This is summarised in Fig 3.

Q1 Hydrogen molecules and chlorine molecules are represented by (H–H) and (Cl–Cl).

What do (H•) and (Cl•) represent?

Q2 Why is the reaction speeded up in sunlight?

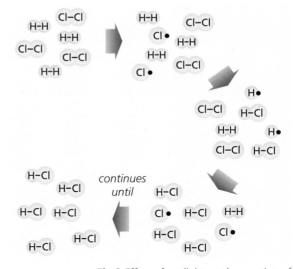

Fig 3 Effect of sunlight on the reaction of hydrogen and chlorine

Another reaction which is affected in a similar way is the decomposition of silver chloride or silver bromide. When silver chloride is freshly precipitated it is white in colour.

silver nitrate + sodium chloride ➡ silver chloride + sodium nitrate
$AgNO_3$ (aq) + NaCl (aq) ➡ AgCl (s) + $NaNO_3$ (aq)

When this is left to stand in sunlight, the precipitate partially decomposes into silver and chlorine and turns purplish. Silver bromide behaves in a similar way. This type of decomposition of silver compounds by light is the basis of photography.

96 Rates of chemical reactions – 3

In this unit you will learn the answers to these questions:
■ How does increasing temperature affect the rate of reaction?
■ Why is reaction rate affected in this way by increasing temperature?

Effect of temperature

Q1 Can you think of everyday examples where reactions are speeded up or slowed down by changing temperature?

The effect of temperature on the rate of a reaction can be studied using the reaction between sodium thiosulphate solution and dilute hydrochloric acid.

| sodium thiosulphate | + | dilute hydrochloric acid | ➡ | sodium chloride | + water + sulphur + | sulphur dioxide |

$$Na_2S_2O_3 \text{ (aq)} + 2HCl \text{ (aq)} \implies 2NaCl \text{ (aq)} + H_2O \text{ (l)} + S \text{ (s)} + SO_2 \text{ (g)}$$

When sodium thiosulphate solution and dilute hydrochloric acid are mixed, the solution goes cloudy. Eventually, it is not possible to see a cross through the beaker (Fig 1).

Q2 Why does the solution turn cloudy?

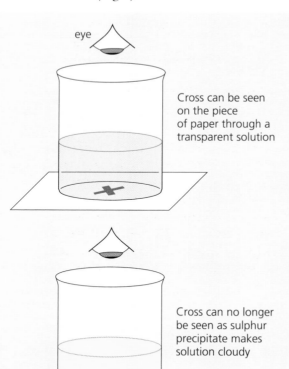

eye

Cross can be seen on the piece of paper through a transparent solution

Cross can no longer be seen as sulphur precipitate makes solution cloudy

In an experiment to investigate the effect of temperature on the rate of reaction, the volumes and concentrations of the sodium thiosulphate solution and dilute hydrochloric acid are kept the same. Only the temperature is changed. The time is measured until the cross just disappears from view through the beaker.

We can see from the results that the time taken for the cross to disappear decreases as the temperature of the solutions rises.

Temperature/ °C	Time for the cross to disappear/seconds
20	280
30	132
40	60
50	33
60	18

ICT Extra!

Use a data-logger to measure how much light passes through the solution at different intervals of time.

Fig 1 *Reaction between sodium thiosulphate solution and dilute hydrochloric acid causes the solution to become cloudy*

Q3 A student carrying out this experiment recorded times as 4.40 min, 2.12 min, 1 min, 0.33 min and 0.18 min. Why are the results wrong?

Q4 It is often said that raising the temperature of a reaction by 10°C doubles the rate of reaction. Do these results support this general statement?

Why does raising the temperature speed up a reaction?

Fig 2 shows the particles of two gases mixed together. These particles are moving rapidly in all directions. Millions of collisions between particles will occur each second and some of these collisions will lead to a reaction. The 'successful' collisions are the ones where the particles hit 'head-on' and the particles contain high energy.

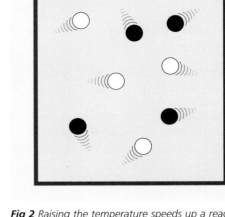

Fig 2 Raising the temperature speeds up a reaction

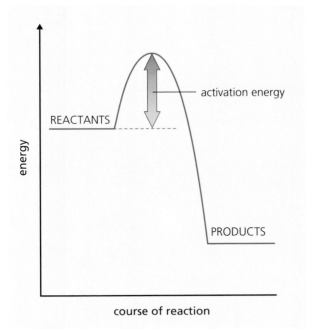

course of reaction

Fig 3 Energy level diagram

Fig 3 shows an energy level diagram which summarises the energy changes in a chemical reaction. The reaction is **exothermic** because the energy of the reactants is greater than the energy of the products. This extra energy is given out to the surroundings. There is an energy barrier, called the **activation energy**, which particles have to get over before a reaction can take place.

Raising the temperature of the mixture of gases will increase the average speed (and energy) of the particles in the mixture of gases. This has two effects.

1 If the particles are speeded up, there will be more collisions per second.

2 More of the collisions will possess the activation energy necessary for a reaction to take place.

97 Rates of chemical reactions – 4

In this unit you will learn the answers to these questions:
- What is a catalyst?
- How does a catalyst operate?

Catalysts

If a jet of hydrogen gas is directed at a piece of platinum gauze, a reaction takes place between the hydrogen and oxygen from the air, forming water. The gauze glows hot and acts as a **catalyst**.

> A catalyst is a substance which alters the rate of a chemical reaction without being used up. The mass of catalyst remains unchanged throughout the reaction.

Decomposition of hydrogen peroxide

Hydrogen peroxide decomposes very slowly at room temperature into water and oxygen.

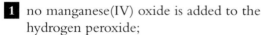

hydrogen peroxide ⟹ water + oxygen
$$2H_2O_2 \text{ (aq)} \implies 2H_2O \text{ (l)} + O_2 \text{ (g)}$$

A wide variety of substances will speed up the decomposition of hydrogen peroxide. One of these substances is manganese(IV) oxide. Fig 1 shows the volume of gas collected at intervals when:

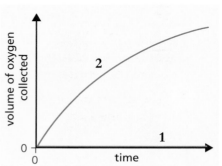

Fig 1 *Volume of oxygen collected from hydrogen peroxide*

1 no manganese(IV) oxide is added to the hydrogen peroxide;

2 one spatula measure of manganese(IV) oxide is added to hydrogen peroxide.

Q1 Draw a diagram of apparatus which could be used for this experiment.

Q2 In order to be sure that the difference in the volume of gas produced is due only to the manganese(IV) oxide, various factors have to be kept the same. List the factors which should be kept the same.

Examples of catalysis

There are many examples of catalysis in industry and everyday life.

1 In the Haber process (Unit 100), finely divided iron is used as a catalyst for the reaction of nitrogen and hydrogen at a temperature of about 450°C.

2 In the Contact process (Unit 101), vanadium(V) oxide pellets act as a catalyst for the reaction of sulphur dioxide and oxygen at a temperature of about 450°C.

3 In the manufacture of nitric acid (Unit 106), a platinum–rhodium gauze acts as a catalyst in the first stage when ammonia and oxygen react together to form nitrogen monoxide and steam.

4 In the manufacture of margarine, a nickel catalyst is used to aid the reaction of hydrogen with unsaturated oils to form margarine. The temperature is about 140°C.

5 Long-chain hydrocarbons are cracked (Unit 70) when crude oil vapour is passed over a heated ceramic catalyst.

6 Catalytic converters are included in car exhaust systems to reduce emissions of carbon monoxide and oxides of nitrogen. The converter contains finely divided platinum.

7 The filler used to make minor body repairs to a car consists of a resin which is hardened by adding a catalyst. This sets in a few minutes to make a material which is so hard it can be sandpapered.

Fig 2 *A catalytic converter from a car*

How a catalyst speeds up a chemical reaction

The following points about catalysts are important to remember.

1 A catalyst does not produce any more of the product, but only the same amount at a faster rate.

2 The mass of catalyst remains unchanged at the end of the reaction.

3 Catalysts are often finely divided powders, pellets and fine gauzes.

4 Catalysts are often transition metals or transition metal compounds.

Q3 Explain why usually only a small mass of catalyst is required to convert large masses of reactants into products.

Q4 Catalysts are often finely divided powders, pellets and fine gauzes. What does this suggest about the way that some catalysts work?

Many catalysts act via an **intermediate compound**, using the fact that transition metals can show variable oxidation states. Let us take the decomposition of hydrogen peroxide using manganese(IV) oxide as an example of the intermediate compound theory. The reaction takes place in two steps.

Step 1 Hydrogen peroxide oxidises manganese(IV) oxide to manganese(VII) oxide.

$$2H_2O_2 + 2MnO_2 + [O] \Rightarrow Mn_2O_7 + 2H_2O$$

Step 2 The manganese(VII) oxide then decomposes into manganese(IV) oxide and oxygen.

$$Mn_2O_7 \Rightarrow 2MnO_2 + O_2 + [O]$$

In Unit 94 the energy level diagram was given for an exothermic reaction. In order that the collisions could lead to a reaction, a certain minimum amount of energy was required – called the activation energy. A catalyst lowers this activation energy (Fig 3). This means that more collisions will now lead to a reaction and so the reaction will be faster.

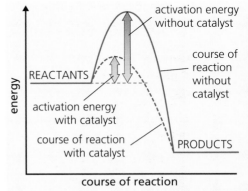

Fig 3 *Effect of a catalyst on the activation energy*

Inhibitors

Sometimes it is necessary to slow down reactions by adding negative catalysts or **inhibitors**. For example, sulphur dioxide is added to lemon juice to stop it oxidising and going bad. Phosphoric acid is added to hydrogen peroxide to slow down its decomposition.

98 Enzymes

In this unit you will learn the answers to these questions:
- ■ **What are enzymes?**
- ■ **Under what conditions do enzymes operate?**
- ■ **What are enzymes used for?**

Enzymes are proteins that control vital biological processes. They often act as biological catalysts. In the human body enzymes control the breakdown of food and reactions which make chemicals such as fats, carbohydrates, proteins and DNA. Enzymes are used today in a wide range of industrial processes. These include fermentation (Unit 72), baking, cheese making, tenderising meat and treating leather. The table summarises some of the enzymes used in industrial processes.

One of the most familiar household uses is in biological washing powders. Although the first biological washing powder was produced in 1913, only in the last twenty years have they been widely used.

Enzyme	Examples of use
α-amylase	stain removal, paper manufacture, making syrups
cellulases	making animal feed from straw
lipases	speeding up the ripening of cheese
proteases	stain removal, making leather pliable, making biscuit flour
catalase	preservative in soft drinks, rubber manufacture
glucose oxidase	preservative in soft drinks, detecting diabetes
pectinase	clearing fruit juices
streptokinase	treating blood clots and bruises
invertase	making soft-centred chocolates

Enzyme decomposition of hydrogen peroxide

The enzyme catalase is present in blood to prevent the build-up of dangerous peroxides. If a small piece of liver is added to hydrogen peroxide, a rapid evolution of oxygen is seen.

The catalase acts as a catalyst and speeds up the decomposition of hydrogen peroxide.

$$2H_2O_2 \text{ (aq)} \Rightarrow 2H_2O \text{ (l)} + O_2 \text{ (g)}$$

Catalase is an extremely effective catalyst. One molecule of catalase will decompose 40 000 molecules of hydrogen peroxide each second.

However, unlike chemical catalysts, which work under a wide range of conditions, enzymes are only able to work under limited conditions. Fig 1 shows graphs of the effectiveness of some enzymes under different conditions.

Q1 Which two conditions are being varied?

Q2 From the graphs, what conditions would be most effective for the operation of these enzymes?

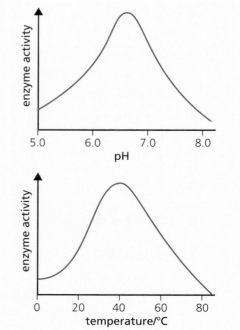

***Fig 1** Effectiveness of some enzymes under different conditions*

How do enzymes work?

You can think of enzyme molecules as pieces of a jigsaw puzzle. In Fig 2, the enzyme molecule will fit together with reactant A but not with reactants B or C. When the enzyme molecule and reactant molecule fit together, a reaction can take place. This is summarised in Fig 3.

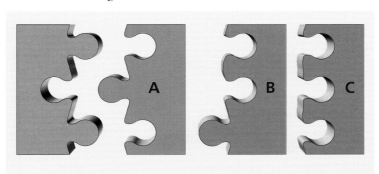

Fig 2 *Enzyme molecules are like pieces of a jig-saw puzzle*

Fig 3 *Summary of enzyme action*

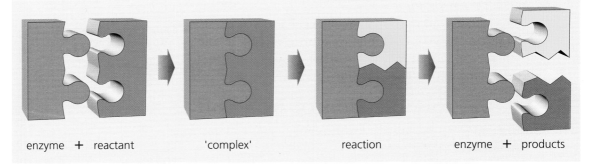

enzyme + reactant   'complex'   reaction   enzyme + products

Biological washing powders

Fig 4 shows a label from a biological washing powder.

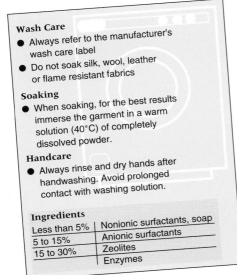

Wash Care
- Always refer to the manufacturer's wash care label
- Do not soak silk, wool, leather or flame resistant fabrics

Soaking
- When soaking, for the best results immerse the garment in a warm solution (40°C) of completely dissolved powder.

Handcare
- Always rinse and dry hands after handwashing. Avoid prolonged contact with washing solution.

Ingredients

Less than 5%	Nonionic surfactants, soap
5 to 15%	Anionic surfactants
15 to 30%	Zeolites
	Enzymes

Q3 Refer to the table (page 206). Which enzymes is the washing powder likely to contain?

Q4 Why should biological washing powders not be used with silk, wool and leather?

Q5 When soaking stains in biological washing powder, why is it better to use water at 40°C rather than hotter water?

Q6 Why should the powder be completely dissolved before the clothes are added?

Q7 Why should the clothes be thoroughly rinsed after washing?

Q8 What effect can biological washing powders have on the skin?

Fig 4 *Biological washing powder*

99 Reversible reactions and equilibrium

In this unit you will learn the answers to these questions:
■ What are reversible reactions and how is an equilibrium established?
■ How can the position of an equilibrium be moved?

Reversible reactions

When magnesium burns in oxygen, solid magnesium oxide is formed.

$$2Mg\ (s)\ +\ O_2\ (g)\ \Rightarrow\ 2MgO\ (s)$$

This reaction cannot be reversed. Many reactions are like this and result in permanent change.

When blue copper(II) sulphate crystals are heated, steam is produced and white anhydrous copper(II) sulphate is formed. If cold water is added to anhydrous copper(II) sulphate, the mixture gets hot and blue copper(II) sulphate is re-formed. This reaction can be summarised by the equation:

copper(II) sulphate + heat $\rightleftharpoons$ anhydrous copper(II) sulphate + water
$$CuSO_4.5H_2O\ (s)\ +\ heat\ \rightleftharpoons\ CuSO_4\ (s)\ +\ 5H_2O\ (g)$$

The $\rightleftharpoons$ sign in the equation shows that the reaction is reversible. A **reversible reaction** is a reaction which can go from left to right or right to left, depending upon the conditions.

Q1 What other examples of reversible reactions can you find?

Reversible reaction of iron and steam

If steam is passed over heated iron, hydrogen and an oxide of iron are formed.

$$3Fe\ (s)\ +\ 4H_2O\ (g)\ \Rightarrow\ Fe_3O_4\ (s)\ +\ 4H_2\ (g)$$

If hydrogen gas is passed over heated iron oxide, steam and iron are produced.

$$Fe_3O_4\ (s)\ +\ 4H_2\ (g)\ \Rightarrow\ 3Fe\ (s)\ +\ 4H_2O\ (g)$$

Depending upon conditions, the reaction can go in either direction and can be represented by the equation:

$$3Fe\ (s)\ +\ 4H_2O\ (g)\ \rightleftharpoons\ Fe_3O_4\ (s)\ +\ 4H_2\ (g)$$

Equilibrium

If iron and steam are heated at 300°C in a closed metal globe so that the products of the reaction cannot escape, Fig 1 represents the situation inside the globe at the start and at one-day intervals for the first three days.

At first the iron reacts with steam to produce hydrogen and iron oxide. As the masses of hydrogen and iron oxide increase, the reverse reaction becomes possible and speeds up. After one day there is no further change in the masses of iron, iron oxide, steam and hydrogen in the globe, providing no change is made to the conditions.

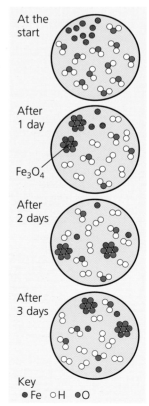

At the start

After 1 day

Fe_3O_4

After 2 days

After 3 days

Key
● Fe ○ H ● O

Fig 1 *Iron and steam heated at 300°C. The system reaches equilibrium*

The reaction has not, however, stopped but is in a system of **equilibrium**. When a system is in equilibrium the forward and reverse reactions are still continuing but both are taking place at the same rate so there is no change in any concentration of reacting substance or product.

Factors affecting an equilibrium

An equilibrium mixture of iron, iron oxide, hydrogen and steam with unchanging concentrations can be disturbed by altering a condition. If the equilibrium moves to produce more iron oxide and hydrogen (i.e. the forward reaction for a time becomes faster than the reverse reaction) the equilibrium is said to move to the right. The system is said to move to the left if the equilibrium changes to produce more iron and steam.

Consider a reaction where **A**, **B**, **C** and **D** represent reacting substances and products:

$$A + B \rightleftharpoons C + D + heat$$

The forward reaction is **exothermic**, that is, heat is evolved as the forward reaction proceeds. The table shows the changes which affect this equilibrium.

Factor	Type of equilibrium affected	Effect on equilibrium
increase in concentration of A and/or B	any	moves to the right
decrease in concentration of A and/or B	any	moves to the left
increase in concentration of C and/or D	any	moves to the left
decrease in concentration of C and/or D	any	moves to the right
increase in pressure	reactions involving gases	may move to the left, right or remain unchanged (see note 1)
catalyst added	certain reactions only	no change
increase in temperature	exothermic forward reaction endothermic forward reaction	moves to the left moves to the right (see note 2)
decrease in temperature	exothermic forward reaction endothermic forward reaction	moves to the right moves to the left

Notes

1 The resulting change in the equilibrium position when pressure is increased depends on the number of gas molecules on the left-hand side and on the right-hand side of the equation. If there are more molecules on the left-hand side, increasing the pressure moves the equilibrium to the right. For example:

$$2SO_2 (g) + O_2 (g) \rightleftharpoons 2SO_3 (g)$$
3 gas molecules on the LHS   2 gas molecules on the RHS

If there are more gas molecules on the right-hand side, increasing the pressure moves the equilibrium to the left.

If there are equal numbers of gas molecules on both sides of the equation, increasing the pressure has no effect on the equilibrium.

$$3Fe (s) + 4H_2O (g) \rightleftharpoons Fe_3O_4 (s) + 4H_2 (g)$$
4 gas molecules on the LHS   4 gas molecules on the RHS

2 Increasing the temperature helps to establish the equilibrium more quickly. This is because it speeds up both the forward and reverse reactions.

100 The Haber process

In this unit you will learn the answers to these questions:
- What is the Haber process?
- What is the major use of ammonia?

Why is nitrogen important?

Nitrogen is absorbed by plants through the roots as a solution of nitrates. The nitrogen is used to build up proteins in the plants. When plants grow they use up nitrogen and so repeated agricultural use can reduce the yield of crops grown because there is not enough nitrogen in the soil.

Q1 When a protein, e.g. milk powder, is mixed with calcium hydroxide (an alkali) and heated, a strong-smelling gas is produced which turns damp red litmus paper blue. This gas is ammonia, NH_3. What does this tell us about the composition of proteins?

To overcome this, farmers used to rely on animal manure and crop rotation. To add to these sources of nitrogen, guano, a natural fertiliser from Chile, was imported. This consisted of the droppings of seabirds. However, these supplies were used up by the beginning of the twentieth century. The famous scientist Sir William Crookes warned that the exhaustion of these deposits rich in nitrogen would lead to worldwide starvation if an alternative could not be found.

A new source of nitrogen compounds was therefore needed for agriculture, and also to meet the demands of the dyeing and explosives industries.

The Haber process

In 1904 the German chemist Fritz Haber suggested that nitrogen from the air and hydrogen from water could be combined together to form ammonia. By 1908 he was able to demonstrate this in the laboratory using high pressures and a catalyst of osmium or uranium. With the help of Carl Bosch, but not without considerable problems of carrying out the process on an industrial scale, he was able to set up large-scale factories using a specially developed iron catalyst.

Ammonia is produced in very large amounts by the Haber process.

Fig 1 *Fritz Haber (1868 – 1934). Despite Haber's great scientific advances and his work for his home country, Germany, during the First World War, as a Jew he was forced to escape from Germany in 1933 and finished his life at Cambridge University. He was awarded the Nobel Prize for Chemistry in 1918.*

Hydrogen is obtained from the cracking of methane or naphtha (Unit 69). Methane and steam are passed over a nickel catalyst at high temperatures and pressures.

methane + steam $\Rightarrow$ carbon monoxide + hydrogen

CH_4 (g) + H_2O (g) $\Rightarrow$ CO (g) + $3H_2$ (g)

Carbon monoxide is removed from the gas as this would poison the catalyst in the Haber process. The hydrogen is mixed with nitrogen from the air in the ratio of 3 parts of hydrogen to 1 part of nitrogen by volume.

The mixture of nitrogen and hydrogen is compressed and passed over a heated catalyst. The catalyst consists of finely divided iron with promoters to reduce the risk of catalyst poisoning. The catalyst is heated to about 450°C to start the reaction, and then this temperature is maintained because the forward reaction is exothermic. Depending upon the conditions, part of the mixture of nitrogen and hydrogen is converted into ammonia. The equation is:

$$\text{nitrogen} + \text{hydrogen} \rightleftharpoons \text{ammonia}$$
$$N_2\ (g) + 3H_2\ (g) \rightleftharpoons 2NH_3\ (g)$$

The mixture of gases, containing ammonia, is cooled and ammonia liquefies and can be separated. The unreacted nitrogen and hydrogen mixture is recycled. The process is summarised in Fig 2.

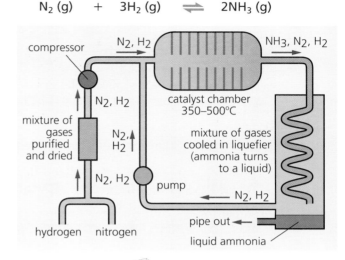

Fig 2 The Haber process

Getting the maximum yield of ammonia

In Unit 97 the conditions required to obtain the maximum yield of products from a system in equilibrium are discussed.

$$\text{nitrogen} + \text{hydrogen} \rightleftharpoons \text{ammonia} + \text{heat}$$
$$N_2\ (g) + 3H_2\ (g) \rightleftharpoons 2NH_3\ (g) + \text{heat}$$

In the above equilibrium, there are more molecules on the left-hand side than on the right-hand side. An increase in pressure will push the equilibrium to the right, increasing the yield of ammonia. Obviously, there are practical implications to increasing the pressure of the reactants. Increasing the pressure makes the cost of the plant (capital costs) much greater.

The reaction to produce ammonia is exothermic. If the temperature of the surroundings is lowered, the equilibrium will move to the right, evolving more heat to counteract the effect of the decrease in temperature of the surroundings. This produces more ammonia. Lowering the temperature slows down the reactions. It also increases the life of the catalyst.

ICT Extra!

From a data book get information about percentage of ammonia at different temperatures and pressures. Use this data in a spreadsheet.

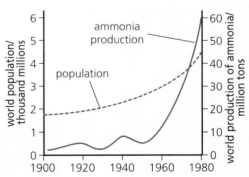

Fig 3 Ammonia production and the growth of population 1900 – 1980

Use of ammonia

Fig 3 shows a graph of the world ammonia production from 1900 to 1980, together with the growth of population. You will see the rapid growth in the mass of ammonia produced. This growth has been due to the development of the Haber process.

Fig 4 shows a pie diagram of the uses of ammonia. You will see that most of the ammonia is turned into fertilisers.

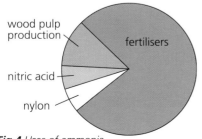

Fig 4 Uses of ammonia

211

101 The Contact process

In this unit you will learn the answers to these questions:
- **What is the Contact process?**
- **What conditions will produce the best yield of sulphuric acid?**
- **What are the uses of sulphuric acid?**

The Contact process is a process to produce sulphuric acid from sulphur or minerals rich in sulphur. It was first devised in 1831 by Peregrine Phillips and it replaced other processes which produced less pure acid. There are three stages to the process. The second stage involves a reversible reaction, and establishing suitable equilibrium conditions in this stage is a key to producing sulphuric acid economically.

Stage 1
Sulphur dioxide is formed from burning sulphur or minerals rich in sulphur.

sulphur + oxygen ➡ sulphur dioxide
$$S\ (s)\ +\ O_2\ (g)\ \rightarrow\ SO_2\ (g)$$

iron pyrites + oxygen ➡ iron oxide + sulphur dioxide
$$4FeS_2\ (s)\ +\ 11O_2\ (g)\ \rightarrow\ 2Fe_2O_3\ (s)\ +\ 8SO_2\ (g)$$

The sulphur dioxide produced is then purified to remove impurities such as arsenic which would poison the catalyst. The gas is passed through charged electrostatic plates in the dust precipitators to remove charged dust particles. It is then washed with water and dried.

Stage 2
Sulphur dioxide and air are passed over a heated catalyst in the catalyst chamber.

sulphur dioxide + oxygen (from the air) ⇌ sulphur trioxide + heat
$$2SO_2\ (g)\ +\ O_2\ (g)\ \rightleftharpoons\ 2SO_3\ (g)\ +\ heat$$

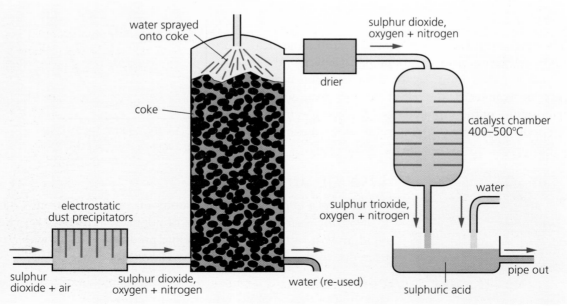

Fig 1 *The Contact process*

A low temperature is suggested from a study of the equilibrium (Unit 99) because the forward reaction is exothermic. At a low temperature there would be a good yield of sulphur trioxide but the reaction would be very slow. A compromise of about 450°C is struck. The catalyst used now is vanadium(V) oxide in the form of pellets. An effective catalyst would be platinum. This is less easily poisoned but is no longer used because it is more expensive.

Increasing the pressure would also produce a larger yield of sulphur trioxide in the resulting equilibrium mixture but, in practice, the extra costs of increasing the pressure outweigh the benefits.

Fig 2 A sulphuric acid plant

Stage 3

The sulphur trioxide is removed from the mixture of gases and converted to sulphuric acid. The sulphur trioxide is not directly dissolved in water because this reaction is too violent on a large scale. Instead, it is dissolved in concentrated sulphuric acid to form oleum (fuming sulphuric acid). This is then diluted with the correct volume of water to make concentrated sulphuric acid.

$$\text{sulphur trioxide} + \text{conc. sulphuric acid} \implies \text{oleum}$$
$$SO_3 (g) + H_2SO_4 (l) \implies H_2S_2O_7 (l)$$

$$\text{oleum} + \text{water} \implies \text{conc. sulphuric acid}$$
$$H_2S_2O_7 (l) + H_2O (l) \implies 2H_2SO_4 (l)$$

The overall reaction is:

$$\text{sulphur trioxide} + \text{water} \implies \text{conc. sulphuric acid}$$
$$SO_3 (g) + H_2O (l) \implies H_2SO_4 (l)$$

Because all of the impurities were removed from the gases before reaction, the acid produced is 99.5% pure. Fig 1 summarises the Contact process.

Q1 Why is it more important to control the conditions of stage 2 rather than stages 1 or 3?

Uses of sulphuric acid

Sulphuric acid has a wide range of uses and the amount of sulphuric acid used in a country is certainly a measure of that country's prosperity. Fig 3 shows a pie diagram of the uses of sulphuric acid.

Sulphuric acid is used to make fertilisers such as ammonium sulphate and calcium superphosphate. It is also used to make detergents. Soapless detergents are made by treating hydrocarbons from petroleum refining with concentrated sulphuric acid. Soapless detergents are preferable to soaps for many purposes because they lather well with water without forming any scum.

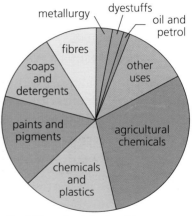

Fig 3 Uses of sulphuric acid

KS4 102 **Acids and alkalis**

acid

alkali

In this unit you will learn the answers to these questions:
- What are acids, bases and alkalis?
- What are typical reactions of acids?
- How can acids and alkalis be detected?

There are many examples of acids and alkalis in everyday life.

Acid	Formula	Salt produced
sulphuric acid	H_2SO_4	Na_2SO_4
hydrochloric acid	HCl	NaCl
nitric acid	HNO_3	$NaNO_3$

Acids are compounds which contain hydrogen which can be replaced by a metal to form a salt. In the laboratory there are three common mineral acids, as shown in the table.

Q1 From your knowledge of apples, lemons and vinegar, suggest what kind of taste acids have?

Q2 Which element is present in all acids?

Q3 Hydrochloric acid and nitric acid are said to be **monobasic** acids and sulphuric acid is a **dibasic** acid. Suggest the meaning of the words monobasic and dibasic.

There are also many **organic acids** composed of carbon, hydrogen and oxygen. Examples are citric acid, tartaric acid and ethanoic acid. Many of these organic acids are solids.

A **base** is an oxide or hydroxide of a metal. It reacts with an acid to form a salt and water only. An **alkali** is a base which is soluble in water. A solution of an alkali contains an excess of hydroxide, OH^-, ions. The common laboratory alkalis are listed (right).

potassium hydroxide	KOH
sodium hydroxide	NaOH
calcium hydroxide	$Ca(OH)_2$
ammonia solution	NH_3 (aq)
(ammonium hydroxide)	or NH_4OH

Properties of acids

Apart from using indicators, acids have other properties in common:

1 Reaction with magnesium

Acids react with magnesium to produce hydrogen. This burns with a squeaky pop. For example:

magnesium + hydrochloric acid ➡ magnesium chloride + hydrogen

2 Reaction with sodium carbonate crystals

Acids react with sodium carbonate crystals to produce a colourless gas. This colourless gas, carbon dioxide, turns limewater milky. For example:

sodium carbonate + hydrochloric acid ➡ sodium chloride + carbon dioxide + water

3 Reaction with black copper(II) oxide

Acids react with copper(II) oxide to produce a blue or green solution. For example:

copper(II) oxide + hydrochloric acid ➡ copper(II) chloride + water

Indicators

Acids and alkalis can be detected using indicators. Indicators are substances which change colour when acids and alkalis are added. Examples of good plant indicators are solutions from red cabbage, red roses, beetroot and elderberries.

In the laboratory the plant extract which is most commonly used to detect acids and alkalis is **litmus**. Litmus is extracted from a lichen. Litmus changes colour between red and blue.

| in acid solution | – red |
| in alkali solution | – blue |

Solutions which are not acidic or alkaline are said to be **neutral**. Litmus is purple in neutral solutions.

Although litmus can detect acids and alkalis, it cannot compare the strengths of acids and alkalis. The comparative strengths of acids and alkalis is given by the **pH** scale. This is a scale from 1 to 14. A substance is an acid if it has a pH less than 7 or alkaline if it has a pH greater than 7. A neutral substance has a pH of exactly 7. The pH of a solution can be found in two ways.

1 *Using mixtures of indicators called **Universal Indicator**.* This changes to a number of colours rather than just the one of a simple indicator such as litmus. The table gives the colours for a simple form of Universal Indicator. For example, if Universal Indicator is added to a solution and the solution turns blue, the solution has a pH of 8 and is a very weak alkali.

	pH	Colour of Universal Indicator	Examples in the home	Examples in the laboratory
STRONG ACIDS	1		car battery acid	mineral acids
	2			
	3	red		
	4		lemon juice, vinegar	ethanoic acid
WEAK ACIDS	5	orange		
	6	yellow	soda water	carbonic acid
NEUTRAL	7	green	water, salt, ethanol	
WEAK ALKALIS	8	blue	soap, baking powder	sodium hydrogencarbonate
	9	blue-purple		
STRONG ALKALIS	10			ammonia solution
	11		washing soda	
	12	purple	oven cleaner	
	13			sodium and potassium hydroxides
	14			

Fig 1 *The glass probe of a pH meter measuring the pH of a solution*

2 *Using a pH meter.* A pH meter is an electrical device used to measure the pH accurately. A glass probe is put into the solution being tested and the pH can be read from a dial or a digital readout immediately.

In this unit you will learn the answers to these questions:
■ What is neutralisation?
■ What examples of neutralisation are there in the world around us?

When an acid is mixed with an alkali, in the correct proportions, a neutral solution is formed. This process is called **neutralisation**.

One product of neutralisation is water. Any neutralisation can be represented by the equation:

$$H^+ (aq) + OH^- (aq) \Rightarrow H_2O (l)$$

These reactions are exothermic. There is a temperature rise when the two solutions are mixed.

Uses of neutralisation

1 **Soil testing**

A soil with a pH value between 6.5 and 7.0 is suitable for growing most plants. If the pH falls below 6.0, the soil will become too acidic for growing some plants. If the pH rises to 8.0 it will again be poor for plant growth because very alkaline soil is short of vital minerals necessary for plant growth.

Acidic conditions	Alkaline conditions
rhododendron	cherry
azalea	juniper
lavender	laburnum
wallflowers	lilac
stocks	birch
heather	broom
hydrangea	holly

The table shows plants which grow well in acidic and alkaline conditions.

You may be able to decide what the soil is like in your area by looking at the trees and plants which grow well in gardens around you. The pH of the soil can be found by mixing a sample of the soil with distilled water and adding pure, insoluble barium sulphate powder. The barium sulphate helps the solution to clear. Universal Indicator is then added and the colour of the solution compared with a Universal Indicator colour chart. Alternatively you could test the mixture of soil and distilled water with a pH meter.

Excess acidity of soils is an important cause of crop failure. It has been estimated that if this was always corrected properly there would be a one-fifth increase in food production.

Excess acidity of soils (or soil sourness) is caused by rainwater washing out alkalis from the soil and by rain containing acids. The excess acidity can be removed by neutralising it with alkalis.

Calcium oxide (or quicklime) and calcium hydroxide (or slaked lime) are frequently used to make the soil less acidic. They are made from limestone (calcium carbonate).

$$\text{calcium carbonate} \xrightarrow{\text{heat strongly}} \text{calcium oxide} \xrightarrow{\text{add water}} \text{calcium hydroxide}$$
$$CaCO_3 \Rightarrow CaO \Rightarrow Ca(OH)_2$$

Calcium hydroxide and calcium oxide are quick-acting. In order to correct excess soil acidity, these alkalis should be used in autumn or winter. Calcium carbonate can also be used. It is less soluble and acts more slowly.

2 Acids in digestion

There is about 1000 cm³ of dilute hydrochloric acid in your stomach. It is there to help you digest the food you eat. The food is broken down into simpler substances which can be used by your body. These substances are the vital supplies that your body needs for all kinds of jobs including building, repair and providing energy.

Indigestion is caused by too much acid in the stomach. It can be cured by taking antacids such as bicarbonate of soda (sodium hydrogencarbonate). These substances are weak alkalis and neutralise excess acidity.

3 Insect bites and stings

Insect bites or stings involve the injection of a small amount of chemical below the skin. This causes irritation. Nettle stings and ant bites inject acid into the skin. Bee stings also involve the injection of an acid. The sting or bite should be neutralised by using calamine lotion (a suspension of zinc carbonate) or sodium hydrogencarbonate. Both are weak alkalis. In neutralising the acid they reduce the irritation.

Wasp stings are different. They are best treated by applying vinegar (ethanoic acid) because the sting involves the injection of an alkali.

Fig 1 Close up of a wasp sting

4 Acidity in lakes

Many inland lakes are becoming too acidic because of acids in the atmosphere. This over-acidity can affect the life in the lake. Fish can die. The water in the lake can be neutralised by adding blocks of limestone.

5 Removing acidic gases from gases leaving power stations

Coal-fired power stations produce sulphur dioxide which can affect the environment. The sulphur dioxide can be removed by passing the gases over limestone. The limestone neutralises the acidic gases in the gases escaping from the factory. Calcium sulphate is produced and can be used in making plasterboards.

Fig 2 Fish killed by acid in lakes

Q1 Why is it important to remove acidic gases from power station gases?

ICT Extra!

Experiments where acids arnd alkalis react are called titrations. You can download software from (http://wwwchem.uwimona.edu.jm:1104/software/titr.html) which will enable you to simulate many titrations.

104 Salt formation – 1

In this unit you will learn the answers to these questions:
■ How can soluble salts be produced?
■ What are the rules for the solubility of salts?

Salts

A **salt** is produced when hydrogen ions in an acid are replaced by metal or ammonium (NH_4^+) ions. For example:

hydrochloric acid ➡ sodium chloride
HCl ➡ NaCl

The hydrogen ion is replaced by a sodium ion.

nitric acid ➡ ammonium nitrate
HNO_3 ➡ NH_4NO_3

The hydrogen ion is replaced by an ammonium ion.

Sulphuric acid contains two replaceable hydrogen ions per molecule. For this reason it is called a **dibasic acid**.

sulphuric acid ➡ sodium hydrogensulphate ➡ sodium sulphate
H_2SO_4 ➡ $NaHSO_4$ ➡ Na_2SO_4

The salt formed when one of the hydrogen ions in sulphuric acid has been replaced is called sodium hydrogensulphate and is an **acid salt**. It has some of the properties of the acid and some of the properties of the salt.

Any metal carbonate, chloride, sulphate or nitrate will be a salt. In general, salts are solids with high melting points. Some salts crystallise, containing water of crystallisation. An example of this is hydrated copper(II) sulphate, $CuSO_4.5H_2O$. The method used to prepare a salt depends upon whether the salt is soluble in water or insoluble in water.

Solubility of salts

The table shows the solubility of a number of salts at room temperature.

Key: s soluble in water
ss slightly soluble in water
i insoluble in water

Metal	Chloride	Nitrate	Sulphate	Carbonate
sodium	s	s	s	s
calcium	s	s	ss	i
zinc	s	s	s	i
barium	s	s	i	i
magnesium	s	s	s	i
lead(II)	i	s	i	i
potassium	s	s	s	s
iron(II)	s	s	s	i
ammonium	s	s	s	s
copper(II)	s	s	s	i
silver	i	s	ss	i

> **Q1** Copy and complete the following sentences by putting in the correct metals.
> **All salts of potassium, sodium and ammonium are soluble in water.**
> **All nitrates are soluble in water.**
> **All chlorides are soluble in water except _____ and _____.**
> **All sulphates are soluble in water except _____ and _____.**
> **All carbonates are insoluble in water except _____, _____ and _____.**

These are the solubility of salt rules which you should know. You will then be able to decide which method you should use to prepare a particular salt.

Preparation of soluble salts

There are four possible starting materials for preparing each soluble salt:

1 the metal;

2 the metal oxide (a base);

3 the metal hydroxide (an alkali);

4 the carbonate.

The appropriate acid needs to be used:
- hydrochloric acid to prepare chlorides;
- nitric acid to prepare nitrates;
- sulphuric acid to prepare sulphates.

For example, magnesium sulphate can be prepared using dilute sulphuric acid and magnesium, magnesium oxide, magnesium hydroxide or magnesium carbonate (Fig 1). The choice of which one of these should be used depends upon:

1 price;

2 availability;

3 the speed of the reaction – not too fast nor too slow.

The following word equations summarise the possible reactions.

Fig 1 Preparation of magnesium sulphate – a soluble salt

105 Salt formation – 2

In this unit you will learn the answers to these questions:
- How can insoluble salts be prepared?
- How can electrical conductivity measurements be used to study the precipitation reaction?
- What can insoluble salts be used for?

Unit 104 listed the rules for solubility of salts at room temperature. These are:

All salts of potassium, sodium and ammonium are soluble in water.
All nitrates are soluble in water.
All chlorides are soluble in water except lead and silver.
All sulphates are soluble in water except barium and lead.
All carbonates are insoluble in water except potassium, sodium and ammonium.

Preparation of insoluble salts

Insoluble salts are prepared by **precipitation**. Two suitable aqueous solutions are mixed together so that the insoluble salt precipitates.

For example, to prepare barium sulphate, choose a salt containing barium which is soluble in water to make one aqueous solution, e.g. barium nitrate (or barium chloride). (A useful tip here: remember that all nitrates are soluble in water and nitrates are often the best salt to use.) The other solution could be made using sodium sulphate or potassium sulphate.

The following equations summarise the reactions which take place:

barium nitrate + sodium **sulphate** ➡ **barium sulphate** + sodium nitrate
$Ba(NO_3)_2$ (aq) + Na_2SO_4 (aq) ➡ $BaSO_4$ (s) + $2NaNO_3$ (aq)

barium nitrate + potassium **sulphate** ➡ **barium sulphate** + potassium nitrate
$Ba(NO_3)_2$ (aq) + K_2SO_4 (aq) ➡ $BaSO_4$ (s) + $2KNO_3$ (aq)

barium chloride + sodium **sulphate** ➡ **barium sulphate** + sodium chloride
$BaCl_2$ (aq) + Na_2SO_4 (aq) ➡ $BaSO_4$ (s) + $2NaCl$ (aq)

barium chloride + potassium **sulphate** ➡ **barium sulphate** + potassium chloride
$BaCl_2$ (aq) + K_2SO_4 (aq) ➡ $BaSO_4$ (s) + $2KCl$ (aq)

All of these reactions could be summarised by one ionic equation:

Ba^{2+} (aq) + SO_4^{2-} (aq) ➡ $BaSO_4$ (s)

The method used to prepare barium sulphate is summarised in Fig 1. The barium sulphate produced is pure and dry.

The progress of a precipitation reaction

Barium sulphate can also be prepared by mixing solutions of barium hydroxide (containing barium ions) and sulphuric acid (containing sulphate ions).

barium hydroxide + sulphuric acid ➡ barium sulphate + water
$Ba(OH)_2$ (aq) + H_2SO_4 (aq) ➡ $BaSO_4$ (s) + $2H_2O$ (l)

A solution of barium hydroxide has a pH value of 13. It is a strong alkali.

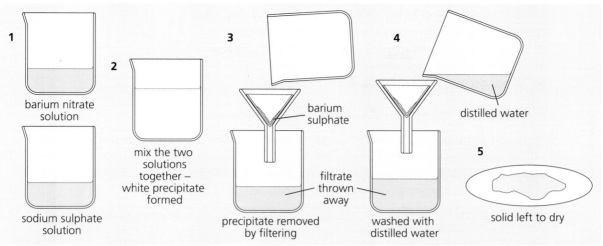

Fig 1 *Preparation of barium sulphate – an insoluble salt*

When sulphuric acid is added to the barium hydroxide solution, three things happen.

1 A white precipitate of barium sulphate is formed.

2 The pH of the solution is reduced from 13 down to 7 when all of the barium sulphate has been precipitated and all of the acid and alkali have been used up. Adding more acid will reduce the pH below 7 as excess acid will remain. The course of the reaction could be followed using indicators or, better, a pH meter.

3 The electrical conductivity of the solution could be followed during the reaction. As the barium sulphate is precipitated, barium ions and sulphate ions are removed and the electrical conductivity is reduced.

Fig 2 shows apparatus which could be used to follow the electrical conductivity of the solution during the experiment together with a graph of the results obtained.

Q1 Why is an alternating current used rather than a direct current?

Q2 Explain the shape of the graph obtained.

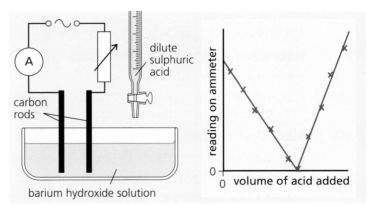

Fig 2 *Following the electrical conductivity of the reaction between barium hydroxide solution and sulphuric acid*

Uses of insoluble salts

Many insoluble salts are used in the paint industry as pigments. Pigments give the paint its colour. Many insoluble salts have characteristic colours, e.g. copper carbonate is green.

Toxic materials in waste water are removed by precipitation followed by filtration. Heavy metals such as lead and cadmium are removed by precipitating insoluble salts.

106 Fertilisers

In this unit you will learn the answers to these questions:
- Which elements are essential for plant growth?
- How is nitric acid manufactured from ammonia?
- How is ammonium nitrate manufactured?
- What factors affect the choice of fertiliser?

Essential elements for plant growth

For good plant growth, quantities of nitrogen, phosphorus and potassium are required. Other elements are required in smaller amounts. Elements such as boron and iron are required in very small amounts and are called **trace elements**. The table shows the importance of nitrogen, phosphorus and potassium.

Element	Importance of the element to a growing plant	Natural sources	Artificial fertilisers
nitrogen	necessary for the growth of stems and leaves	dried blood (14% N), hoof and horn (14% N)	sodium nitrate, calcium nitrate, ammonium sulphate, ammonium nitrate, urea
phosphorus	essential for root growth	slag, bone meal	ammonium phosphate, calcium superphosphate
potassium	for the production of flowers	wood ash	potassium sulphate

Q1 A fertiliser bag is labelled 'NPK 15:5:10'. What does this mean?

Q2 Which two substances in the 'Artificial fertilisers' column of the table could be mixed to produce a fertiliser which would provide nitrogen, phosphorus and potassium?

Industrial production of ammonium nitrate and ammonium sulphate

Ammonia is manufactured by the Haber process (Unit 100). Much of this ammonia is converted into nitric acid in a three-stage process.

Stage 1

A mixture of 10% ammonia and 90% air is passed over a heated platinum/rhodium alloy gauze catalyst.

ammonia + oxygen ➡ nitrogen monoxide + steam
$$4NH_3 (g) + 5O_2 (g) \implies 4NO (g) + 6H_2O (g)$$

Stage 2

The mixture of gases is allowed to cool.

nitrogen monoxide + oxygen ➡ nitrogen dioxide
$$2NO (g) + O_2 (g) \implies 2NO_2 (g)$$

Fig 1 *Ammonia plant*

Stage 3

The mixture of gases dissolves in water to produce nitric acid.

nitrogen dioxide +   water   + oxygen ⇒   nitric acid
$4NO_2$ (g)   + $2H_2O$ (l) + O_2 (g) ⇒ $4HNO_3$ (l)

Manufacture of ammonium nitrate from ammonia and nitric acid

Ammonium nitrate is the most widely used fertiliser in Great Britain. It can be prepared by reacting ammonia solution and nitric acid.

ammonia + nitric acid ⇒ ammonium nitrate
NH_3 (aq) + HNO_3 (aq) ⇒ NH_4NO_3 (aq)

In the final stage, the solution of ammonium nitrate is evaporated. Solid ammonium nitrate is melted and sprayed down a tall tower (Fig 2). As the droplets fall they meet an upward flow of air. The fertiliser solidifies and forms small, hard pellets called **prills**. These are easy to handle and to spread onto the fields.

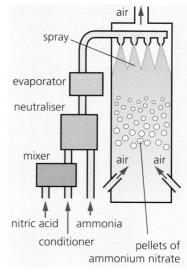

Fig 2 *Ammonium nitrate production*

Q3 Plan an experiment to prepare a sample of ammonium sulphate in the laboratory. Ammonium sulphate is a soluble salt.

Choosing the most suitable fertiliser

The factors which affect the choice of a nitrogen fertiliser include:

- *Percentage of nitrogen in the fertiliser.*

    Work out the percentage of nitrogen in ammonium nitrate, NH_4NO_3
    Using the relative atomic masses (page 179):
    Mass of 1 mole of ammonium nitrate = $14 + (4 \times 1) + 14 + (3 \times 16) = 80$ g
    Mass of nitrogen in 1 mole of ammonium nitrate = $(2 \times 14) = 28$ g
    Percentage of nitrogen
    $= \frac{28}{80} \times 100 = 35\%$

    Q4 Work out the percentage of nitrogen in ammonia, NH_3.

- *Cost.* If two fertilisers have similar percentages of nitrogen and similar solubilities, the choice may be made on price.

Ideas and evidence

Solubility in water.
Plants absorb fertilisers in solution through their roots. If a fertiliser is very soluble in water, it will be quick-acting. However, a very soluble fertiliser is quickly washed off the field and into drainage ditches, brooks and rivers. This will reduce the effectiveness of the fertiliser and will also cause water pollution. Ammonia is oxidised to nitrates by bacteria, using up dissolved oxygen in the river. The nitrogen fertiliser also makes the water plants grow better. When these die and decay they use up more oxygen in the water and the water becomes stagnant. Fish die and other river life is affected.

Fig 3 *A tractor distributing solid fertiliser*

Physical processes

This part of the book is divided into six sections. Most of these deal with topics that you have studied before, and they aim to advance your knowledge and understanding of these areas of science. The last section is concerned with radioactivity, a topic which you may not have met previously in your science studies.

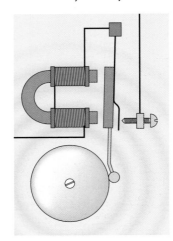

Electricity and magnetism is of fundamental importance to our everyday lives. Two hundred years ago, Volta made the first battery. Nearly a hundred years later, thanks to Faraday's discoveries about electromagnetism, Britain had its first power station. In the last twenty years the technological revolution has reached the home with microwave cookers, video recorders and personal computers now being commonplace in many households.

The section starts with a study of electric current and how it transfers energy around a circuit. The meaning of terms such as 'voltage', 'power' and 'resistance' is explained in the context of using mains electricity. While you are studying these topics, it is expected that you will experiment and make electrical measurements using safe, low-voltage circuits. Safety is an important consideration when using mains voltages, so there are units on how to use electricity safely, as well as costing the use of different appliances at home.

Electrostatic effects range from sticking charged balloons on ceilings to dangerous situations involving lightning and sparks. After studying these, the section examines some aspects of electromagnetism. This is particularly important to all of us, as the electricity supply industry uses electromagnetism to generate electricity and distribute it throughout the country.

The second section is about **Forces and motion**. It begins with a study of the deformation of materials when subjected to forces, something that is important to all designers who use materials in their everyday work. After examining the effects of pressure on gases, concepts such as speed, velocity and acceleration are studied, leading to Newton's discoveries about the relationship between force, mass and acceleration. Although Newton first put forward his ideas some three hundred years ago, his theories are still used by motor vehicle manufacturers in their attempts to improve the safety of travel, and by astronomers to predict the movement of planets.

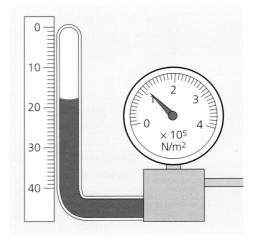

The third section, **Waves**, is all about communication. Humans have always communicated using sound and light, but radio, television and, more recently, satellite communications have made our world a much richer place. Similarities and differences between the different types of wave are studied, as well as their uses and dangers in domestic and non-domestic situations.

In studying waves you will learn about an important scientific tool: using models to describe real-life situations. By using models we can improve our understanding of phenomena and events that take place on a sub-microscopic scale. You will also learn how the use of optical fibres is revolutionising our whole communications network so that when making a long-distance telephone call, it sounds as clear as when you are telephoning someone who lives just down the road.

The **Earth and beyond** is the subject of the fourth section. Recent discoveries using space probes and the Hubble telescope have changed many ideas about the planets in the Solar System, and the stars that make up the galaxy. Astronomy is much more than just making observations; these observations are used to refine or reject old theories about the origin and future of the Universe and to put forward new ideas. It is a fascinating branch of science in which new discoveries are being made every day.

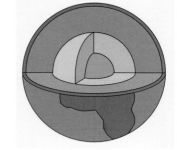

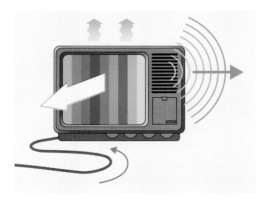

The fifth section is about **Energy resources and energy transfer**. It starts by examining how things heat up and cool down by energy transfer, and how we use energy transfer processes at home and at work. Keeping warm is an important aspect of living in this country for at least nine months of the year, and if we are lucky we are concerned with keeping cool for the other three months. An understanding of how energy moves about is important if we are to put our heating and cooling systems to effective use.

We also need to understand about efficient use of energy resources in order to make our fuel reserves last until renewable energy sources have been developed to a stage where we can rely on them to provide all our energy needs.

Finally in this section, energy transfer by forces at work is studied. Energy and power are quantified in the context of objects that move and change position.

Radioactivity is the subject of the last section. This is a topic which is often in the news, and an understanding of the basic processes is necessary to anyone who likes to keep in touch with current affairs. The known dangers and uses of radioactivity are studied in a way that should help you to make informed judgements about issues concerned with radioactivity.

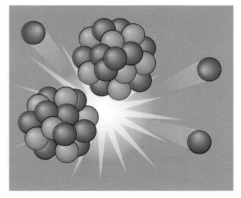

107 Measuring current

In this unit you will learn the answers to these questions:
- How do we use an ammeter to measure current?
- How does the current in a series circuit differ to that in a parallel circuit?

Using an ammeter

Ammeters are used to measure electric current. There are two types of ammeter: **digital** and **analogue**. Digital meters are easy to read because they display the current as a number, usually rounded off to two decimal places. Analogue meters have a pointer that moves over a scale. You need to take care to make sure that you interpret the scale correctly.

Current is measured in **amperes**, or amps for short. Fig 1 shows how an ammeter can be used to compare the current that goes into a lamp with the current that comes out. Note how current is always drawn as passing out from the positive terminal of the cell or power pack and back in at the negative terminal.

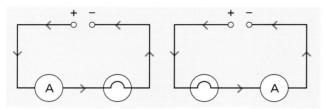

Fig 1 Measuring the current into and out of a lamp

The results of these measurements reveal an important result. Lamps and other electrical devices do not use up any current. The current that passes into the lamp is equal to the current that passes out.

Current in a series circuit

A **series circuit** is one where the current passes through one thing after another. Fig 2 shows a lamp in series with an ammeter, a motor and a switch. The lamp acts as a visual sign that the motor is switched on. The current from the power supply passes through each component in turn as it completes a circuit. As you answer **Q1**, remember that the current passing out of the lamp is equal to that going in.

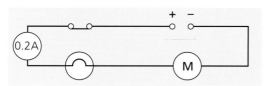

Fig 2 A lamp in series with a switch, an ammeter and a motor

Q1 The ammeter shows that the current entering the lamp is 0.2 A.
- **a)** How much current leaves the lamp?
- **b)** How much current enters the motor?
- **c)** How much current leaves the motor?
- **d)** If two more ammeters were added to the circuit, one between the lamp and the motor and one between the motor and the negative power supply terminal, what would you notice about all three ammeter readings?

The current in a series circuit is the same everywhere, so it does not matter whereabouts in a series circuit you place an ammeter to measure the current, the reading is the same in any position. The same is true for a switch, it is equally effective in switching the current on and off in any position. This can be a problem with some Christmas tree lights that use series circuits. If one lamp filament 'blows' and breaks the circuit all the lamps go out!

Current in a parallel circuit

Most of the mains-operated circuits that we use at home are **parallel circuits**. In a parallel circuit each device or component can be switched on and off without affecting the others. Fig 3 shows how you can measure the current at different points in a parallel circuit. You do not need to have four ammeters available to make the circuit shown in Fig 3, you can use one ammeter and put it in each position in turn.

Using the parallel circuit, you can switch the lamp and the motor independently; you do not have to have them both on or both off.

The black spots on the circuit diagram are junctions in the circuit. At these points the current divides as it goes into the two separate branches and rejoins after some has travelled through the lamp and some through the motor.

Your measurements of electric current in a parallel circuit show you that, unlike the series circuit, different size currents can pass in different components. In Fig 3, all the current passes through ammeter A_1 before splitting at the junction, some passing through the lamp and some through the motor. The currents then rejoin before returning to the power supply.

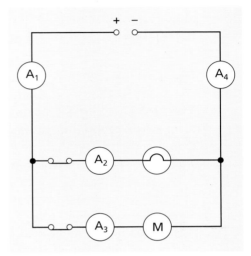

Fig 3 *Measuring current in a parallel circuit*

An important rule for parallel circuits is that the current that passes into a junction is equal to the current passing out. For the circuit in Fig 3, this means that the reading on ammeter A_1 is equal to the sum of the readings on A_2 and A_3. Ammeter A_4 reads the same as A_1 because it measures the current after it has rejoined.

Q2 Study the circuits shown in Fig 4 and write down the readings on the ammeters A_1, A_2, A_3 and A_4.

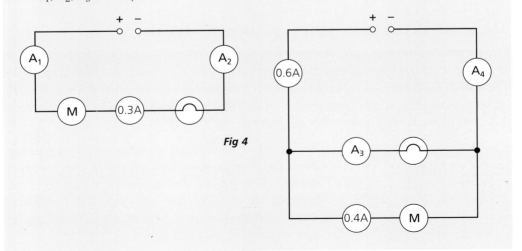

Fig 4

108 Circuits and energy transfer

In this unit you will learn the answers to these questions:
■ How is energy transferred from a battery or power supply
   to components in electric circuits?
■ What effects do electric currents have on lamps, motors and heaters?

In Unit 107 you learned that components such as lamps and motors in electric circuits do not use up any current. This unit examines the job that electric currents do in circuits and the energy transfers that take place.

Energy from electricity

Electricity is the energy source that we use the most in our everyday lives at work and at home. One reason for this is its ready availability; it can be switched on and off and can be easily supplied to wherever we want to use it. There are three important things that electricity can be used to provide: **heat**, **movement** and **light**. Toasters, sandwich makers and electric fires all give out heat. Televisions, filament lamps and fluorescent tubes give out light. The sound from a radio, television or hi-fi is caused by the movement of the loudspeaker cone and we also rely on movement from electricity when we use a vacuum cleaner or washing machine.

Heat, movement and light have one thing in common; they are all forms of **energy**. The things that we plug into the electricity supply take energy from electricity and transfer it into energy in one or more of these three forms. Fig 1 shows the energy flow through a television set.

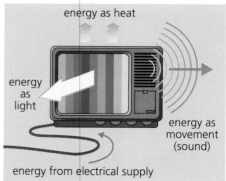

Fig 1 *Energy flow through a television*

Where does the energy come from?

Energy that we obtain from electricity comes from batteries or the mains supply. In each case it comes from energy that is released when a chemical reaction takes place. The job of an electric current is to transfer this energy to where we want it. Electric currents have energy that they gain from the battery or mains supply and give up as they pass through the components in a circuit.

Q1 Draw energy flow diagrams for the following devices:
  a) a kettle
  b) a radio
  c) a hairdryer

An electric circuit is just a means of moving energy from the energy source to wherever the energy is needed. The job of the current is to act as a go-between; it provides the link between the energy source and the device that then transfers the energy into movement, heat and light.

How does a current transfer energy?

An electric current is a movement of **charged particles**. In metals these particles are electrons, which carry a negative charge. In gases, such as in a fluorescent tube and sodium street lights, and in conducting liquids (electrolytes) there are both positively and negatively charged particles that move.

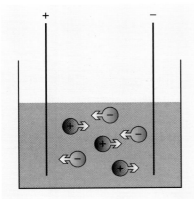

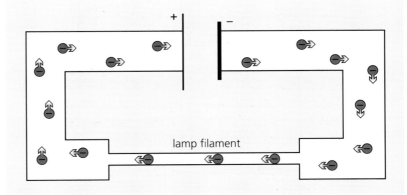

Fig 2 *The movement of charged particles in an electrolyte*

Fig 3 *A model of charge flow in a circuit. Free electrons move in the direction negative to positive*

Think of a simple circuit consisting of a single cell, a lamp and two connecting wires. Metals contain lots of electrons that are free to move about. When the circuit is switched on, the electric force repels them from the negative terminal of the cell and attracts them towards the positive.

The electrons travel easily in the connecting wires. They are accelerated by the electric forces and only occasionally do they collide with the metal particles in the wires. There are many more collisions in the thin wire of the filament in the lamp, where the electrons have to travel faster. The particles in the filament become heated as energy is transferred to them from the electrons.

Very hot metals give out light. The tungsten in a filament lamp is heated to a temperature of about 2000°C due to collisions between moving electrons and the tungsten particles.

Q2 Describe the differences between electrical conduction in metals, electrolytes and ionised gases.

Q3 Ionised gases are similar to electrolytes, except the particles are less concentrated. Draw a diagram to show how electric current is conducted by an ionised gas.

Q4 In a mains fluorescent lamp, the alternating voltage changes direction 100 times every second. Describe the movement of the charged particles when a current is passing.

In this unit you will learn the answers to these questions:
- How is a voltmeter used in a circuit?
- What factors affect the current in a circuit?
- How does voltage differ in series and parallel circuits?

In Unit 108 you learned how an electric current transfers energy. This unit examines the factors that determine the size of the electric current that passes in a circuit and how to measure voltage.

How easy?

Using the same number of batteries or the same power pack setting, you can compare the current that passes through three different components such as a lamp, a heater and a motor. The table shows the readings obtained using a digital ammeter and a power pack set at 4 V.

Device	Current/A
heater	0.65
lamp	0.21
motor	0.36

Q1 Arrange the three components in order, with the best conductor first and the worst conductor last.

All components used in circuits have some opposition to electric current. The more opposition they have, the less current passes. Of the components shown in the table, the heater has the least opposition or **resistance**. For the same voltage, the lamp allows less current to pass because it has more resistance.

The variable resistor

Fig 1 shows a circuit that uses a variable resistor. You should try this using both a lamp and a motor. Note what happens to the current and to the lamp or motor when you change the setting on the variable resistor.

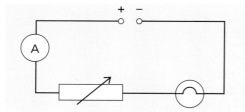

Fig 1 *Using a variable resistor*

Variable resistors change the current that passes in a circuit by changing the resistance. Increasing the resistance causes less current to pass so the lamp dims or the motor slows. Reducing the resistance increases the current that passes in a circuit. Variable resistors, along with other components, are used in light-dimming circuits at home and in theatres. A variable resistor also forms the basis of the volume control circuit on a radio or television.

Changing the voltage

Current only passes through a component such as a lamp or a motor when there is a voltage across it. Fig 2 shows how to connect a voltmeter to measure the voltage across a lamp in a simple circuit. Note how a voltmeter is always connected in parallel with a component.

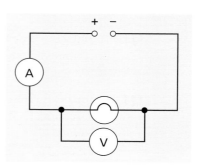

Fig 2 *Using a voltmeter*

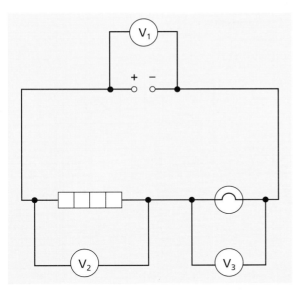

Fig 3

By increasing the number of batteries or the power supply setting, you can see how the current and the brightness of the lamp depend on the voltage.

Q2 Fig 3 shows how you can use a voltmeter to measure voltages in a circuit that has two components in series. V_1 measures the power supply voltage, V_2 and V_3 measure the voltages across the heater and the lamp. What do you notice about V_1, V_2 and V_3? Try the circuit with other pairs of components.

Q3 Make a circuit with two components in parallel. Connect a voltmeter first across the power supply, then across each component in turn. What do you notice about the readings?

The results of your measurements show that components in parallel always have the same voltage across them, but in a series circuit the voltages across the individual components add up to equal the power supply voltage.

Series or parallel?

In Unit 107 you learned that the current in a series circuit is the same in all components. In a parallel circuit different currents can pass in individual components and each one can be switched independently of the others.

Another reason for using parallel circuits at home and for the low-voltage circuits in motor vehicles is that no matter how many components are switched on, the voltage stays the same. If you have your bedroom light on and someone puts the kettle on it doesn't affect the brightness of your light.

The lamps in Christmas tree lights are low voltage because it would be dangerous to have high voltages within the reach of young children. Some sets of lights use a transformer (see Unit 121) to change the mains voltage to a lower value. In these sets of lights the lamps are wired in parallel. A more common method is to connect twenty 12 V lamps in series to the mains supply.

Q4 Explain why twenty 12 V lamps on a Christmas tree can be safely connected to the mains supply if they are connected in series, but not if they are connected in parallel.

110 Measuring resistance

In this unit you will learn the answers to these questions:
- How is resistance related to current and voltage?
- Does the resistance of a component depend on the current passing?

In Unit 109 you learned that the current in a circuit depends on the resistance and the voltage. This unit starts with resistance calculations and then examines the resistance of different circuit components.

Calculating resistance

The more resistance a component has, the less current passes for a given voltage. When connected to the mains supply, the current in a filament lamp is 0.25 A but that in a kettle element is 10 A. The kettle element allows more current to pass because it has less resistance than the filament lamp.

Resistance is calculated using the equation

$$\text{resistance} = \text{voltage} \div \text{current} \quad \text{or} \quad R = \frac{V}{I}$$

The unit of resistance is the ohm (Ω).

Example

Calculate the resistance of a kettle element if the current is 10 A when it is connected to the 240 V mains.

Answer

$R = V \div I$
$\quad = 240\,\text{V} \div 10\,\text{A}$
$\quad = 24\,\Omega$

Q1 Use the resistance equation to complete the table.

	Device	Voltage/V	Current/A	Resistance/Ω
a	60 W household lamp	240	0.25	
b	iron	240	4.6	
c	1 kW (1000 W) heater	240		57.6
d	60 W car headlamp	12		2.4

Measuring resistance

The resistance of a wire-wound resistor or a piece of resistance wire can be measured using the circuit shown in Fig 1. Using a variable resistor allows the current to be adjusted so that resistance can be measured over a range of values of current and voltage. Provided that the resistor or wire is not allowed to get hot, the resistance is the same.

Fig 2 shows two graphs of the results of an experiment to investigate the resistance of a metal wire at a constant temperature. The graph of voltage against current is a straight line through the origin. This shows that voltage and

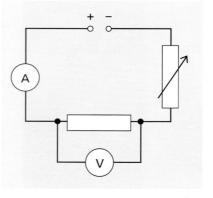

Fig 1

current are in direct proportion to each other. If one of them is doubled or halved then so is the other. The constant gradient of this graph shows that the resistance is not changing, as can be seen by looking at the graph of resistance against current. These graphs show the typical behaviour of a metallic conductor. Provided the temperature does not change, the resistance has a constant value.

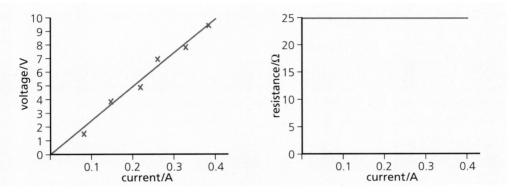

Fig 2 *Voltage, current and resistance at constant temperature*

Changing the temperature

When a filament lamp is first turned on, the heating effect of the current causes the temperature of the filament to rise very rapidly. As the temperature changes, so does the resistance. The potential divider circuit shown in Fig 3 can be used to increase the voltage across a filament lamp gradually and note how the current changes. The results can then be used to plot graphs of voltage against current and resistance against current.

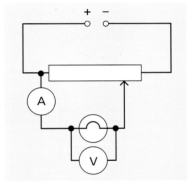

Fig 3

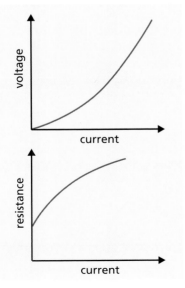

The graphs look very different to those for a metal kept at a constant temperature. Fig 4 shows typical results for a filament lamp.

The increasing gradient of the voltage–current graph shows that the resistance of the lamp filament increases as more current passes. The resistance–current graph shows the way in which the resistance changes. Resistance of a metal to electric current is due to the conducting electrons colliding with the particles of the metal. The more frequent the collisions, the greater the resistance. Increasing the temperature of a metal causes an increase in the energy and amplitude of the vibrations of the metal particles. This results in more frequent collisions between the electrons and the metal particles, hence the increase in resistance.

Fig 4 *Voltage, current and resistance at changing temperature*

111 Circuit components

In this unit you will learn the answers to these questions:

- How do light and temperature affect the resistance of a light-dependent resistor and a thermistor?
- How does the current in a diode vary with the applied voltage?

The way in which current varies with voltage for a resistor and a filament lamp was studied in Unit 110. This unit extends the study to some other common circuit components.

The thermistor

As its name implies, a thermistor is a device that has a resistance which changes with temperature. You can buy thermistors whose resistance increases when the temperature increases but most common ones do the reverse; as the temperature rises their resistance goes down.

As you do not need to change the current to experiment with a thermistor, a resistance meter is the easiest way to measure the resistance. If you do not have access to a resistance meter then you need a power pack or battery, an ammeter and a voltmeter. Fig 1 shows a circuit diagram and a way of controlling the temperature of the thermistor.

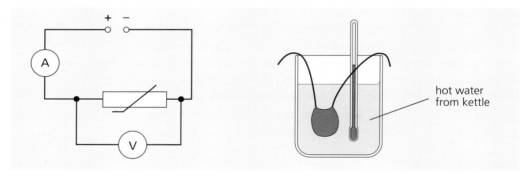

Fig 1 *Testing a thermistor*

Thermistors are useful because of the large change in resistance that occurs when the temperature changes. The change in resistance is much greater than that of a metal wire over the same change of temperature. This makes thermistors very sensitive; they can detect tiny changes in temperature. The graph in Fig 2 shows how the resistance of a typical thermistor changes over the range 0°C to 100°C.

> **Q1** Describe how you could vary the temperature of a thermistor over the range 0°C to 100°C.

Thermistors are used as temperature sensors in incubators for newborn babies. Their extreme sensitivity also makes them useful in instruments that detect the heat from a human body buried after a disaster such as an earthquake.

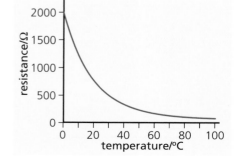

Fig 2 *Behaviour of a thermistor*

The diode

A potential divider circuit similar to the one used in Unit 109 can be used to investigate the current in a diode as the voltage is varied. Unlike most circuit components, a diode has two different patterns of behaviour depending on how it is connected into a circuit. Current can pass in the direction shown by the arrow in the circuit symbol provided that the voltage is above a minimum value, 0.6 V in the case of a silicon diode. In the opposite direction it has a very high resistance, allowing no current at all to pass.

Fig 3 *The circuit symbol for a diode*

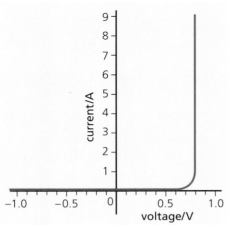

Fig 4 *Current and voltage in a silicon diode*

The graph, Fig 4, shows how the current in a silicon diode varies with the voltage. After it starts to conduct when the voltage is 0.6 V, the resistance of the diode decreases and continues to decrease as more and more current passes.

Diodes are used, along with transformers and other components, to produce a low voltage direct current, suitable for powering electronic equipment such as radios, keyboards and computers, from the high voltage alternating current mains.

ICT Extra!

Use data logging to investigate the relationship between the current in a diode and the voltage across it.

The light-dependent resistor (LDR)

Light-dependent resistors are used for exterior lamps that only come on in the dark and they control the current in the circuits that switch street lighting on and off automatically. LDRs are easily damaged by too much current passing in them and so it is not possible to experiment using an ammeter and voltmeter. If you have a resistance meter available you can see the effect on the resistance when the amount of light illuminating the LDR is changed. The resistance of a typical LDR changes from 1 kΩ (1000 Ω) in daylight to 10 MΩ (10 000 000 Ω) in total darkness.

When used in a control circuit to switch something on or off an LDR is placed in series with another resistor. Fig 5 shows how you can experiment with such a circuit. Changing the illumination of the LDR causes the voltage across it to change. This can be used to trigger a logic gate or transistor to operate another circuit containing, for example, a mains-operated lamp.

Q2 Write a sentence about each component in this unit. Describe what the component does when placed in a circuit.

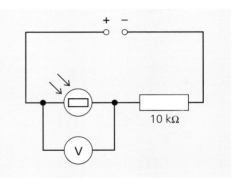

Fig 5 *Testing an LDR*

112 Understanding current and voltage

In this unit you will learn the answers to these questions:
- ■ How is current related to charge flow?
- ■ How does voltage measure energy transfer?

In Unit 108 you learned how charge transfers energy as it moves round a circuit. This unit uses the model of charge flow to explain the meaning of measurements of current and voltage.

Current and charge

In circuits containing metallic conductors, the only particles that are free to move are electrons. Metals contain positive ions, neutral atoms that have lost one or two of their outermost electrons. These electrons are 'free' to move about in the metal and are affected by electric forces. Any movement of charge is an electric current, but the flow rate depends on more than just the speed of movement.

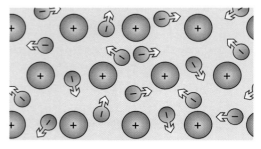

Fig 1 The free electrons and positive ions in a metal

Imagine a wide, slow-moving river compared to a fast-moving stream. Water in the river is travelling slower than that in the stream but the river has a much bigger flow rate. If you stood on the riverbank, more water would go past you each second than if you stood at the side of the stream.

Just as each molecule in the river is a tiny amount of water, each electron in a metal carries a tiny amount of charge, 1.6×10^{-19} coulomb (C). The flow of charge in a metal is due to vast numbers of charge-carrying electrons flowing at low speeds, typically a few millimetres per second. The size of an electric current is a measure of the charge flow past any point each second:

$$\text{current} = \text{charge flow} \div \text{time} \quad \text{or} \quad I = \frac{Q}{t}$$

In the circuit shown in Fig 2, one coulomb of charge flows through the lamp each second. One coulomb is the charge carried by 6.25×10^{18} electrons, so you can see that a large number of charge carriers are needed to transfer the energy from a power pack to a lamp.

Q1 Use the charge equation to complete the table.

	Device	Current/A	Charge flow/C	Time/s
a	battery charger		60	300
b	torch	0.15		60
c	kettle	10		360
d	hairdryer		3000	600

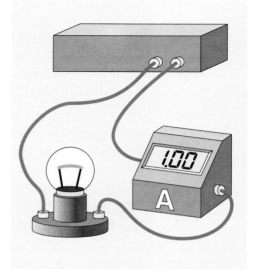

Fig 2 One coulomb of charge flows through the ammeter and the lamp each second

Voltage and energy transfer

A circuit is a way of transferring energy from the mains supply, power pack or battery to the electrical devices we use to do useful jobs. You have learned how the energy is transferred by the charge carriers. The voltage of a battery or power supply describes the energy transfer to each coulomb of charge. A voltmeter connected to a source of electricity measures this energy transfer:

voltage = energy transfer ÷ charge   or $V = E/Q$

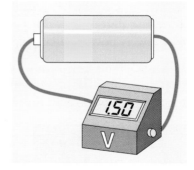

Fig 3 The battery supplies 1.5 J of energy to each coulomb of charge

In making a complete circuit, the energy gains and losses of the charge should balance. Fig 4 shows the energy transfer for a circuit consisting of a 12 V power supply in series with a lamp and a heater.

The figures show that, as a coulomb of charge makes a complete circuit, 12.00 J of energy are transferred from the power supply to the charge. In passing through the components, a coulomb of charge transfers 2.75 J of this energy to the lamp and 9.20 J to the heater. The other 0.05 J is the energy transfer in the connecting wires. These are normally thick so that charge passes easily through them. The small amount of energy that is transferred in the connecting wires is usually neglected when doing circuit calculations.

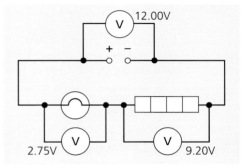

Fig 4

Resistance and energy transfer

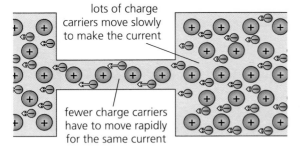

lots of charge carriers move slowly to make the current

fewer charge carriers have to move rapidly for the same current

Fig 5

Q2 The heater in Fig 4 has more resistance than the lamp filament. If both are made from metal wire, what differences could account for the higher resistance of the heater? Use the model in Fig 5 to explain your answer.

In the circuit shown in Fig 4 the charge transfers more energy in the heater than it does in the lamp. The energy transfer is caused by the resistance to charge flow.

Fig 5 shows a model of charge moving from a connecting wire through the lamp filament. The filament has fewer conducting electrons than the same length of connecting wire and so the charge has to move faster to maintain the same flow rate, or current. This leads to heating of the filament as the electrons transfer their energy in collisions with the metal particles. The greater the number of collisions, the more energy is transferred as an electron passes through, and the greater the resistance to charge flow.

113 Power in circuits

In this unit you will learn the answers to these questions:
- ■ What determines the power of an appliance?
- ■ How is power calculated?

In the previous unit you studied how measurements of current and voltage are related to charge flow and energy transfer. This unit explains how these measurements together can be used to measure the power of a device.

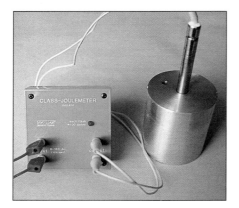

Fig 1 *Using a joulemeter to measure the energy transferred to a heater*

Device	Energy transfer in one minute/J
kettle	15 000
vacuum cleaner	4800
lamp	360

Comparing the energy transfer

The electricity meter that you have at home does not measure the current or the voltage. It measures the energy that is delivered to your home by the current passing in the wires. You can use a joulemeter in a similar way to measure the energy provided from a power supply to a low voltage lamp, heater or motor. Some joulemeters measure the energy transferred directly from the mains supply. Using either a low voltage or a mains joulemeter allows you to compare the energy transfer when electricity is used to provide lighting, heat or movement.

The table compares the energy transferred in one minute from the mains supply to a kettle, a vacuum cleaner and a lamp.

The kettle is the most powerful of the devices shown because it transfers energy at the greatest rate. Power is the energy transfer per second (see also Unit 155). It is calculated using the equation:

$$\text{power} = \text{energy transfer} \div \text{time taken} \quad \text{or} \quad P = \frac{E}{t}$$

Power is measured in **watts** (W) when the energy is in joules and the time in seconds.

Q1 a) Use the equation to calculate the power of the kettle, the vacuum cleaner and the lamp.

b) To bring one litre of water to the boil in a kettle requires 380 000 J of energy to be transferred from the mains supply to the water. Calculate how long it would take the kettle in **a)** to boil one litre of water.

Current, voltage and power

Energy transfer is the job of electric current, so the more current that passes in a circuit the more energy you would expect to be transferred each second. The other factor that affects the rate of energy transfer is the voltage, the amount of energy transferred by each coulomb of charge as it passes round a circuit.

Fig 2 shows an ammeter and voltmeter being used to measure the electrical power supplied to an electric motor. The meter readings show that 3 C of charge pass through the motor each second and each one transfers 12 J of energy. The total energy transfer each second is therefore three lots of 12 J, i.e. 36 J. Power is being supplied to the motor at the rate of 36 J/s or 36 W.

For any electrical device, the power is calculated by multiplying the current and the voltage:

$$\text{power} = \text{current} \times \text{voltage} \quad \text{or} \quad P = IV$$

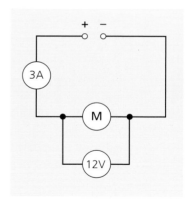

Fig 2 *Measuring electrical power*

Q2 Use the equation $P = IV$ to fill in the blanks in the table.

	Device	Voltage/V	Current/A	Power/W
a	torch lamp	3	0.15	
b	toaster	240	6.5	
c	car headlamp	12	5	
d	electric train	1500	1000	

Fig 3 *This could cause overheating in the mains cable*

Calculating the current

When using mains appliances at home and at work, it is important to avoid overloading the cables and sockets that the current passes through. An overloaded circuit is a common cause of domestic fires. Whilst it is safe to operate a computer, printer and monitor from a single socket outlet, it is not safe to have a kettle and a hairdryer working from a single socket at the same time.

No more than 13 A should pass through a standard mains socket to avoid overheating. Manufacturers of electrical appliances do not usually state the current that passes in the appliance when it is being used. They do state the power and the mains voltage that the appliance is designed to operate from. Fig 4 shows the plate that gives this information about a vacuum cleaner. The current that passes in the vacuum cleaner can be calculated using the electrical power equation in the form $I = P \div V$.

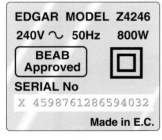

Fig 4 *A manufacturer's rating plate from a vacuum cleaner*

The current in the vacuum cleaner, $I = P \div V$
$$= 800\,\text{W} \div 240\,\text{V}$$
$$= 3.33\,\text{A}$$

Q3 By calculating the curent passing from the mains supply, decide whether the following combinations would overload a 13 A socket. Assume the mains is 240 V.

a) A 1500 W hairdryer and a 2000 W convector heater.

b) A 4 W clock, a 15 W radio and a 60 W lamp.

114 Using electricity safely

In this unit you will learn the answers to these questions:
■ What do the live, neutral and earth wires do?
■ Why are earth wires, fuses and circuit breakers necessary?

In studying electricity, it is safe to experiment with circuits powered by a low-voltage source. Higher voltages are used at home because high-powered appliances such as kettles and cookers would need enormous currents if the electricity was supplied at low voltage. This in turn would require thick, unwieldy cables to carry the currents without overheating. There are dangers in using high voltages, and this unit looks at the precautions necessary to ensure that mains electricity is used safely.

The mains supply

For an electrical appliance to work, there needs to be a complete circuit. A route is needed for the current to pass from the energy source to the appliance and then return. Fig 1 shows the arrangement where the mains electricity supply enters a house. Notice how the incoming cable has three wires. Energy is supplied to a house through the live wire. The neutral wire is needed to make a complete circuit and the earth wire is literally connected to the earth through the cold water pipes of the house. Normally no current passes in the earth wire. It is only there to protect the user if something goes wrong.

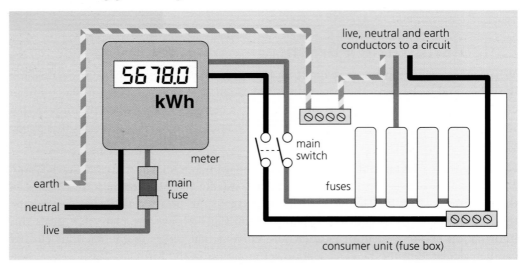

Fig 1 Mains electricity supply

The incoming live and neutral wires consist of very thick cables capable of carrying a current in excess of 100 A without overheating. The main fuse in the live wire is to protect against fire hazard. It melts if a fault causes too large a current. An excessive current passing into the house would overload the cables and could set them on fire.

Fig 2 A cartridge fuse

Fuses or circuit breakers

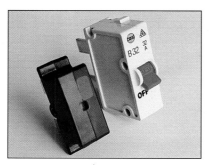

In the consumer unit, or 'fuse box', the live wire is connected to each circuit. Normally there are one or two circuits for the sockets in a house, together with separate circuits for lighting, a cooker, a shower and an immersion heater. Each circuit is protected by a fuse or circuit breaker. Like the main fuse, those in the consumer unit are to protect from fire hazard if too much current should pass through the cables.

Fig 3 *Consumer unit fuse and circuit breaker*

Newer houses often have circuit breakers fitted instead of fuses. These have several advantages: they are more reliable, they can easily be reset when a fault has been rectified and they cannot be tampered with. It has been known for householders to replace 'blown' fuses with thick copper wire, thus removing the protection.

Protecting the user

Fig 4 shows how a metal-cased appliance such as a convector heater is connected to the mains supply. In this case the plug fuse has two purposes: one is to protect from fire by breaking the circuit if too much current passes in the flexible cable. The second is that, along with the earth wire, it protects the user from the danger of electrocution.

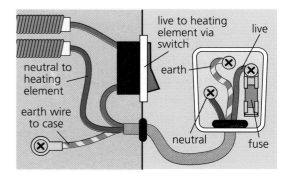

Fig 4

Suppose the live wire became frayed and came into contact with the metal casing or, through repeated movement, the cable became damaged where it enters the heater. This would cause the casing to become live. Anyone touching this would receive a severe shock as current passed through them to earth. The earth wire prevents this from happening by providing a low-resistance path to earth. If the casing does become live, a large current passes from the live wire straight to earth, causing the fuse wire to melt and break the circuit.

An electric drill does not have an earth wire. Its plastic casing does not conduct electricity so there is no danger of electrocution. It is said to be double-insulated. Double-insulated appliances have a symbol like this ▣ on the manufacturer's rating plate – you can see one on the plate from a vacuum cleaner shown in Unit 113.

Q1 Different appliances at home are wired to the mains supply using cables of different thickness.
   a) Explain why cables of different thickness are used.
   b) Explain why, if the cable connecting an iron to the mains supply is replaced, it is important to use the correct size of cable.

Q2 Describe the **two** functions of an earth wire.

---

115 Paying for electricity

In this unit you will learn the answers to these questions:
- How much does electricity cost?
- What are the different ways in which we use electricity for heating?

Once every three months, householders receive a bill from their electricity supply company. The bill is for the energy supplied through the mains. This unit looks at how electricity is costed and how electricity is used for heating.

Another unit of energy

The energy transferred when an appliance is used can be calculated using:

> **energy transfer = power × time   or $E = Pt$**

Using this equation, you can work out that a 2500 W kettle which takes four minutes to boil some water transfers 2500 W × 240 s = 600 000 J of energy. Multiply this by the number of times a kettle is boiled in a three-month period, then take into account the energy transfer by all the other household appliances, and you come up with a very large number!

Electricity supply companies use a larger unit of energy, the kilowatt-hour (kWh), which is equivalent to 3 600 000 J. It is calculated using the equation above, but instead of using the watt and the second for units of power and time, it uses the kilowatt and the hour, as its name implies.

> **energy in kWh = power in kW × time in h**

Fig 1 *This electricity meter measures the energy in kWh*

Q1 Use the equation

energy in kWh = power in kW × time in h

to complete the table. Assume that each kWh of electricity costs 8p.

	Appliance	Power/kW	Time used/h	Energy transfer/kWh	Cost/p
a	vacuum cleaner	0.8	0.5		
b	lamp	0.06	8		
c	kettle	2.5	0.75		
d	television set	0.12	5		

Example

Calculate the energy transfer, in kWh, by a 2.5 kW immersion heater which is used for 30 minutes each day for a week.

Answer

energy = power × time
        = 2.5 kW × 3.5 h
        = 8.75 kWh

The cost of energy from electricity is, including tax, about 8p per kWh so the cost of using the immersion heater is 8.75 × 8 = 70p per week.

Electrical heating

Heat, light and movement are the three things we use electricity for at home. Of the three, appliances designed to transfer energy to heat are the most powerful and cost the most to run. Some of the appliances shown in Fig 2 are designed to heat the space around us. Others heat water, for washing, cooking and drinking. Electric current is also used to heat irons and hairdryers and in different ways to cook food.

Kettles, immersion heaters and convector heaters all use convection currents (see Unit 148) to transfer the heat away from the heating element into the surrounding air and water. Heating of the element occurs when a large current, about 10 A, passes through it. Most electric kettles switch themselves off when they have boiled but immersion heaters must not be allowed to boil the water. They are fitted with a thermostat, usually set to about 50°C, to switch off the current when the water has reached the desired temperature.

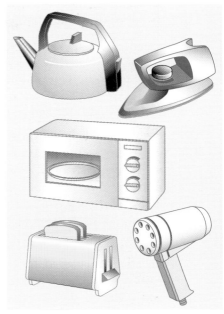

Fig 2

Q2 Give **two** reasons why it would be dangerous for the water in a hot water cylinder to reach boiling point.

Ovens and hairdryers also use heating elements. Like the immersion heater, an oven has a thermostat that switches off the current when a certain temperature has been reached. Many electric ovens also have a fan to give an even temperature throughout the oven. Hairdryers need fans to give a large air flow. It would take too long to dry your hair if you relied on convection currents from a hairdryer!

Q3 a) Explain why the temperature in an oven without a fan is uneven.
b) Suggest why some recipes say 'bake in the top of the oven'.

Microwave cookers heat food in a different way. They generate radio waves with a frequency of 2450 MHz. Waves of this frequency are readily absorbed by water and salt particles in food, causing them to become heated. Radiant heaters also give off energy in the form of electromagnetic radiation (see Unit 150). The infrared radiation is absorbed by objects in the room, causing them to become warmed. This is in contrast to a convector heater, which heats the air in the room.

Q4 When in use, the outside of a conventional oven can become warm to the touch, but a microwave oven remains cool. Explain why this is.

Q5 a) Explain why the air inlet to a hairdryer should never be covered.
b) What is the purpose of the thermal cut-out fitted to a hairdryer?

116 Static charge

In this unit you will learn the answers to these questions:
- How do balloons and other objects become charged?
- Why do some charged objects attract each other while others repel?

Electric currents are due to forces that make charges move. When a quantity of electric charge is isolated so that it cannot move, it can cause large forces on the charges in nearby objects. This unit looks at ways in which electric charge can be isolated.

Separating charges

Rubbing a balloon on a jumper or rubbing a polythene rod with a duster causes both objects to become charged. Polythene takes electrons from the duster and becomes negatively charged. The duster has a deficit of electrons and so has an overall positive charge.

The charged duster and the rod both exert forces on other, uncharged, objects. They will attract the hairs on your head, pick up small pieces of paper and deflect a stream of water from a tap. These effects are due to the charged rod and duster exerting forces on the charges in other objects.

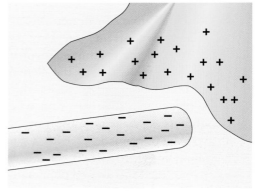

Fig 1 *The charges on a polythene rod and a duster*

Attraction and repulsion

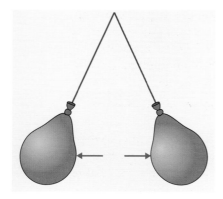

Fig 2 *Objects with the same type of charge repel each other*

Two charged balloons or polythene rods push away from each other. A balloon charged by rubbing with the duster is attracted to the duster. These observations show that two objects with the same type of charge, both negative or both positive, repel each other. A negatively charged object is attracted to a positively charged one.

> **Q1** A polythene rod becomes negatively charged when rubbed with a duster. Explain how you could use a charged polythene rod to find out the type of charge on a balloon that has been rubbed with a duster.

Although insulators such as rubber, polythene and nylon can attract and repel each other when they are charged, they all attract small pieces of paper and the hair on your head. This is known as **induction** and is caused by the movement of small amounts of charge carried by positive and negative ions. A perfect insulator does not allow any movement of charge, but the moisture in paper contains both positive and negative ions, and these ions can move.

Fig 3 shows how the negatively charged polythene rod attracts positive ions in the paper and repels negative ions. The positively charged part of the paper is attracted to the rod.

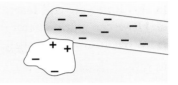

Fig 3 *How a piece of paper is attracted to a charged polythene rod*

When you wash your hair with shampoo you remove the natural oils that allow the movement of charge in the form of positive and negative ions. Without these, your hair easily becomes charged by friction and can stick out, as all the hairs repel each other. Using a conditioner prevents this from happening by coating your hair with an oily liquid which allows charges to move off your hair, preventing a build-up of charge.

> **Q2** Use diagrams to explain how hair can be attracted to a positively charged acetate rod.

Creating a high voltage

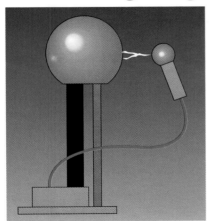

A van de Graaff generator uses static charge to generate very high voltages. Charge is deposited on a metal dome which has to be well insulated from its surroundings. The van de Graaff generator shows one of the dangers of a build-up of static charge. When the voltage is high enough the electric force from the dome can pull electrons from air particles. When this happens the air becomes ionised and conducts electricity, creating a spark. The high voltage generated by a small van de Graaff generator used in schools is enough to cause a spark over an air gap of several centimetres.

Fig 4 *The spark is caused by the charge from the dome passing through the air*

Humans can also become charged up to very high voltages. The friction forces when you walk, or even shuffle about on a plastic chair, can cause charge separation. Synthetic materials such as nylon are very good insulators and do not allow the charge to pass from your body to earth. Walking across a synthetic carpet can put enough charge on your body to make you a very high voltage source of electricity. This high voltage can ionise the air when you are close to an earthed or metal object, causing a spark as the charge passes from you. Although this might give you a shock, there is no danger of electrocution because the amount of electric current involved is tiny.

Some of the dangers of sparks caused by a build-up of charge are described in Unit 117.

> **Q3** A person can become charged while sitting on a plastic stool or chair.
> **a)** Draw a diagram to explain how this happens.
> **b)** Explain why the person feels a shock when he or she touches the metal chair leg.

117 Dangers and uses of static charge

In this unit you will learn the answers to these questions:
- How can static charge be hazardous?
- What useful jobs can static charge do?

In Unit 116 you learned that static charge can exert large forces on other charges. This unit examines situations where care has to be taken to avoid this build-up of charge and situations where the force from static charges is put to use.

Refuelling

Friction forces cause charge to be separated whenever two materials rub together. Unless the materials are very good insulators the charge is carried away by ions and is not allowed to build up. Petrol and other liquid fuels are very good insulators and when a car or aircraft is being refuelled the flow of liquid into the fuel tanks can cause **charge separation**. If you watch an aircraft being refuelled at an airport you will see that an **earthing lead** is always attached to the aircraft body before any fuel is put in. This

Fig 1 *Refuelling an aircraft needs earth bonding*

allows charge to pass safely to earth, so preventing sparks that would be caused by static charge creating a high voltage and ionising the air.

Following a recent outbreak of fires at petrol stations in Germany involving one particular model of car, a scientist was asked to investigate. He found that the car in question had a metal sleeve around the plastic inlet pipe that leads to the tank. This sleeve was not connected to the car body, allowing charge to build up on it as petrol flowed into the tank, as shown in Fig 2. The high voltage due to this charge could cause a spark to pass to an earthed object such as the finger of the person holding the nozzle, igniting the petrol vapour. The car manufacturer solved the problem by connecting the metal sleeve to the car body, allowing the charge to become spread out and preventing a high voltage from being generated.

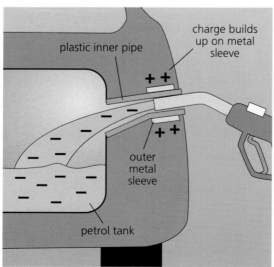

Fig 2 *A dangerous build-up of charge*

Q1 The scientist who investigated the fires also found that some garages were putting a plastic sheet over the ground so that they could clear up petrol spillages easily. Suggest how this could have contributed to the problem.

Keeping the air clean

Before coal is burned at a power station, it is turned into a fine powder. This ensures that it burns quickly and the maximum amount of energy is extracted from it. It also means that the ash that remains when the coal has burned is in the form of a fine dust. This fine dust is carried along with the waste gases and does not merely fall in a heap. This ash would be emitted as smoke from the power station chimney if it were not first of all removed.

After leaving the boiler, and before going to the chimney, the waste gas carrying the fine ash passes through an **electrostatic precipitator** which uses electric charge to remove most of the ash from the gases. Fig 3 shows how the gases pass between plates with a very high voltage between them. The air between the plates is ionised by this high voltage, the negative ions attach themselves to the ash, and the ash is then attracted to the anode. Hammers repeatedly hit the anode plates to remove the ash. Ash from power stations forms a useful building material; it is used to make building blocks for housing.

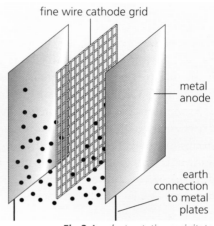

Fig 3 An electrostatic precipitator

Painting with charge

Electrostatic induction is used to ensure good paint coverage of metal panels such as car doors. Panels being painted are connected to earth and sprayed with a positively charged powder. The powder near the panel attracts negative charges and these travel from the earth to the panel. This is an example of charging by induction. Attractive forces between the powder and the negatively charged panel ensure that the powder reaches and covers all the metal. Baking in an oven gives a hard finish to the powder-covered panels.

Q2 The painting process would be equally effective if negatively charged powder was used. Explain how negatively charged powder would be attracted to the metal panels.

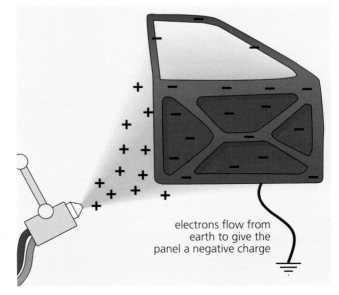

Fig 4 Electrostatic painting

In this unit you will learn the answers to these questions:
- ■ What pattern of magnetic field is produced by the current in a coil of wire?
- ■ What makes an electromagnet strong?
- ■ How do bells and relays work?

Electric current causes heating when it passes through an object that has resistance. The production of movement using electricity is due to the magnetic field of an electric current. This unit looks at this magnetic field and some everyday uses of it.

The field of a coil

Every electric current has its own magnetic field. We do not often notice the effects of the magnetic fields due to electric currents because they are very weak. Fig 1 shows the magnetic field pattern around a single current-carrying wire. You can experiment with this using compass needles or iron filings to detect the magnetic forces. Remember that the direction of a magnetic field is the direction of the force on the N-seeking pole of a compass or other magnet.

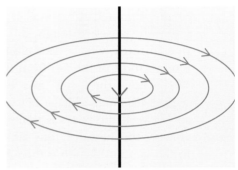

Fig 1 The magnetic field due to a current-carrying wire

A stronger magnetic field can be obtained by winding the wire into a **coil**. Using an arrangement like that shown in Fig 2a you can investigate the field pattern both outside and inside a coil of wire. Fig 2b shows the results of such an experiment.

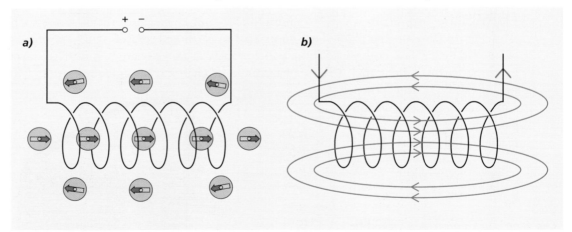

Fig 2 a) *Using compass needles to investigate the magnetic field due to a current in a coil of wire*
b) *The field due to a current in a coil of wire*

Like the field of a current in a single wire, the field of a current passing in a coil is weak. With an iron nail used as a core, the field becomes much stronger and you have an **electromagnet** that can do simple jobs such as lifting iron and other magnetic materials. Other factors affecting the strength include the number of turns of wire and the size of the current passing.

Q1 How could you investigate how the strength of an electromagnet depends on the core material, the number of turns of wire and the current?

An electromagnetic switch

By using a coil with an iron core, an electromagnet can be made which only requires a small current to operate it but can exert enough force to press a pair of switch contacts together. Such a device is called a **relay**. Relays are useful for automatic switching; for example, an outside light that comes on at night when someone walks down your driveway. The sensor circuit in these lights operates from a low-voltage d.c. and the lamp operates from mains voltage. A relay uses a small current from the low-voltage circuit to switch on a larger current in the high-voltage circuit. Such a relay is shown in Fig 3. Relays are also used extensively in motor vehicles. They enable thin wires to be used for the switches that the driver operates while thick wires are used between the relay and high-current devices such as the windscreen heater.

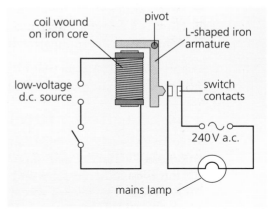

Fig 3 *A relay circuit*

Q2 Write down the sequence of events that causes the lamp to be switched on when the current to the relay coil in Fig 3 is switched on.

The electric bell

An electric bell uses an electromagnet to attract a piece of soft iron called an **armature**. When the armature is attracted by the electromagnet, a small gong is struck and the bell 'dings'. The clever part about a bell mechanism is that it switches the electromagnet off each time the bell 'dings'. A spring then pulls the armature back, thus switching the electromagnet on again and the whole process repeats itself. The switching circuit in a bell is often called a '**make-and-break**' mechanism because it repeatedly makes and then breaks the electromagnet circuit. You can see the make-and-break mechanism in Fig 4.

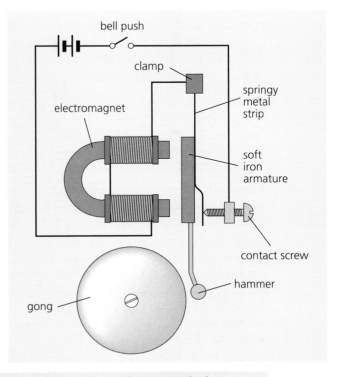

Fig 4 *An electric bell*

Q3 The make-and-break mechanism has an adjusting screw that controls the frequency of the 'dings'. Try to explain how this works.

119 The d.c. motor

In this unit you will learn the answers to these questions:
- How do magnetic fields exert forces?
- How is a turning effect produced in a motor?
- What does a commutator do?

Motors use electromagnetism to produce forces that cause rotation. This unit examines the forces when magnetic fields interact and how these are put to use in the d.c. motor.

The magnetic force

A current that is at right angles to a magnetic field experiences a force. Fig 1 shows how you can investigate the force using some wire and a horseshoe magnet. You should record the effect of varying the current, reversing the current and reversing the direction of the magnetic field.

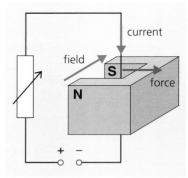

Fig 1

The magnetic field, current and force are all at right angles to each other. You can work out the direction of the force on a wire using the **left-hand rule**. With the thumb and first two fingers of your left hand all at right angles to each other:

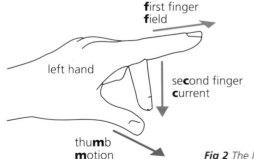

Fig 2 The left-hand rule

1 point your **f**irst finger in the direction of the magnetic **f**ield,

2 point your se**c**ond finger in the direction of the **c**urrent,

3 your thu**m**b points in the direction of **m**otion.

The motor

The magnetic force is used in motors to produce a turning effect or moment. Fig 3 shows the forces on each side of a loop of wire in a magnetic field; use the left-hand rule to check these. Each force has a moment about an axis through the centre of the loop; these moments both have a turning effect in the anticlockwise direction.

Fig 3

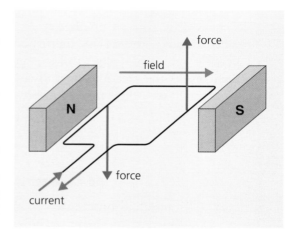

Q1 Sketch the loop in a vertical position and draw the direction of the forces on the sides of the loop. Is there still a turning effect?

The loop experiences the greatest turning force when it is horizontal and no turning force when it is vertical. You can feel this by making a loop out of copper wire and holding it between the poles of a horseshoe magnet or between opposite poles of a pair of slab magnets while passing a current in the loop.

Q2 Imagine that the loop in Fig 3 has been allowed to turn through 180°. It looks the same as in Fig 3, except that the current in each side appears to have been reversed. Sketch the forces now acting on each side of the loop. What is likely to happen to it next?

Keep turning

Your answer to **Q2** should have shown you that, once the loop has completed half a revolution, the turning effect of the forces is in the opposite direction. This would not make a very useful motor.

To keep the loop turning in the same direction, the current needs to be reversed each time the loop has moved through half a revolution. Fig 4 shows how this is done by using a **split–ring commutator** to connect the loop to the source of electric current. Each time the loop passes through the vertical position, the connections to the loop are reversed, keeping the current passing clockwise around the loop. This keeps the rotation of the loop in the same direction all the time.

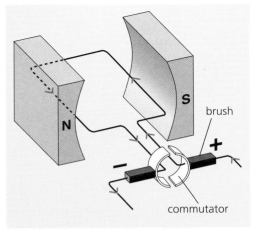

Fig 4 Using a commutator

Practical motors

Although the motors we use at home are designed to operate from the alternating current mains rather than direct current, they work on the same principle. Motors such as those used to power electric trains use direct current since d.c. motors can produce much bigger forces than a.c. motors.

There are three main differences between a practical motor and the simple motor studied in this unit. Instead of using a loop, motors use a coil to produce a greater turning effect. They also have several coils wound on a single armature. This enables just one coil to be used at a time, when its position is such that the turning effect is at its greatest. The third difference is the magnets – practical motors use electromagnets instead of permanent ones.

Fig 5 A practical motor

120 **Electromagnetic induction**

In this unit you will learn the answers to these questions:
■ What causes an induced voltage?
■ What factors affect the size and direction of the voltage?
■ How does a dynamo work?

Our whole lifestyle depends on electromagnetic induction; producing electricity by changing magnetic fields. The battery as a source of electric current was invented by Volta around 1800 and in 1831 Faraday succeeded in generating a current using a changing magnetic field. Fifty years then elapsed before the opening of the first power station in Great Britain, at Godalming in Surrey. This unit describes Faraday's discoveries.

Inducing a current

Fig 1 shows an arrangement for investigating the current that passes in a coil of wire when a magnet is moved inside it. Tiny currents are generated in these experiments, so very careful observation is needed. You should try the effect of:

1 moving the magnet quickly and slowly,

2 reversing the direction of movement,

3 holding the magnet still inside the coil,

4 reversing the poles of the magnet.

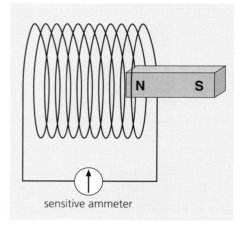

sensitive ammeter

Fig 1

It does not have to be the magnet that moves to generate a current. You can achieve similar results using a coil of wire and a horseshoe magnet or pair of slab magnets, as shown in Fig 2. Careful observation shows that current is generated when the wire is moved at right angles to the magnetic field. Again, you should experiment by varying the speed and direction of motion as well as the number of turns of wire on the coil.

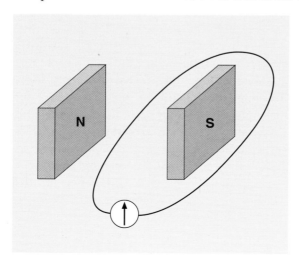

The currents that you have observed are caused by a voltage being **induced** in a wire whenever the magnetic field around it changes. Faster movement causes the magnetic field to change at a greater rate, and a bigger voltage is induced. Reversing the magnetic field or direction of movement reverses the induced voltage, causing the current to pass in the opposite direction.

Fig 2

Increasing the current

The induced current in the above experiments is tiny, and certainly not enough to light up a small lamp. By winding a coil of wire on an iron core a bigger voltage is induced which in turn causes a bigger current. An alternating current is generated when a magnet is turned round next to a coil wound on an iron core, as shown in Fig 3.

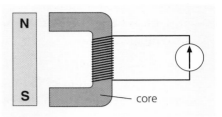

Fig 3

The induced voltage can be studied more closely if the output is connected to a cathode ray oscilloscope while the magnet is turned round using a hand drill. The trace on the oscilloscope is shown in Fig 4. Notice that the trace has both positive and negative values, showing that the voltage is alternating.

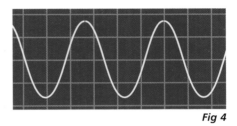

Fig 4

Q1 Describe two changes that occur to the oscilloscope trace when the speed of rotation of the magnet is changed. Explain why each change takes place.

The dynamo

A **dynamo** on a bicycle and a **generator** in a power station both work on the principle that a magnetic field rotating inside a coil generates a voltage in that coil. Fig 5 shows the structure of a dynamo. The cylindrical magnet creates a magnetic field in the iron core. With the magnet in the position shown, the left-hand part of the iron core acts as a N-seeking pole and the right-hand part acts as a S-seeking pole. These poles are reversed when the magnet has turned through half a revolution.

As the cycle wheel turns the magnet rotates, causing the magnetic field in the iron core to change direction. Repeated reversal of this magnetic field generates an alternating voltage in the coil of wire.

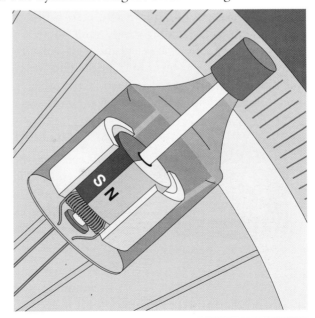

Fig 5 A dynamo

Q2 Describe the advantages and disadvantages of using a dynamo for cycle lights.

121 Transformers

In this unit you will learn the answers to these questions:
- ■ **What do transformers do?**
- ■ **How do the numbers of turns on transformer coils affect the current and voltage?**

In Unit 120 you studied how electromagnetic induction is used to generate an electric current. This unit examines another use of electromagnetic induction, which is of particular importance to the electricity supply industry.

Changing fields

A voltage is induced in a conductor when the magnetic field around it changes. Fig 1 shows how the induced voltage can be investigated when an electromagnet is switched on or off. Switching on the current in the left-hand coil causes a pulse of current in

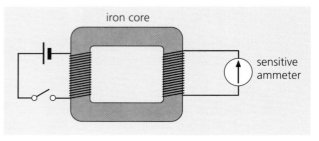

Fig 1 Investigating induced voltages

the right-hand coil. A pulse of current passes in the opposite direction when the current in the left-hand coil is switched off. There is *no* induced current in the right-hand coil when a *steady* current passes in the left-hand one.

These results can be explained using the principles of electromagnetic induction. Switching on the current in the left-hand coil makes it into an electromagnet which has its own magnetic field. That field passes through the iron core as well as the surrounding air. The right-hand coil experiences a change of magnetic field around and within it, so a voltage is induced. Once the current has reached its steady value there is no longer a change in the magnetic field and no induced voltage. Switching off the current causes the reverse to happen. The magnetic field collapses, inducing a voltage as it does so. This voltage is in the opposite direction to the one induced when the field was created.

ICT Extra!

Use a spreadsheet to analyse data about the relationship between the input and output voltages and the numbers of turns of wire on the coils.

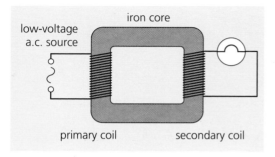

Fig 2 A transformer

The transformer

Replacing the d.c. source with an a.c. source, as shown in Fig 2, gives a magnetic field in and around the iron core which is changing all the time. This causes an alternating voltage to be induced in the right-hand coil. A lamp or an a.c. voltmeter is needed to detect this induced voltage.

A transformer has two coils of wire, usually wound on an iron core. An alternating voltage applied to the **input**, or **primary**, **coil** induces an alternating voltage in the **output**, or **secondary**, **coil**. Energy is transferred from the input to the output through the changing magnetic field.

Changing the voltage

Transformers are used to change the size of an alternating voltage. Using the brightness of a lamp as an indicator of the output voltage, or an a.c. voltmeter if one is available, you should experiment to see how the output voltage depends on the number of turns of wire on the two coils.

Fig 3 *This train uses a transformer to step down the voltage from the overhead power lines*

Results of these experiments show that the output voltage depends on the ratio of the numbers of turns of wire on the coils. A **step-up transformer** has more turns on the secondary coil than on the primary and the output voltage is bigger than the input. **Step-down transformers**, used to make an alternating voltage smaller, have fewer turns of wire on the secondary coil than on the primary coil.

The relationship between the input and output voltages of a transformer is given by the equation:

$$\frac{\text{primary coil voltage}}{\text{secondary coil voltage}} = \frac{\text{number of primary turns}}{\text{number of secondary turns}} \quad \text{or} \quad \frac{V_p}{V_s} = \frac{N_p}{N_s}$$

Remember this is just a ratio. It simply states that the voltages are in the same ratio as the numbers of turns. So if a step-up transformer has three times the number of turns on the secondary as on the primary, the secondary voltage is three times the primary voltage.

Q1 Use ratios or the transformer equation to complete the table.

	Number of primary turns	Number of secondary turns	Primary voltage/V	Secondary voltage/V
a	50	200	12	
b	100		6	36
c		100	240	12
d	1000	12000		240

Transformers are very efficient devices. Some energy is wasted as heat in the wires and the core, but this is usually neglected. It is assumed that all the power in the primary coil is transferred to the secondary coil.

power in the primary coil = power in the secondary coil or $V_p I_p = V_s I_s$

A transformer cannot provide more power from the output than it takes in at the input. When a transformer is used to increase the voltage there is a decrease in the current. If the secondary voltage is twice that of the primary, then the current in the secondary is half the primary current. The ratio of the currents in the coils of a transformer is the inverse ratio of the turns or voltages:

$$\frac{\text{primary coil current}}{\text{secondary coil current}} = \frac{\text{number of secondary turns}}{\text{number of primary turns}} \quad \text{or} \quad \frac{I_p}{I_s} = \frac{N_s}{N_p}$$

122 Power transmission

In this unit you will learn the answers to these questions:
- ■ How is electricity generated?
- ■ Why are high voltages used to transmit electricity?
- ■ What are transformers used for in power transmission?

In the two previous units you have learned how electromagnetic induction is used to generate electricity and change the size of an alternating voltage. This unit describes how these principles are used to supply us with electricity.

The generator

Generators in power stations work in a similar way to the cycle dynamo described in Unit 120, except that they are driven by **turbines**. Coal-fired power stations and nuclear power stations generate high-pressure steam to drive the turbines. In modern gas-fired power stations the turbines are driven by the high-energy waste products from the burning gas. These work in a similar way to aircraft jet engines.

Fig 1 shows the turbines in a hydroelectric power station. The generator in a power station has three sets of wire coils, inside which an electromagnet rotates fifty times each second. This generates alternating current at 25 000 V with a frequency of 50 Hz. A 500 MW generator produces a large current, so very thick wire is used for the coils.

Fig 1 Water-driven turbines

Power into the grid

We do not receive our electricity from any one particular power station. All the electricity generated is fed into the **national grid**, a network of cables that links together the whole country. The electric current in these cables transfers energy as heat, which results in power losses. Fig 2 shows how you can demonstrate the power loss in a transmission wire using a safe low-voltage supply.

To minimise the power losses in transmission, the current has to be kept as small as possible. A typical coal-burning power station has four generators, each producing 500 MW of power at 25 000 V. A total current of 80 000 amps would be required to transmit this power at 25 000 V. Using transformers, the voltage is increased at the power station, allowing the power to be fed into the national grid at a reduced current.

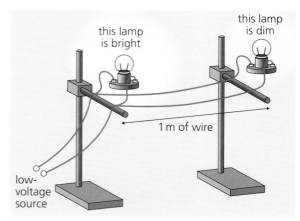

Fig 2 Demonstrating power loss

Power around the country

Most of the national grid uses overhead cables to take the power from the power stations to the users. These cables do not need electrical insulation because the air gap between them and the ground is big enough to prevent sparking. Apart from cost, another advantage of not using insulation is that the air also acts as a coolant and prevents the cables from overheating. The cost of using underground cables is very high for two main reasons. Very good electrical insulation is required for cables at such high voltages. This electrical insulation is also a good thermal insulator, so the cables have no natural coolant. Underground cables are cooled by oil flowing through them, increasing both the cost of the cable and the running costs.

Fig 3 These pylons are ugly, but the alternative is expensive

Power to the consumer

Before going to consumers, the voltage of the electricity supply has to be reduced. Fig 4 shows how this is done in stages. Some industry uses electricity at a high voltage, 11 kV or 33 kV, but 240 V is supplied to domestic users. The last stage in the stepping down process is at a substation close to your home. Power is supplied to these substations and travels to your home through underground cables.

You can see from Fig 4 that, for efficient distribution of electrical power, transformers are used extensively. They provide a cheap way of increasing the voltage for transmission and reducing it again to a safe level for consumers. The need to use transformers is the reason for using a.c. rather than d.c. for our mains electricity supply.

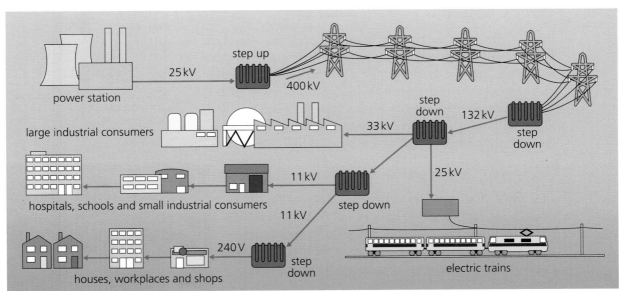

Fig 4 The national grid

Q1 Discuss the advantages and disadvantages of using underground cables rather than overhead cables for the national grid.

123 Changing shape

In this unit you will learn the answers to these questions:
- Do all materials stretch in a regular way?
- Which materials are elastic?
- What is the difference between the 'elastic limit' and the 'limit of proportionality'?

Some materials are useful because they stretch easily. Rubber bands are stretched when they are used to hold things together. Socks often contain a material such as nylon so that they stretch when you put them on. Rubber and nylon are both **elastic** materials; they return to their original shape when the stretching force is removed. Plasticine is easy to stretch but it keeps its new shape; it is a **plastic** material.

Investigating stretching

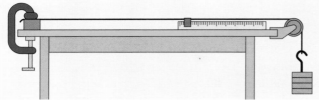

Fig 1 Comparing materials

Fig 1 shows how you can compare the stretchiness and elasticity of different materials. Suitable materials to use include 32 swg copper wire, nylon fishing line and rubber. Safety goggles should be worn in case the material being tested breaks.

The graph (Fig 2) shows how the extension of a length of copper wire increases when the force is increased. The graph is a straight line up to point P, showing that the extension is proportional to the force. Copper, like other metals, is said to obey **Hooke's law** up to this point, known as the **limit of proportionality**.

Beyond the limit of proportionality copper becomes less stiff. The same increase in force causes a greater stretch than below the limit of proportionality. At the point labelled E on the graph the copper sample has lost its elasticity. If the force is removed it will not return to its original size and shape. Increasing the force beyond this eventually causes the wire to break; this is shown as point B on the graph.

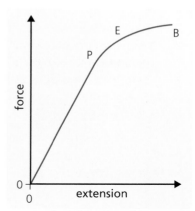

Fig 2 Stretching of copper wire

Storing energy

The force that stretches a material does work on it, causing energy to be stored in it. Archers use this energy to propel an arrow at a target. Bungee-jumpers and trampolinists use the energy stored in stretched elastic to bounce back up after falling down.

Q1 Describe the energy transfer that takes place when the girl shown in Fig 3 bounces on the trampoline.

Fig 3

The driver of a car travelling at 60 mph has a lot of kinetic energy. Seat belts are designed so that they stretch and absorb this energy if a collision occurs. However, seat belts only restrain the body. The driver's head carries on moving forwards, causing the neck muscles to stretch as they absorb the energy. The increasing force in the muscles stops the driver's head from moving forwards and pulls it backwards, transferring energy back to kinetic energy of the head. Head restraints fitted to cars stop the head from continuing to move backwards and protect the driver from damage to the neck and back.

Designing car tyres

Unlike metal wires, rubber does not obey Hooke's law. The graph (Fig 4) shows the pattern of stretching for a sample of rubber. The slope of the graph indicates the stiffness of the rubber.

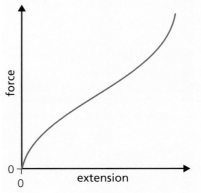

Fig 4 *Stretching of rubber*

> **Q2** Describe how the stiffness of rubber changes as it is stretched.

Rubber absorbs some energy each time it is stretched. You can demonstrate this by repeatedly stretching and relaxing a rubber band – it becomes warm.

Tyres on a car travelling at 60 mph are deformed and returned to their original shape about 20 times each second, causing heating. If the tyre pressure is low, more deformation and heating occurs. This raises the pressure of the air inside the tyre and can cause a 'blow–out'. This is the result of high air pressure in the tyre causing the tyre to explode.

The ideal car tyre has a stretchy tread so that it adjusts to the shape of the road and gives a good grip. The tyre wall does not need to change shape and so it should be made of a stiffer material which does not stretch so much.

Traditional car tyres are made of carbon, which is hard-wearing, and rubber, which is springy. New tyres are being introduced which use silica instead of carbon. The resulting material absorbs less energy when it deforms and returns to shape, so reducing both the heating of the tyre and fuel bills.

> **Q3** Unlike carbon, silica does not conduct electricity. Explain why tyres made with silica instead of carbon could cause a problem if there is a build-up of static charge on the car.

Fig 5 *Energy-saving car tyre*

124 Gases under pressure

In this unit you will learn the answers to these questions:
- How does the pressure of a gas depend on its volume?
- What does Boyle's law tell us about the effects of changing the pressure or volume of a gas?

Gases can be compressed easily, but solids and liquids cannot. This unit studies the behaviour of gases under pressure.

A particle model

Air trapped in a stoppered syringe or bicycle pump can be squashed or stretched by pushing or pulling on it. When you squash air you can feel it pushing back as the pressure increases.

Gases consist of large numbers of particles in constant motion. The motion is random, which means that there is no order or direction to it. At any time, there are

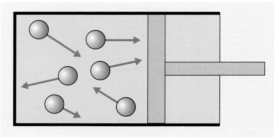

Fig 1 The particles of a gas move with a range of speeds in all directions

particles moving in all possible directions. As they move at high speeds, typically 300 m/s in air at room temperature, collisions with the container walls are frequent. Gas pressure is a result of the force exerted on the walls by the particles when they hit the walls and rebound.

This model of a gas can be used to explain why the pressure increases when a gas is squashed into a smaller volume. Imagine the piston shown in Fig 1 being pushed in. The result is that the same number of particles now have less space to move in, so individual particles collide with the walls more frequently. The walls are subjected to more collisions each second, so the force and pressure due to these collisions increases.

Q1 Describe and explain what happens to the pressure of the trapped air in Fig 1 if the piston is moved to the right.

Increasing the pressure

Fig 2 shows apparatus that can be used to measure the changing volume of air when the pressure on it is increased. Air would dissolve in water, so oil is used to trap the air. Pressure applied from a pump is transmitted through the oil, squashing the air.

If each pair of values of pressure and volume is multiplied together the result is, within the limits of the precision of the measurements, always the same. A graph of pressure against 1/volume gives a straight line which can be traced back to the origin,

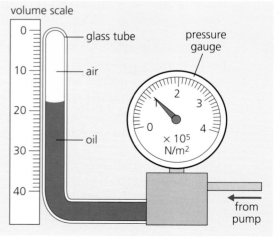

Fig 2 Demonstrating Boyle's law

as shown in Fig 3. These results show that the pressure is inversely proportional to the volume. This means that if one quantity is doubled, the other one halves.

Boyle's law describes how gases behave when the pressure on them is changed. It states that:

> **The volume of a fixed mass of gas kept at a constant temperature is inversely proportional to its pressure.**
>
> **This can be written as:**
>
> $$pV = \text{constant} \qquad \text{or} \qquad p \propto \frac{1}{V}$$

Example Some air in a syringe has a volume of $80\,\text{cm}^3$ and a pressure of $1.1 \times 10^5\,\text{Pa}$. Calculate the pressure of the gas when the volume is decreased to $55\,\text{cm}^3$.

Answer Multiplying the pressure by the volume gives the same number in each case, so if the new pressure of the gas is p then:

$$1.1 \times 10^5 \times 80 = p \times 55$$

so $\quad p = \dfrac{1.1 \times 10^5 \times 80}{55} = 1.6 \times 10^5\,\text{Pa}$

Storing gases

The photographs (Fig 4) show two kinds of container used for storing gases.

Camping gas is butane, a gas which liquifies easily when put under pressure. If you shake a cylinder of camping gas you can hear the liquid moving inside. Because it is stored as a liquid, a large quantity of butane can be stored in a small container. Thin aluminium is used for small gas cylinders so that the cylinder pierces easily to allow the gas out.

Carbon dioxide, which is used to make fizzy drinks, does not liquefy. The pressure of the gas in a carbon dioxide cylinder can be over a hundred times atmospheric pressure, so the cylinders are made of thick cast iron which can withstand this pressure.

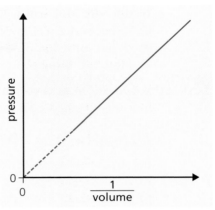

Fig 3 *Graph showing Boyle's law*

Q2 Calculate the pressure of the gas in the example if the volume is increased to $120\,\text{cm}^3$.

Ideas and evidence

Brown and Einstein
Evidence for the motion of particles was first reported by Robert Brown, an amateur biologist who worked on classifying different types of pollen. He noticed that pollen grains suspended in water had a jiggling, haphazard motion, but he was unable to explain the cause of this. More than a century later Einstein explained the motion of the pollen grains in terms of their being bombarded by water particles. He also predicted the amount and speed of movement of the pollen grains. These predictions were later confirmed in experiments carried out by the French scientist Jean-Baptiste Perrin.

Fig 4 *Storing gases under pressure* **a)** *camping gas,* **b)** *carbon dioxide*

Q3 Explain why carbon dioxide cylinders should never be stored in direct sunlight.

In this unit you will learn the answers to these questions:
- What is the relationship between the speed, distance travelled and time taken?
- What information does a distance–time graph give?
- How are displacement–time graphs interpreted?

Forces are needed to make things move, speed them up and slow them down. This unit is concerned with measuring the speed of moving objects.

Calculating the speed

Fig 1 shows how you can use a computer to measure the speed of a toy car as it passes through an infrared beam. The computer measures the length of time that the infrared beam is interrupted by the piece of card attached to the car. Knowledge of the length of the card enables the computer to calculate the speed of the car using the formula:

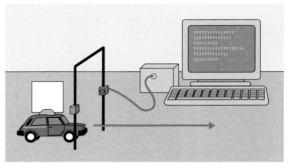

Fig 1 *Using a computer to measure the speed of a toy car*

> **average speed = distance travelled ÷ time taken   or $v = d/t$**

The speed is an average because the car may have been speeding up or slowing down as it passed through the beam.

Using the symbols v for speed, d for distance and t for time, the speed formula can be written in three different ways:
$$v = d/t, \quad d = v \times t \text{ and } t = d/v.$$

Q1 Use the speed formula to calculate the average speed of:
a) a bus that travels 60 miles in 2 hours,
b) a sprinter who runs 100 m in 12.5 s.

Q2 Calculate the time taken to travel:
a) 150 miles at an average speed of 40 mph,
b) 300 m at an average speed of 12 m/s,
c) 6000 miles at an average speed of 500 mph.

 ICT Extra!

Use data logging to measure the speed of objects as they pass through an infrared beam.

If you are going on a long journey by car you need to be able to make an estimate of your journey time so that you know what time to set off from home. At an average speed of 60 mph on a motorway, a 300 mile journey should take 300 miles ÷ 60 mph = 5 hours.

Using graphs

A **distance–time** graph can be used to represent a journey. Fig 2 is a distance–time graph of a bicycle ride.

You can gain a lot of information about the journey by looking at the slope, or gradient, of the line. This gradient represents the speed of the cyclist.

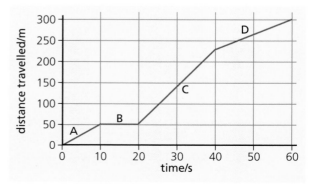

Fig 2 *A distance–time graph*

Q3 Without doing any calculations, write out a brief description of the bicycle ride.

Calculating the gradient of the line gives the actual speed of the cyclist at any point on the journey. The gradient of part C of the graph is $(225 - 50)/20$, representing a speed of $8.75\,\text{m/s}$.

Q4 Calculate the speed of the cyclist at parts A and D of Fig 2, and the average speed for the journey.

One important piece of information that the graph does not give is where the journey ended. You can tell that the cyclist travelled a total distance of 300 m but there is no information about the direction in which the cyclist was travelling.

A **displacement–time** graph gives more information than a distance–time graph. Displacement is the distance an object moves from a certain position. It can have both positive and negative values to show movement in opposite directions. Fig 3 is a displacement–time graph for a child on a swing. It shows her swinging away from the mid-point of the swing, then returning and swinging away in the opposite direction.

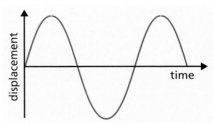

Fig 3 *A displacement–time graph of a swing*

Not only can the displacement have both positive and negative values, the gradient of the graph can also be positive or negative. If the positive value represents speed in one particular direction, then the negative value represents the speed in the opposite direction. So the gradient of a displacement–time graph gives information about both the speed of an object and the direction in which it is moving. These two quantities together, the speed and the direction, are called the **velocity**.

Fig 4 is a displacement–time graph that represents the movement of a lift. Part A of the graph represents the lift travelling from the eighth to the fifteenth floor of a building. The gradient of each part of the graph represents the velocity of the lift, i.e. its speed and direction. You can tell therefore that the lift was moving down during part C. The gradient of this part of the graph is -2, representing a velocity of $2\,\text{m/s}$ downwards.

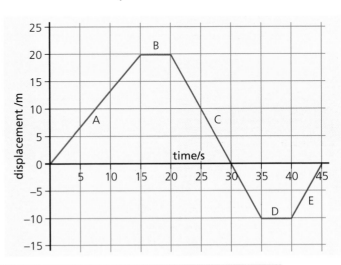

Fig 4 *A displacement–time graph of a lift*

Q5 a) Describe the movement of the lift that Fig 4 represents.
    b) Calculate the velocity during parts A and E of the graph.
    c) How far did the lift travel altogether, and where was it after 45 s?

In this unit you will learn the answers to these questions:
■ What are the factors that affect stopping distance?
■ How does stopping distance depend on speed and the driver's reaction time?

In the last unit you studied how to calculate speed and velocity. Drivers of vehicles need to judge how fast it is safe to drive in different conditions. If they drive too fast then they may not be able to stop the vehicle when something unexpected happens; this can lead to accidents. This unit is concerned with the factors that determine vehicle stopping distances.

Braking distance

The speed limit on roads where there are a lot of houses is usually 30 mph, equivalent to a speed of 14 m/s. Sometimes there are road signs to warn drivers to take extra care. Fig 1 shows the signs that warn drivers of a school or pedestrian crossing. These signs are intended to make drivers more alert and ready to brake if necessary.

Fig 1 *Warning signs*

On a dry road in good conditions, a car travelling at 14 m/s takes about 2 s to stop after the brakes are applied. The average speed while braking is 7 m/s (this is the average of the initial speed and the final speed).

Q1 Show that a car that brakes from a speed of 14 m/s and stops after 2.0 s travels 14 m.

A braking distance of 14 m is quite a long way, and yet cars travelling at motorway speeds are often to be seen with a shorter distance than this between them.

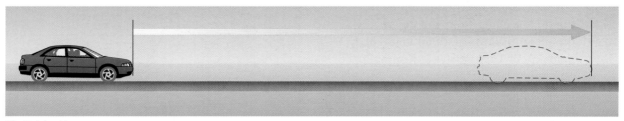

Fig 2 *A braking distance of 14 m*

Q2 The braking time from a speed of 28 m/s is twice that from a speed of 14 m/s, so the car in **Q1** would take 4.0 s to brake from a speed of 28 m/s. Calculate the distance the car travels in braking from this speed. (Do not forget to use the car's average speed in your calculation.)

If you compare the answers to **Q1** and **Q2**, you can see that when the speed of a car doubles, its braking distance *becomes four times as big*. Not only does it take twice as long to stop, its average speed is also twice as great (see Unit 156).

Some of the factors that can affect braking distance are the type of road surface, weather conditions, the weight of the vehicle and the condition of its tyres and brakes. Water acts as a lubricant and a film of water between a tyre and the road would cause the vehicle to slide over the road surface. Tread on tyres is very important because it allows the tyre to push water out from underneath the tyre, so the tyre stays in direct contact with the road.

Fig 3 *Tyre tread*

Stopping distance

Good drivers are always ready for the unexpected. If a child steps out from between two parked cars the driver's reaction time, that is the time between the driver seeing the child and pressing the brake pedal, is very important.

Fig 4 *Small children stepping out from behind parked cars present particular problems to drivers*

An alert driver can react in 0.6 s, but this time is lengthened if the driver is tired, has been drinking alcohol, or is paying too much attention to the car hi-fi system. During the time it takes the driver to react, the car carries on moving at a steady speed. The distance travelled by the car in this time is referred to as '**thinking distance**' in the Highway Code.

Stopping distance is the total distance travelled by a vehicle while the driver is reacting and braking.

ICT Extra!

Use the spreadsheet to plot best-fit line graphs of thinking distance, braking distance and stopping distance against speed, and to determine the relationship between each of the distances and the speed of a vehicle.

Q3 a) Assuming a reaction time of 0.6 s, calculate the 'thinking distance' for a car travelling at 14 m/s and one travelling at 28 m/s.
　　b) Use the braking distances you calculated in **Q1** and **Q2** to calculate the total stopping distances from these speeds.

The Highway Code recommends that on roads carrying fast traffic, drivers should leave a 2 second time gap between themselves and the vehicle in front.

Q4 a) How far is a two second time gap for cars travelling at 28 m/s (60 mph)?
　　b) Explain why this is considered to be a large enough gap.

127 Forces in and out of balance

In this unit you will learn the answer to this question:
- How is an object's motion affected by the forces acting on it?

Unless you are travelling downhill, if you want to keep a bicycle moving you have to keep pedalling. This unit is concerned with the forces that act on objects that are slowing down, speeding up or travelling at a constant speed.

What makes a bicycle go?

Like buses, trains, cars and lorries, bicycles are driven by **friction**. Anyone who has ever ridden a bicycle onto a patch of ice realises that without friction there is no propulsion. When a cyclist pushes on the pedals the force is transmitted through the chain to the rear wheel. The rear wheel pushes backwards against the road, as shown in Fig 1. Friction between the road surface and the

Fig 1 The push of a bicycle wheel on the road surface

Fig 2 The push of the road surface on the wheel

tyre prevents the tyre from sliding. The friction force pushes forwards on the tyre, propelling the cycle in the forwards direction.

Two forces are involved in moving any vehicle that uses wheels. The backward push of the wheels on the road or track is matched in size by the forward push of the friction force that acts betwen the two surfaces. This friction force is the **driving force**.

> **Q1** We rely on friction to walk. Describe the forces between the floor and a shoe when a person walks.

What slows a bicycle down?

There are several forces that combine together to slow you down when you stop pedalling a bicycle. One of them is the **air resistance**. You have to exert a force to push the air out of the way so that your body and bicycle can pass. Racing cyclists try to reduce the effect of air resistance by adopting a crouching position.

Resistive forces also act on the tyres. This is called **rolling resistance** and is caused by the tyres changing their shape as they go round. You can minimise the effects of rolling resistance by keeping the tyres pumped up to the recommended pressure.

A third resistive force comes from the **friction** in the wheel bearings, but provided that these are kept lubricated they do not offer much resistance to motion.

Fig 3 This racing cyclist keeps a low profile to reduce the effect of air resistance

Going on a bicycle ride

Resistive forces only act when a bicycle is moving, so at the instant a cyclist sets off the only force acting is the driving force. Once the cyclist is moving the resistive forces start to act but so long as the total resistive force is smaller than the driving force the forces are unbalanced and the cyclist accelerates.

As the cyclist goes faster, the resistive forces increase. The further the cyclist travels each second, the more air has to be pushed out of the way and the more times the tyres change their shape. Eventually the resistive forces are equal to the driving force and the cyclist now travels at a constant speed. Because the forces are equal in size but act in opposite directions, they are said to be balanced forces.

Cyclists usually stop pedalling when they brake, so as a cyclist slows down and stops the resistive force is the only force acting. Fig 4 shows the forces acting on a cyclist when speeding up, travelling at constant speed and braking.

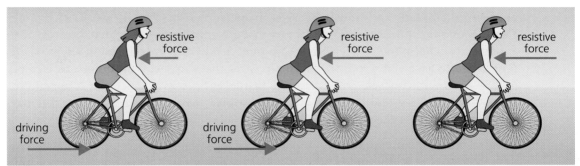

Fig 4 The cyclist on the left is speeding up, the one in the centre is travelling at a constant speed and the one on the right is slowing down

The forces on a sky diver

Like a cyclist, a sky diver has two forces acting on her. The Earth pulls her down and air resistance acts upwards.

Q2 Draw diagrams to show the relative size of the forces acting on a sky diver when she:
  a) is speeding up, having jumped out of the aircraft,
  b) is travelling at constant speed before she opens her parachute,
  c) has just opened her parachute.

Q3 The graph (Fig 5) shows how the vertical speed of the sky diver changes from when she leaves the aircraft to when she reaches the ground.
  a) Describe how the speed of the sky diver changes.
  b) Which parts of the graph show when the forces on the sky diver were balanced?
  c) At which part of the graph was the air resistance greater than the sky diver's weight?

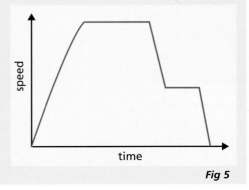

Fig 5

128 Acceleration

In this unit you will learn the answers to these questions:
■ What does acceleration mean?
■ What is a negative acceleration?
■ How is acceleration calculated?

When the forces acting on a moving object are unbalanced, the result is a change in velocity. In the previous unit you studied how the speed of a cyclist increases when the driving force is bigger than the resistive force. This unit develops the idea further into a study of acceleration.

The New

Presto

... and its 'nearest' rival

	Presto	Lento
Fuel injection	✔	✗
Airbags	✔	✗
CD player	✔	✗
ABS brakes	✔	✗
0 – 60mph	7.5 sec	8.6 sec

Fig 1 Comparing cars

Speeding up

Car manufacturers spend millions of pounds in advertising their goods. They often make comparisons between their cars and those of rival manufacturers. Safety, economy and reliability are factors that are commonly compared, but cars that are meant to appeal to younger drivers are more likely to be advertised in terms of the time taken to accelerate from 0 to 60 mph. A car that can speed up from 0 to 60 mph in 7.5 s has a greater acceleration than one that takes 8.6 s. In practice this is unrealistic, since there are very few occasions when a sensible driver would want to accelerate from 0 to 60 mph in the shortest possible time.

Imagine a milk float and a small car setting off together from some traffic lights. The milk float reaches its top speed of 8 m/s after a time interval of 5 s. The car accelerates to a speed of 14 m/s in 7 s. Which has the greater acceleration?

For an object moving in a straight line, **acceleration** is how much it speeds up by each second.

> The definition of acceleration is:
> increase in velocity / time   or $a = (v_2 - v_1) / t$

Using this definition, the acceleration of the milk float is 8 m/s ÷ 5 s = 1.6 m/s per s and that of the car is 14 m/s ÷ 7 s = 2.0 m/s per s. Note the unit of acceleration, which is usually written as m/s² or m s⁻².

> **Q1** Use the definition to calculate the acceleration of:
> **a)** a cyclist who speeds up from 0 m/s to 10 m/s in 4 s,
> **b)** a car that speeds up from 15 m/s to 30 m/s in 9 s,
> **c)** an aircraft that speeds up from 10 m/s to 60 m/s in 10 s.

The acceleration formula can also be applied to objects as they slow down. For a car reducing its speed from 35 m/s to 20 m/s in 10 s, the increase in velocity is −15 m/s. The negative sign shows that the velocity has decreased. The acceleration of the car is −15 m/s ÷ 10 s = −1.5 m/s². The negative acceleration in this case shows that the car is decelerating.

Fig 2 This aircraft needs a large acceleration to reach its take-off speed before the end of the runway

Using graphs

Fig 3 is a **speed–time graph** for part of a car journey. You can gain a lot of information by studying the graph without doing any calculations. You can see that after 60 s the car stopped and set off again 10 s later. What the graph does not tell you is whether the car was still travelling in the same direction.

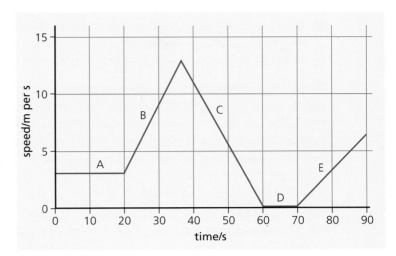

Fig 3 *A speed–time graph*

The gradient of a speed–time graph represents the size of the acceleration of an object. A positive gradient means that it is speeding up and a negative gradient represents a slowing down.

Q2 Calculate the acceleration represented by sections B, C and E of the graph.

Information about the direction of travel can be obtained by studying a **velocity–time graph**. You learned in Unit 125 that the velocity of an object describes both its speed and its direction, so velocity can have negative as well as positive values.

Fig 4 shows a velocity–time graph for part of a car journey. You can see that after accelerating, travelling at a steady speed, braking and then stopping, after 60 s the car starts to travel in the opposite direction. The negative acceleration shown on part E of the graph represents the car speeding up, but in the opposite direction to the one it set off in.

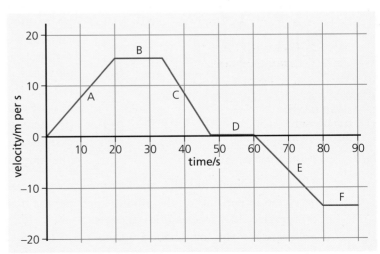

Fig 4 *A velocity–time graph*

Q3 a) Calculate the value of the acceleration represented by parts A, C and E of the graph.
   b) Use the speed equation to calculate the distance travelled by the car on the outward part of its journey.
   c) After 90 s, how far is the car from the place it set off from?

129 Force, mass and acceleration

In this unit you will learn the answers to these questions:
- ■ How does the acceleration of a moving object depend on its mass and the size of the unbalanced force?
- ■ What is the relationship between force, mass and acceleration?

Unit 127 explained how the movement of an object depends on the relative sizes of the forces acting on it. To speed up or slow down requires an unbalanced force. In Unit 128 you learned how to calculate the size and direction of an acceleration. This unit is concerned with the way in which acceleration depends on the size of the unbalanced force and the mass of the object being accelerated.

Measuring acceleration

A jumbo jet and an inter-city passenger train have roughly equal masses, about 300 tonnes (300 000 kg). The top speed of the train is about the same as the take-off speed of the jumbo jet, but the aircraft needs to have a much greater acceleration. The train does not run out of track until it reaches its destination but the aircraft has to accelerate to a speed of 75 m/s before it runs out of runway. A large force is needed to accelerate a jumbo jet when it takes off!

Fig 1 This jet engine can exert a force of 1 MN

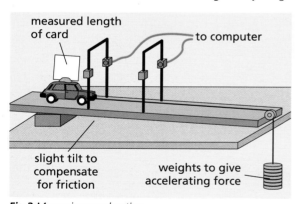

Fig 2 Measuring acceleration

More than 300 years ago, Isaac Newton carried out experiments which enabled him to describe how acceleration depends on the size of the unbalanced force and the mass it acts on. Fig 2 shows how you can use a computer and some light-sensitive or infrared switches to carry out your own experiments. You may have used a similar arrangement to measure speed when studying Unit 125. Measuring acceleration is more complex as it is necessary to measure two speeds and the time interval between them.

Using equipment like that shown in Fig 2, you can experiment to find out how the acceleration depends on the pulling force and the mass of the car. If you plot your results as graphs of acceleration against pulling force and acceleration against 1/mass you should obtain graphs like those shown in Fig 3. In each case the graph is a straight line through the origin, showing that the acceleration is proportional to the pulling force and inversely proportional to the mass being accelerated. So, for a fixed mass,

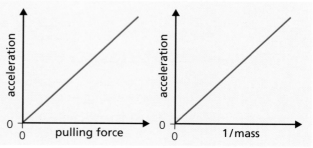

Fig 3 Relationship between acceleration, force and mass

doubling the pulling force causes the acceleration to double, but, for a fixed force, doubling the mass of the object halves the acceleration.

The relationship

Putting together the results of the experiment gives the formula:

$$\text{force} = \text{mass} \times \text{acceleration} \quad \text{or} \quad F = ma$$

Fig 4

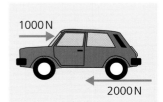

1000 N

2000 N

It is important to realise that the force is the unbalanced or resultant force when all the forces have been taken into account. In the experiment the car was accelerated down a slight slope to counterbalance the effects of resistive forces. When calculating the acceleration of a car the resistive forces need to be considered.

Example The diagram (Fig 4) shows a car of mass 800 kg. Calculate the acceleration of the car.

Answer The unbalanced, or resultant, force accelerating the car = 2000 N − 1000 N = 1000 N in the forwards direction.
The acceleration of the car = force ÷ mass
$$= 1000\,\text{N} \div 800\,\text{kg} = 1.25\,\text{m/s}^2$$

ICT Extra!

Use data-logging equipment to investigate the relationship between the size of an unbalanced force and the acceleration it causes on objects with different masses.

Car safety

The results of a head-on collision between two cars can be horrific and, fortunately, very few of us are ever involved in such an event. The deceleration of the cars when this does happen is large as the cars stop within a very short time interval. Consequently very large forces are exerted on the cars themselves.

Crumple zones are designed to reduce these forces by allowing the car to crumple, increasing the time it takes the car to stop. This reduces the deceleration and the force exerted on the cars.

Fig 5 *Seat belts reduce deceleration*

The seat belts that protect the driver and passengers are designed to stop the people inside the car so that they do not carry on moving, hitting the windscreen or the seat in front. The seat belts are not rigid – they are designed to stretch a small amount. This stretching of the seat belts increases the time it takes the driver and passengers to stop, thus reducing the force that the seat belt exerts on them.

130 **Falling down**

In this unit you will learn the answers to these questions:
- What forces are involved when two objects interact?
- What affects the size of the Earth's pull on an object?
- Why do heavy and light objects have the same free-fall acceleration?

In previous units you have studied the motion of objects with both balanced and unbalanced forces and seen how unbalanced forces cause a change in velocity. This unit is a study of the vertical motion caused by the Earth's gravitational pull.

The Earth's pull

Newton realised that gravitational forces act between all masses, but the effects are only noticeable when one of them is very massive. As a result we notice the effects of the gravitational forces due to planets, but not those due to ourselves!

Another of Newton's important discoveries was that objects exert forces on each other, so if one object pulls or pushes a second, then the second object pulls or pushes the first with an equal-sized force in the opposite direction. You came across this idea in Unit 127 when considering the force that propels a bicycle.

Fig 1 The forces between you and the Earth are equal in size but opposite in direction

It may be comforting to know that although the Earth is pulling you towards it, you are pulling the Earth towards you with an equal-sized force. However this won't help you if you fall. The effect of your pull on the Earth's mass is negligible so rather than it moving to meet you, you move towards the Earth.

The size of the Earth's pull is called its gravitational field strength, or *g* for short. Close to the surface of the Earth this has a value of 10 N/kg, so each kg of your body mass is pulled towards the centre of the Earth with a force of 10 N. This downward pull is the force called weight, which can be calculated using the formula:

weight = mass × gravitational field strength or $W = mg$

Q1 Why is it incorrect to say that 'a bag of sugar weighs 1 kg'?

Q2 Potatoes can be bought in 50 kg sacks.
- **a)** How much does a sack of potatoes weigh on the Earth?
- **b)** The Moon's gravitational field strength is 1.5 N/kg. How much would a sack of potatoes weigh on the Moon?

Free-fall acceleration

If you hold a 1p coin in one hand and a 10p coin in the other, and then let them go at the same time from the same height, you find that they reach the ground together. Releasing a coin and a sheet of paper together may not give the same result, unless you do it in a vacuum. In the absence of air resistance, all objects have the same free-fall acceleration, regardless of their mass.

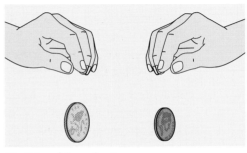

Fig 2 *Free-fall acceleration*

Fig 3 *Galileo's famous experiment – did he ever do it?*

This came as a revelation at the time of Galileo in the sixteenth century. In fact his proclamation that heavy objects do not fall faster than light objects cost him his job as professor of mathematics at the University of Pisa. However, Newton's work around 100 years later revealed a simple explanation: a 2 kg mass is twice as heavy as a 1 kg mass, so there is twice the pulling force acting on it from the Earth. But there is also twice as much mass to be accelerated, so as force = mass × acceleration the two masses should accelerate at the same rate.

Comparing the equations

force = mass × acceleration

and

weight = mass × gravitational field strength

for an object falling freely with no resistive forces acting, you can see that they are equivalent. Consequently 'gravitational field strength' and 'free-fall acceleration' are the same physical quantity, having the same value of 10 N/kg or 10 m/s^2.

Ideas and evidence

Galileo Galilei
As an old man, Galileo told the story of how, having failed to convince people by argument, he had dropped a large ball and a small ball from the top of the leaning tower of Pisa. Experimental proof was very rare in the sixteenth century, when scientific ideas were debated but not tested. Galileo reports that, due to the effects of air resistance, the large ball reached the ground fractionally ahead of the smaller one. Despite this demonstration, many people clung to the view that a heavy object falls at ten times the speed of one with only one-tenth of the weight.

ICT Extra!

Use data logging to measure free-fall acceleration.

Q3 **a)** Use the equation $W = mg$ to calculate the weight of a 5 kg mass and a 10 kg mass.

b) Now use $F = ma$ to calculate the acceleration of each mass due to the Earth's pull.

c) Explain why a feather does not have the same acceleration as a 50p coin when they are dropped together.

d) You may have seen the famous film where an astronaut on the Moon releases a hammer and a feather at the same time. Explain why they reach the ground together.

Fig 4 *An astronaut releasing a hammer and a feather on the Moon*

131 Turning forces

In this unit you will learn the answers to these questions:
- What are the factors that determine the turning effect of a force?
- How is the moment of a force calculated?
- What is the principle of moments?

We use forces to turn things round whenever we move an arm or a leg, cut with scissors or ride a bicycle. This unit is a study of how those forces are used to the best effect and how structures depend on the turning forces being balanced.

Turning round

You steer a bicycle with your hands placed at the end of the handlebars rather than near the middle, and when you push open a swing door it opens easily if you apply your push as far away from the hinge as possible. The effect that a force has in causing an object to move in a straight line depends on the size of the force. When forces are used to turn things round both the direction of the force and its point of action need to be considered.

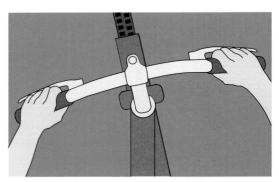

Fig 1 Using turning forces

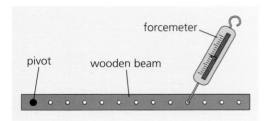

Fig 2 Experimenting with turning forces

Q1 List six everyday examples of forces being used to turn objects round.

Fig 2 shows how you can experiment by using a forcemeter to make a wooden beam turn round. You should try the effect of applying the force at different places and at different angles, measuring the force you need to turn the beam.

The results of this experiment show that the force has the greatest turning effect when it is applied as far away from the pivot as possible and at right angles to a line from the point of action to the pivot.

The measurement of the effectiveness of a force in causing rotation is called its **moment**. The moment of a force is calculated using the formula:

moment = force × perpendicular distance to pivot

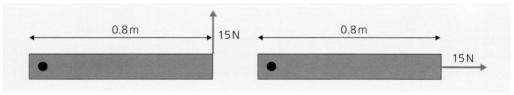

Fig 3 This force has the greatest turning effect   and this has no turning effect at all

The force shown on the left in Fig 3 has a moment of $15\,N \times 0.8\,m = 12\,Nm$. The moment of that on the right is 0 since the perpendicular distance from the force line to the pivot is zero.

Q2 Calculate the moments of the forces shown in Fig 4.

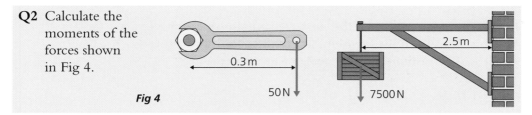

Fig 4

A question of balance

When we turn on a tap or pedal a bicycle, we want the forces we exert to rotate the tap or bicycle crank. Structures such as bridges and machines such as cranes have to be designed so that they are stable. This means that any force that has a turning effect has to be counterbalanced with a force that has an equal turning effect in the opposite direction.

The **principle of moments** applies to situations where there are two or more turning forces in balance. It states that:

> **when an object is in equilibrium the sum of the clockwise moments about a pivot must equal the sum of the anticlockwise moments.**

When you hold a drink in your hand there are two turning forces acting on your forearm, as shown in Fig 5. The weight of the drink has a clockwise moment that is counterbalanced by the upward pull of the biceps. Because the biceps are positioned very close to the pivot, they have to exert large forces to counterbalance the effect of forces at the hand. The principle of moments can be used to calculate the size of the force needed to counterbalance the weight of the drink. Each force has the same moment, so

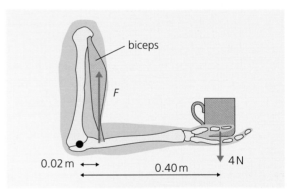

Fig 5 Turning forces acting on your forearm

$$F \times 0.02\,\text{m} = 4\,\text{N} \times 0.40\,\text{m}$$
$$F = \frac{(4\,\text{N} \times 0.40\,\text{m})}{0.02\,\text{m}}$$
$$F = 80\,\text{N}$$

Q3 a) There is another force, not shown in Fig 5, that has a turning effect on the forearm. Which force is missing from the diagram?

b) Taking this extra force into account, is the force from the biceps bigger or smaller than 80 N? Explain why.

Using levers

Levers use forces to turn things round. A lever used to remove a tight lid from a tin does so by **force magnification**. In this case the force exerted by the lever is much closer to the pivot then the force that the person exerts.

Other levers **magnify distance**. When an angler uses a fishing rod a small movement near the base of the rod produces a large movement of the fish.

Q4 The arm shown in Fig 5 is an example of a lever. Explain whether it magnifies force or distance.

132 **Sound reflections**

In this unit you will learn the answers to these questions:
- How do reflections of sound affect the acoustics of rooms?
- How is ultrasound used at sea and in medicine?

Hearing yourself speak

When you talk in a room that has been emptied of furniture, you can hear your voice make a 'ringing' sound. Without furniture in the room to absorb the energy of the sound, the large flat surfaces of the walls are excellent reflectors of sound waves. Like a ball bouncing between the walls, the sound is reflected several times before it becomes inaudible. The effect is known as **reverberation**. It can cause speech to sound unclear as each sound is mixed with echoes of sounds made a fraction of a second earlier. The control of reverberation is very important in large halls, particularly those

Fig 1 The acoustics of the Albert Hall have been improved by using large baffles in the ceiling. These absorb the sound, reducing the reverberation time

where music is played. If there is too much reverberation the music sounds 'fuzzy', but too little gives a 'flat' tone, as the individual notes do not blend into each other.

To separate a sound from its echo, a large distance is needed between the sound source and the reflecting surface. Since sound travels at a speed of approximately 330 m/s, a distance of 165 m between the source and the reflector gives a time interval of 1 s between making the sound and receiving the echo. Don't forget that the sound has to travel to the reflecting surface and back again, so at this separation the sound would travel a total distance of 165 m × 2 = 330 m.

Fig 2 Cliff faces make good reflecting surfaces for hearing your own echo

Q1 A boy, standing some distance from a large brick wall, shouts his name and hears the echo 0.6 s later.
  a) The speed of sound in air is 330 m/s. Use the speed equation from Unit 125 to calculate how far the sound travelled between the boy calling his name and hearing the echo.
  b) How far was the boy from the brick wall?

Using echoes

Echoes are used in many ways.

1 At sea to locate shoals of fish and wrecks on the sea bed.

2 By geologists to study the structure of the Earth and locate minerals.

3 By surgeons to study body organs.

Short bursts of high-frequency waves, called **ultrasound** because the frequency is above the human audible range, are used to search for shoals of fish and wrecks on the sea bed. Ultrasound is used because it enables a narrow beam of sound to be sent from a small source with very little spreading by diffraction (see Unit 139). The source is a crystal that vibrates at a very high frequency. The same crystal is also used to detect the reflected waves. Computer equipment can use the reflections to build up a picture of the sea bed or work out the depth of a shoal of fish.

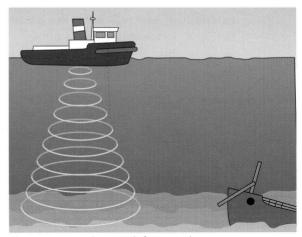

Fig 3 *Using sound to search for a wreck*

Q2 Sound travels in water at a speed of 1500 m/s. A pulse of sound is sent out from a ship and the echo from the sea bed returns 0.44 s later.
a) Use the speed equation to calculate the distance travelled by the sound.
b) How deep is the sea?
c) What would be noticed if a shoal of fish swam under the ship?

Sound in medicine

Ultrasound is used extensively by doctors and surgeons to 'see' inside the body without using X-rays. It is considered to be safer than X-rays because, provided a low power is used, there is no damage to body cells or tissue. Sound scans can be used to examine delicate organs such as the brain and the eye. Sound scans are routine for pregnant women to check on the size and development of the fetus. Fig 4 shows an ultrasound of a 12-week-old fetus in the womb.

The picture is built up by the reflection of ultrasound whenever there is a boundary between body tissues. In this case the fetus reflects more energy than the surrounding amniotic fluid does. The fetus shows up lighter than the fluid.

Q3 Describe the advantages of using ultrasound to scan body organs.

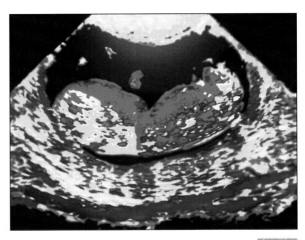

Fig 4 *An ultrasound scan of a fetus*

133 Reflecting light

In this unit you will learn the answers to these questions:
- How do surfaces reflect light?
- How does a plane mirror form an image?
- What are the properties of the image in a plane mirror?

In the last unit you studied how the reflection of sound is put to use. This unit examines how the reflection of light enables us to see, and how sometimes we see things that aren't there.

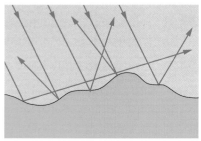

Fig 1 *Light is reflected in all directions by a rough surface*

Seeing

You can see the page of this book because of the way in which light is reflected. Light comes from light sources such as the Sun, flames and lamps. Surfaces that are not perfectly smooth scatter this light by reflecting it in all directions. The surface of this page may look smooth to you, but under a microscope it would appear rough, covered in small hills and valleys.

Fig 1 shows how a rough surface scatters the light that falls on it, making it possible for the light to be detected by eyes in different positions in a room.

Fig 2 *Everybody in the audience can see the band, because light from the lamps is reflected in all directions*

Regular reflection

Mirrors and other smooth surfaces reflect light in a regular and predictable way. The light is reflected from a mirror surface at the same angle as it hits it. Fig 3 shows two pairs of angles that are equal. The angles between the rays and a line drawn at right angles to the surface, marked *i* and *r*, are known as the **angle of incidence** and the **angle of reflection**.

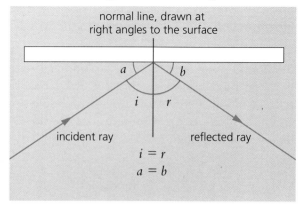

normal line, drawn at right angles to the surface

a *b*

i *r*

incident ray   reflected ray

$i = r$
$a = b$

Fig 3 *The angles of incidence and reflection*

> **Q1** Mirrors can be used in periscopes to turn light through 90°. Draw a diagram to show how two mirrors can be used to make a periscope. Trace the path of light as it passes through the periscope.

Images

When you look into a mirror, you see a likeness of yourself. This likeness is called an **image**. You also see images when looking at the picture on a television or cinema screen. Images do not have to be exact copies. That on a cinema screen is a **magnified** image and when you use a camera to take a photograph the image captured on the film is **diminished** (smaller than the object). The images made by projectors and cameras are upside down (inverted) and they are examples of **real** images. A real image is one that can be caught on a screen. If an image cannot be caught on a screen then it is **virtual**, it is not really there.

Fig 4 Using a convex lens

Fig 4 shows how you can use a convex lens to form a real image on a paper screen. Use the words in the paragraph above to write a description of the image.

The image in a mirror

Is the image in a mirror real or virtual? Upside down or upright? Magnified or diminished? Whereabouts is the image?

You may be able to answer some of these questions from your everyday experience of looking into mirrors. Fig 5 shows how you can use three **ray streaks** from a lamp to locate the position of the image formed by a plane mirror. Once you have found the position of the image, you can use a piece of paper as a screen to test whether the image is real or virtual.

The results of this experiment show that the image formed by a plane mirror is virtual, and it is formed straight behind the mirror, as far back as the object is in front. It is also upright and the same size as the object.

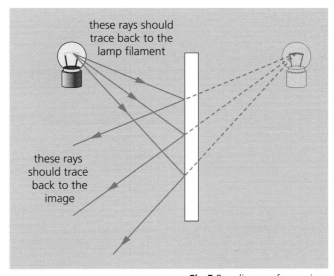

these rays should trace back to the lamp filament

these rays should trace back to the image

Fig 5 Ray diagram for a mirror

Q2 In tracing back the ray streaks to find the position of the lamp and the image of the lamp, what did you assume about the way in which light travels?

Q3 Windows and flat water surfaces act like mirrors. If you stand in a well–lit room and it is dark outside, you can see your image by looking through the window.
a) Draw a diagram to show where your image would be.
b) Explain why a person standing outside would not be able to see your image.

134 Different waves

In this unit you will learn the answers to these questions:
- How are sounds produced and transmitted through the air?
- What is the difference between a transverse wave and a longitudinal wave?
- How do waves transfer energy?

In Unit 132 you studied how sound can be reflected and how the reflections can be put to use. Sound, like light, travels as a wave motion. Waves transfer energy from one place to another without the need for any material to move between the two places. Compare the transfer of energy from the Sun to the Earth with that from a coal mine to a power station. In the case of the power station, the energy is concentrated in a material that has to be moved from the coal mine to transfer the energy.

In this unit you will study different types of wave motion and their similarities and differences.

Making sounds

All sounds are made by vibrating objects. You can see the vibrations of a loudspeaker in slow motion, using a signal generator set to a low frequency. The cone moves in and out repeatedly. Holding a piece of cling film stretched over a wire coathanger near to the loudspeaker shows the effect that the movement of the cone has on your eardrum. The movement from the loudspeaker to your eardrum is transmitted by vibrations of the air particles.

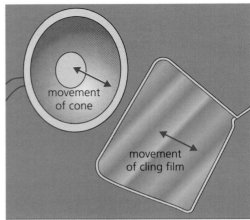

Fig 1 *Vibration of a loudspeaker*

Sound is an example of a **longitudinal wave**. The air particles transmit the wave by vibrating along the direction of wave travel. The air particles that transmit sound from a source such as a loudspeaker to your ear do not travel between the two points, they only vibrate. The vibrations of the air particles cause the air to be alternately squashed and stretched as the wave passes through.

A wave model

A slinky spring can be used to study a model of air transmitting sound. By pushing and pulling the spring in a to-and-fro movement, a longitudinal wave is sent along the spring. Each part of the spring vibrates in the direction of wave travel, causing a series of 'squashes' and 'stretches', or **compressions** and **rarefactions**, to travel along the spring.

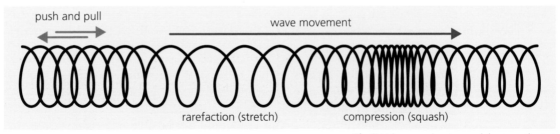

Fig 2 *Using a spring to model a sound wave*

Moving your hand further will increase the amplitude of the vibrations. The amplitude of a wave motion is the greatest displacement from the normal position. Fig 3 shows a vibration with an amplitude of 3 cm. This is much greater than the amplitude of vibration of air particles transmitting a sound, which can be just a few millionths of a metre.

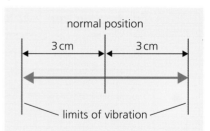

Fig 3

Q1 What is the effect on a sound when the amplitude of the vibrations of the loudspeaker cone is increased?

Q2 Name three sources of sound waves. For each source, describe the vibration and how the amplitude of the vibration can be changed.

ICT Extra!

Use CD-ROM software to find out about wave models.

Another type of wave

Sound and other longitudinal waves are compression waves. If you hit one end of a row of iron railings the sound is transmitted by vibrations of the particles causing alternate compressions and rarefactions to travel through the material.

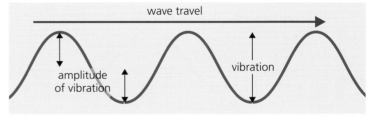

Fig 4 Vibrations of a transverse wave

Surface water waves, light, radio and other electromagnetic waves (see Unit 139) are transverse waves. In a **transverse wave** the vibrations are perpendicular to the direction of travel. A rope or a slinky spring can be used to study the vibration of a transverse wave. Fig 4 shows the vibrations of a transverse wave.

Radio and television signals are carried using transverse waves where the vibration is restricted to one plane, usually vertical or horizontal. The transverse waves from a light source such as the Sun or a lamp have vibrations in all possible directions that are perpendicular to the wave travel. Fig 5 shows the difference between the vibrations of a radio wave and those of light.

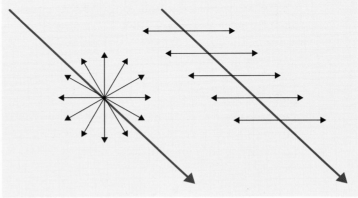

Fig 5 The vibrations of a light wave   *and those of a radio wave*

Q3 Television and radio aerials detect the signal using a pair of metal rods, called a dipole. Aerials are mounted either horizontally or vertically. Suggest why it is important that aerials are mounted in a particular direction.

135 **Wave measurements**

In this unit you will learn the answers to these questions:
- What is the meaning of wavelength and frequency?
- How is the wave equation used to calculate wave speed, wavelength and frequency?

The difference between longitudinal and transverse waves was studied in Unit 134, where you also learned that the amplitude of a wave motion is the measurement of the greatest displacement from the mean position. In this unit you will study other measurements used to describe waves and how these are related to the speed of a wave.

The long and short of it

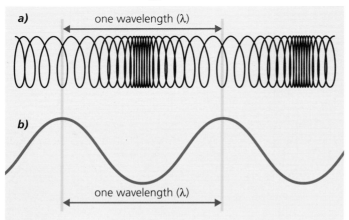

Fig 1 Wavelengths of *a)* longitudinal and *b)* transverse waves

A wave motion is a repetitive motion. A longitudinal wave consists of compression followed by rarefaction, then another compression, and so on. Transverse waves are similar. They consist of a wave peak, then a trough, followed by another peak. One complete cycle is a compression and rarefaction in the case of a longitudinal wave, and a peak and trough in the case of a transverse wave. The whole wave motion is formed by repetitions of this cycle.

The **wavelength** of a wave motion (symbol λ) is the distance from the beginning to the end of one complete cycle of the wave. Fig 1 shows how to measure the wavelength of a longitudinal wave and a transverse wave.

The wavelength of sound ranges from a few centimetres to several metres, but is typically around 1 metre. Light has a wavelength of approximately half a millionth of a metre and the wavelength of radio waves used for broadcasting varies from three metres (VHF) to two thousand metres (long wave).

How often?

The **frequency** of a wave (symbol f) is the number of cycles of the wave that go past any point each second. It is measured in hertz (Hz). Audible sounds range in frequency from approximately 20 Hz to 20 000 Hz. Using the arrangement shown in Unit 134, Fig 1, you can watch the effect on the loudspeaker cone when the frequency of the a.c. supply is increased.

> **Q1** How does increasing the frequency affect the pitch of a sound?

The effect on the wavelength when the frequency of a wave motion is increased can be studied using a slinky spring or rope. Fig 2 shows two waves travelling at the same speed in a rope. You can see that when the frequency of the wave is increased, the wavelength gets shorter.

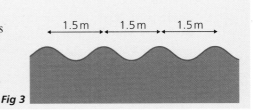

a wave on a rope   a higher frequency wave

Fig 2

High-pitched sounds have a higher frequency and shorter wavelength than low-pitched ones. Light also varies in frequency and wavelength. Blue light has a higher frequency than red light. When they are travelling at the same speed the wavelength of blue light is shorter than that of red.

The wave equation

A wave motion is a repetition of a cycle of compression and rarefaction for a longitudinal wave, or crest and trough for a transverse wave.

Q2 Imagine that you are watching a wave motion such as a surface water wave. The frequency of the wave motion is 3 Hz, which means that three complete waves pass each second. If the wavelength is 1.5 m, what is the speed of the wave? Fig 3 should help you to answer this. It shows the waves that go past in one second. **Fig 3**

The total length of the waves passing each second is 4.5 m, so the speed of the wave motion is 4.5 m/s. The speed of any wave can be calculated by multiplying the length of each wave (the wavelength) by the number of waves per second (the frequency). This is known as the wave equation:

> **wave speed = frequency × wavelength**
> **or $v = f \times \lambda$**

Here are two examples of using the wave equation:

Example 1

A wave transmitted along a spring has a wavelength of 0.8 m and a frequency of 5 Hz. Calculate the speed of the wave.

Answer

$$v = f \times \lambda$$
$$= 5\,\text{Hz} \times 0.8\,\text{m}$$
$$\text{speed} = 4\,\text{m/s}$$

Example 2

The speed of sound in air is approximately 330 m/s. Calculate the wavelength of middle C, which has a frequency of 256 Hz.

Answer

First the equation has to be rearranged to:

$$\lambda = v \div f$$
$$= 330\,\text{m/s} \div 256\,\text{Hz}$$
$$\text{wavelength} = 1.29\,\text{m}$$

Q3 Use the wave equation to work out the missing quantity in each line of the table.

	Wave speed/m per s	Frequency/Hz	Wavelength/m
a		6	3.5
b	1200	40	
c	600		1.25
d		660	0.5
e	5	10	
f	1800		0.2

136 Refraction of light

In this unit you will learn the answers to these questions:
■ What happens when a wave crosses a boundary?
■ When does a change of speed result in a change of wave direction?
■ How does refraction cause virtual images to be formed?

We see using our eyes as detectors and brains to process the information. The eye–brain system assumes that light travels in straight lines. In Unit 133 you saw how this causes the brain to 'see' things that aren't really there when we look at a virtual image in a mirror. This unit is concerned with virtual images formed when light passes from one substance to another.

Changing the speed

Whenever a wave passes from one substance into another, there is a change of speed. The consequences of this speed change can be seen by studying water waves in a ripple tank. Fig 1 shows what happens when water waves are slowed down as they pass into a shallow water region.

Notice how the parts of the waves in the shallow water lag behind those travelling in the deeper water. This change in wave speed is called **refraction**. When the waves emerge from the shallow water they speed up again.

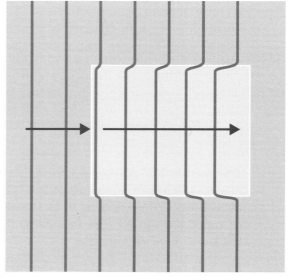

Fig 1 *Using a ripple tank*

Q1 a) The frequency of the waves in the shallow water is the same as that in the deeper water. Describe what happens to the wavelength of the waves when they enter the shallow water.
   b) On a copy of Fig 1, complete the picture by drawing the waves as they speed up when they emerge from the shallow water.

When the waves meet the shallow water region at an angle each wave is slowed down progressively, rather than all at once, and the waves change direction. Fig 2 shows the change in direction of water waves as they enter and leave a shallow water region.

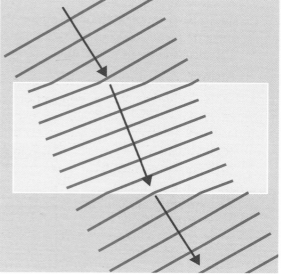

Fig 2 *Refraction causes waves to change direction*

Refracting light

You can use a block of glass or container of water to study the effect of light being slowed down as it passes from air into the water or glass. The change in direction of the light depends on the angle at which it meets the surface. For the same angle of incidence, glass causes a greater change in direction than water does. Fig 3 shows these changes. You will also notice that some light is reflected at each boundary.

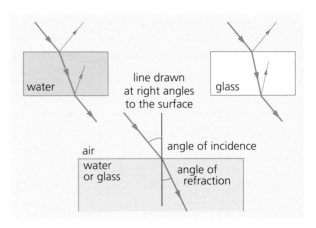

Fig 3 *Refraction in water and glass*

The lower diagram in Fig 3 shows the angles of incidence and refraction drawn relative to a normal line (a line drawn at right angles to the surface). The change in direction is towards this normal line when the light slows down and away from it when the light speeds up.

Image formation

If you look at the bottom of a swimming pool while standing on the poolside, the pool looks to be shallower than it really is. You can see the same effect if you examine the printing in this book, looking at it through a glass block or a beaker of water. Fig 4 shows how you can locate the image formed when light passes through glass.

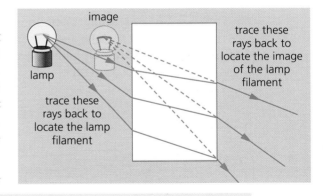

Fig 4 *Ray diagram for a block of glass*

Q2 a) Is the image formed by the glass real or virtual ? Explain how you can tell.
b) Choose words from the list to describe the other properties of the image formed by glass. *diminished inverted magnified same size upright*

The change in direction as light leaves water or glass can be used to explain why the bottom of the swimming pool appears to be nearer than it really is. As light leaves the water it changes direction, moving away from a line drawn at right angles to the water surface. Fig 5 shows how this leads to the formation of a virtual image.

Q3 Imagine that you are swimming under water, looking at someone standing at the poolside. Draw a diagram to show how light from the person would reach your eye. Whereabouts would the person look to be?

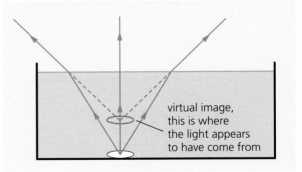

Fig 5 *Refraction produces a virtual image*

285

137 Using total internal reflection

In this unit you will learn the answers to these questions:
- When is light totally internally reflected at a boundary?
- What is total internal reflection used for?

In Unit 136 you studied how a change in speed when light passes from one substance to another can cause the light to change direction and how this leads to the formation of virtual images. This unit starts with a study of another phenomenon that can occur at the boundary between two substances and looks at some of the uses made of this effect.

Light getting faster

When light passes from a transparent substance such as glass or perspex into air, it speeds up. Unless the light hits the boundary at 90°, this change in speed causes a change in direction. As always when a wave passes from one substance to another, some of the light is reflected at equal angles. This is shown in Unit 136, Fig 3.

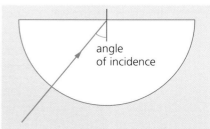

Fig 1

Using a semicircular glass or perspex block allows you to investigate this effect by changing the angle at which the light meets the glass–air (or perspex–air) boundary. Fig 1 shows a suitable arrangement. Provided the light is aimed at the centre of the flat face of the semicircle, it does not change direction as it enters the block. This arrangement enables you to vary the angle of incidence of the light at the glass–air boundary in the range 0° to 90°.

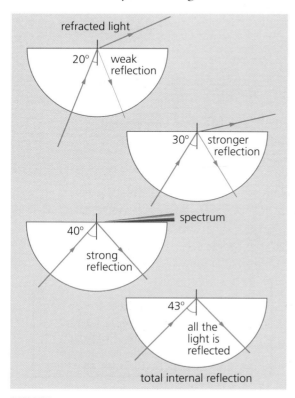

Fig 2 Showing total internal reflection

In doing this experiment, you should pay particular attention to changes that occur to both the light leaving the block and the light reflected as you change the angle of incidence. Fig 2 illustrates some typical results.

For small angles of incidence most of the light leaves the block by refraction, but some is reflected internally. As the angle of incidence is increased, the proportion of the light reflected increases and there is a reduction in the brightness of the refracted light. At an angle of incidence of around 40° the reflected light is very bright and the dim refracted light splits into a spectrum. When light only just emerges by refraction the angle of incidence is called the **critical angle**. For angles of incidence greater than the critical angle, around 42° for glass and perspex, all the light is reflected internally. This is known as **total internal reflection** (TIR).

Seeing round corners

Periscopes, bicycle reflectors and binoculars all use 45°-45°-90° prisms to turn light through an angle of 90° or 180°. Bicycle reflectors consist of hundreds of these prisms made as a single moulding. Fig 3 shows how light enters a prism and undergoes two internal reflections, each one at an angle of incidence that is greater than the critical angle. At each reflection the light is turned through an angle of 90°. So the result is that light from the headlamps of a car travelling behind the cyclist is reflected back to the car driver.

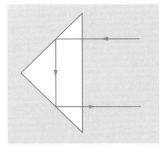

Fig 3 *Ray diagram for a prism*

Q1 a) On a copy of Fig 3, mark in the angles of incidence and reflection at the first internal reflection.

b) Explain how the light is turned through 90° at each reflection.

Q2 Fig 4 shows the arrangement of two prisms in a periscope. On a copy of the diagram, trace the path of two rays of light from the ship, through the periscope, and into the eye.

Fig 4 *Using prisms in a periscope*

Fibre optics

A thin fibre of glass or plastic can be used to transmit light round bends and corners with very little energy loss. In a simple fibre, whenever the light hits the boundary it does so at an angle that is greater than the critical angle, so all the light is reflected back into the fibre. Fig 5 shows how light can travel round a bend in a fibre by travelling in a series of straight lines.

More complex fibres are designed so that the light travels along the core of the fibre and never meets the sides. Fibres like this have many uses. Some of the more important ones are in communications (see Unit 141) and in medicine.

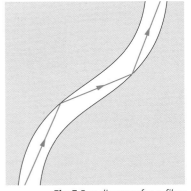

Fig 5 *Ray diagram for a fibre*

Optical fibres are used by surgeons to see inside the body using natural openings such as the mouth or anus or small incisions made for the purpose. You may have seen video programmes of the internal workings of the body made using optical fibres. Such an instrument used for medical purposes is called an **endoscope**. It consists of two bundles of fibres. One carries light into the body, the other transmits the reflected light to a small camera which then displays the picture onto a monitor like a television screen.

Endoscopes allow surgeons to detect problems that would have have required major surgery. They also allow some illnesses to be treated using microsurgery techniques that do not require large incisions to be made. This enables the patient to make a speedier recovery than would have been possible using traditional techniques.

Q3 Describe the benefits that endoscopy has brought to medicine.

287

138 A family of waves

In this unit you will learn the answers to these questions:
- Where does each type of electromagnetic radiation occur within the spectrum?
- When does diffraction of waves occur?

When white light passes through water droplets, the colours are split into a rainbow, or spectrum. A spectrum of visible light can be obtained by sorting the waves that make up white light into an order according to wavelength and frequency. Visible light is only a small part of a large spectrum of waves that have some similar properties and some important differences. In this unit you will learn about the properties of electromagnetic waves. Subsequent units will examine some of the uses of waves from different parts of the electromagnetic spectrum.

The visible spectrum

The visible part of the electromagnetic spectrum ranges from red to a deep blue or violet colour. The colour that light appears to the eye depends on the frequency of the wave motion. Blue light has a higher frequency than red light. In a vacuum, light (and other forms of electromagnetic radiation) travels at a speed of $300\,000\,000$ m/s, usually written as 3×10^8 m/s. When light changes speed as it passes through different substances the frequency does not change, only the wavelength changes. Fig 1 shows the range of frequency of the visible spectrum and the wavelength for light travelling in air or a vacuum.

	red	orange	yellow	green	cyan	blue	violet
frequency / 10^{14} Hz	4.3	5.0		6.0	6.7		7.5
wavelength / 10^{-6} m	0.7	0.6		0.5	0.45		0.4

Fig 1 The visible spectrum

Q1 The speed of light in glass is 2×10^8 m/s. Use the frequencies given in Fig 1 and the wave equation (see Unit 135) to calculate the wavelengths of red and violet light when passing through glass.

The whole family

You can see from Fig 1 that the electromagnetic radiation detected by our eyes extends over a narrow range of frequencies and wavelengths. The whole electromagnetic spectrum covers a vast range of wavelengths and frequencies. Radio waves have the longest wavelength, extending up to thousands of metres. At the opposite end of the spectrum, X-rays and gamma rays can have wavelengths shorter than a millionth of a millionth of a metre (1×10^{-12} m).

Apart from the waves already mentioned, the whole family also includes infrared and ultraviolet radiation, as well as microwaves. Fig 2 shows the position of each type of wave in the spectrum and the range of frequencies and wavelengths. The wavelengths apply to waves travelling in air or a vacuum.

frequency / Hz	10^{20}	10^{17}	10^{14}	10^{11}	10^8	10^5
	gamma rays	ultraviolet	infrared		radio waves	
	X-rays		light	microwaves		
wavelength / m	10^{-12}	10^{-9}	10^{-6}	10^{-3}	1	10^3

Fig 2 The electromagnetic spectrum

Q2 a) Which type of wave has a wavelength shorter than microwaves but longer than light?
b) Which type of wave has a wavelength just beyond the shortest wavelength of the visible spectrum?

ICT Extra!

Use the Internet and CD–ROM software to find out information about uses of the different waves in the electromagnetic spectrum.

Family trends

All electromagnetic waves are transverse waves, they can all be reflected and refracted and they travel at the same speed in a vacuum. The most dangerous to humans are those with a wavelength shorter than that of light. Short wavelength electromagnetic radiation has a higher energy and can be more penetrative than longer wavelength radiation. Another property that varies according to wavelength is diffraction.

Diffraction is the spreading out of waves when they pass the edge of an obstacle or pass through a gap. It is not restricted to electromagnetic waves. Sound waves can be diffracted, as can water waves. Fig 3 shows what happens when surface water waves in a ripple tank pass through gaps of different sizes.

The maximum spreading occurs when the gap is the same size as the wavelength. There is less spreading when the gap is several wavelengths wide. Very little spreading out occurs when waves pass through a gap that is many wavelengths wide.

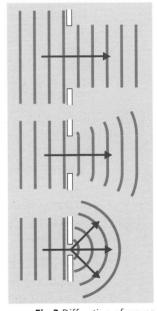

Fig 3 Diffraction of waves

Visible light has a very small wavelength, around $0.5\,\mu m$ ($1\,\mu m = 1 \times 10^{-6}\,m$ or 1 millionth of a metre), so the effects of diffraction can only be observed when light passes through a very small gap. Diffraction is readily observed with radio waves, where the wavelength varies from a few metres (VHF) to thousands of metres (long wave). Long wave radio signals are diffracted as they pass through gaps between buildings and over hills, causing them to spread out. VHF signals do not spread out so easily, making VHF reception more difficult in hilly areas.

Q3 A typical sound wave has a wavelength of around 1 m and a typical light wave has a wavelength of around $0.5\,\mu m$ ($0.5 \times 10^{-6}\,m$). Explain why sound spreads out when it passes through an opening such as a doorway but light does not.

139 At home with waves

In this unit you will learn the answer to this question:
■ **What are the uses and dangers of microwave, infrared and ultraviolet radiation?**

In Unit 138 you studied the electromagnetic spectrum and the similarities and differences between the waves in different parts of the spectrum. The next two units are concerned with the uses and dangers of electromagnetic radiation.

Cooking by radio

Microwaves are short-wavelength, high-frequency radio waves. Microwave cookers generate radio waves at a frequency of around 2500 MHz (2.5×10^9 Hz). Radio waves of this frequency are readily absorbed by water and salt particles in food. As these particles absorb the energy, they become heated and vibrate with a bigger amplitude. Some of the energy is passed on to neighbouring particles, so all the food becomes hot.

Fig 1 shows the inside of a microwave cooker. The microwaves enter from the top of the oven, which has metal sides to reflect any waves that hit them back into the oven. Without the paddle or rotating turntable some parts of the oven would have more energy than others. Microwave cookers use either a paddle to move the wave pattern about or a rotating turntable so that all

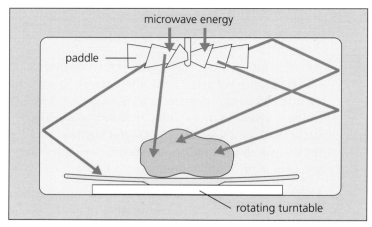

Fig 1 A microwave cooker

parts of the food move through the regions of high and low energy. The glass door of a microwave cooker contains a metal grid which is a good reflector of microwaves.

When food is heated in a conventional oven or in boiling water, the outer layer is heated and the energy is transferred through the food by conduction. This can be a slow process, giving cooking times of 15–20 minutes for vegetables in boiling water and up to 2 hours or more for a family-sized joint of meat. Microwaves heat food more quickly because they can penetrate several centimetres before being absorbed, so the food cooks uniformly throughout. Cooking times for vegetables are reduced to a few minutes.

Another advantage of microwaves is their ability to defrost food rapidly without cooking it, so food can be taken from a freezer and prepared immediately.

Q1 Like all electromagnetic waves, microwaves have a speed in air of 3×10^8 m/s. Calculate the wavelength of microwaves that have a frequency of 2500 MHz.

Q2 a) Explain how a metal grid prevents microwaves from travelling through the glass door.
b) Why is it important that microwaves do not leave the cooker?

Using infrared

Infrared radiation is the name given to electromagnetic radiation with a wavelength longer than light, but shorter than microwaves. We use infrared radiation at home for cooking, heating and operating devices such as televisions and hi-fi by remote control.

All objects give out infrared radiation – the hotter the object the more radiation it gives out. Thermograms use the infrared radiation given out

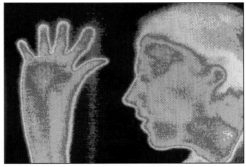

Fig 2 A thermogram

by the body to take a picture. Abnormally warm regions which are caused by cancers and tumours show up as a different colour to normal tissue.

> **Q3** Wrapping hot objects in aluminium foil reduces the energy loss through infrared radiation. What property of infrared radiation does this rely on?

Using ultraviolet

Ultraviolet radiation, although not visible, is commonly used in lighting. Fluorescent tubes pass a current through ionised mercury vapour. When this happens new ions are constantly being created and pairs of negative and positive ions recombine. Energy is given out as ultraviolet radiation when ions combine

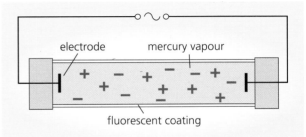

Fig 3 A fluorescent tube

together. This ultraviolet radiation is absorbed by the coating on the inner glass wall of a fluorescent light and is re-emitted as light. Fig 3 shows a fluorescent tube.

Fluorescent lamps are more efficient than ordinary filament lamps. Because they do not rely on heating, there is less energy loss when the lamp is operating. The energy-efficient lamp shown in Fig 4 is a fluorescent tube in a coil.

Sunbeds use mercury vapour lamps without the fluorescent coating, so they emit ultraviolet radiation. Exposure to ultraviolet radiation gives you a suntan, but it can also cause skin cancer, so sunbed-users should take care and limit their exposure to ultraviolet radiation. The increased occurrence of skin cancer is attributed to the fact that more ultraviolet radiation from the Sun reaches us as the ozone layer becomes more depleted.

Fig 4 An energy-efficient lamp

> **Q4** Mercury vapour is a poisonous substance if inhaled. Explain why old fluorescent tubes should never be smashed and suggest how they should be disposed of.

140 Communications

In this unit you will learn the answer to this question:
■ What are the uses of radio waves, microwaves and light in communications?

Electromagnetic waves are fundamental to many aspects of our everyday lives. In the previous unit you studied some uses of microwave, ultraviolet and infrared radiation. This unit examines the use of electromagnetic waves in communications.

Listening to the radio (or watching TV)

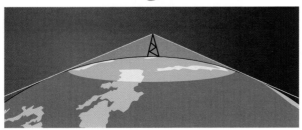

Fig 1 *The lighter shaded area shows where the signal transmitted by the aerial can be detected*

Some radio stations broadcast over a small area but the television channels and many radio stations are broadcast to the whole nation. The way in which radio waves travel depends on their wavelength. Long wavelengths follow the Earth's curvature and can be detected hundreds of miles from the transmitter. However, more information can be transmitted by shorter wavelength, higher frequency waves. The VHF waves used for broadcasting stereo radio have a wavelength of around 3 m and those used for television have a wavelength of around 0.6 m. At these short wavelengths, the waves travel in straight lines. Fig 1 shows that the effect of the Earth's curvature limits the range of these signals. An aerial which is 100 m above ground level has a range of about 35 km, though aerials are often positioned on hilltops to increase this range.

Fig 2 *Microwave dishes on BT tower*

National broadcasts originate from the BT tower in London. They are carried by waves of even shorter wavelength, waves that are in the microwave region of the electromagnetic spectrum. The microwaves are in narrow beams that are passed through a network of repeater stations. At each repeater station the signal is amplified before being passed on to other stations.

The dish behind the transmitting aerial focuses the microwaves into a narrow beam. Diffraction occurs at the dish in a similar way to diffraction when waves pass through a gap. To minimise the effects of diffraction the dish needs to be many wavelengths wide, which is why short wavelength microwaves are used.

Fig 3 *A repeater station*

Q1 Use the information given above, and the speed of electromagnetic radiation given in Unit 139, to calculate the frequency of a television broadcast that has a wavelength of 0.6 m.

The final stage in the journey occurs at your local transmitting station. Here the information from the microwaves is transferred onto waves that your radio or television set can detect. Unlike the repeater stations, which transmit waves in narrow beams to other stations, a transmitter broadcasts the waves in all directions.

> **Q2** To minimise diffraction effects when microwaves are transmitted, the diameter of the dish needs to be about one hundred times the wavelength being used.
> **a)** Explain why television broadcasts from the BT tower do not use the same wavelength that your television set detects.
> **b)** Suggest a suitable wavelength for the microwaves.

Analogue or digital?

Digital signals are replacing analogue signals for all types of communication. In an analogue signal the amplitude or frequency varies continuously with time, but a digital signal has only two possible values, 'on' or 'off'. Fig 4 shows an analogue and a digital signal. Digital signals have two major advantages over analogue ones. Although they become distorted and pick up 'noise' just like analogue signals, they can easily be cleaned up and restored to their original quality. They can also be used to carry more information at the same time.

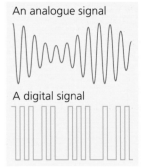

An analogue signal

A digital signal

Fig 4

Making a telephone call

Increasingly, glass fibres are being used for long-distance telephone links. These have several advantages. Very pure glass can carry signals for long distances before the signal needs to be amplified, and they are not affected by geography in the same way that hills can disrupt microwave transmissions. The cables can be easily installed, linking centres of population by laying them alongside railway lines or on the beds of canals. Fibres carry the signals in a digital form, as a series of pulses of laser light. Lasers give out light of a single wavelength so all the light travels at the same speed along the fibre. Fig 5 illustrates a long-distance telephone call being sent along a fibre.

As Fig 5 shows, the digital signal becomes distorted as it travels. This is due to some parts of the pulse travelling further than others as the cable goes round corners and as parts of the pulse are reflected at the edges of the fibre.

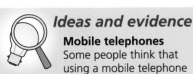

Ideas and evidence

Mobile telephones
Some people think that using a mobile telephone can cause brain damage. This could be due to the absorption of the microwave radiation emitted by these telephones, which has a power of about 1 W. Scientists cannot be sure whether microwave radiation at this level can damage brain cells, and they are not able to carry out experiments to find out the answer. However, the public debate has caused mobile telephone manufacturers to develop new telephones that emit much less microwave radiation.

copper link

telephone exchange

telephone exchange

copper link

Fig 5 A long-distance telephone call

> **Q3** Pulses of white light are sent along an optical fibre. Red light travels faster than blue light in glass. Explain what happens to the pulses and sketch what a pulse would look like after travelling some distance along the fibre.

141 Using X-rays and gamma rays

In this unit you will learn the answer to this question:
■ How are X-rays and gamma rays used in medicine?

In previous units you have learned about uses of long- and mid-wavelength electromagnetic waves. You learned when studying the electromagnetic spectrum that X-rays and gamma rays are both at the short-wavelength end of the spectrum. X-rays and gamma rays differ only in their origin. X-rays come from X-ray tubes and gamma rays come from unstable nuclei. Short-wavelength electromagnetic radiation can have damaging effects on human tissue and it needs to be used with care. In this unit you will study some benefits of X-rays and gamma rays and learn about precautions that need to be taken to avoid unnecessary hazards.

X-ray pictures and X-ray therapy

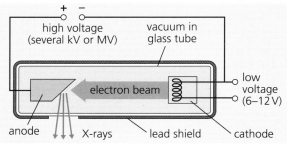

Fig 1 Producing X-rays

X-rays are produced by firing high-speed electrons at a metal target, as shown in Fig 1. Although X-rays are absorbed to some extent by all body tissue, bone absorbs more X-ray energy than flesh does.

X-ray pictures are not taken like a normal photograph, which uses light reflected from objects into the camera. X-rays are passed through the body, forming an image on a photographic plate or fluorescent screen. Fig 2 shows a radiographer examining an X-ray plate. Notice how the bone shows up white on the black-and-white negative. The darker the area on the plate, the more X-radiation it has been exposed to.

When X-rays are absorbed by body tissue, they can cause ionisation by removing electrons from atoms. This can damage molecules that control vital aspects of a cell's behaviour or, if water molecules are ionised, cause the production of hydrogen peroxide which can damage or destroy parts of the cell. The effects on the body of exposure to X-radiation include gene mutations,

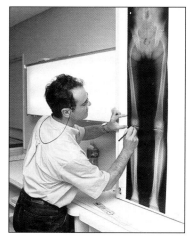

Fig 2 Examining an X-ray

damage to the central nervous system and cancer. For safety, exposure to X-radiation and other forms of ionising radiation is kept to a minimum. Radiographers who operate X-ray equipment do so from behind a lead screen and lead is also used to protect parts of the subject's body that are not being X-rayed.

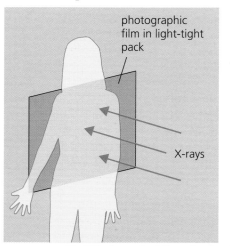

Fig 3 Having a chest X-ray (lead protection not shown)

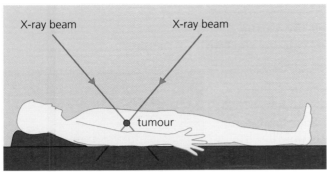

Fig 4 *Using X-rays in cancer treatment*

As well as causing cancer, X-rays can be used to destroy cancer cells. Cancer cells absorb more energy from an X-ray beam than healthy cells do. Fig 4 shows how the body is exposed to X-ray beams from several directions which overlap at the area being treated. This ensures that the cancer receives a high dose of X-rays but the surrounding tissue only gets a low dose.

> **Q1** The X-rays used to kill cancer cells are of shorter wavelength than those used to take X-ray photographs. Explain why long-wavelength X-rays are used for photographs but short-wavelength X-rays are used for therapy.

Using gamma rays to trace and treat

Like X-rays, **gamma rays** can be used to treat cancers. Gamma rays emitted from cobalt-60 are used in a similar way to the X-rays shown in Fig 4.

Another way in which gamma rays are used to treat cancers is by using sources inside the body. The body sends certain chemicals to particular organs and this can be used to concentrate radioactive materials in a chosen part of the body. Cancers of the thyroid can be treated using iodine-131, which emits both beta and gamma radiation when it decays. In this treatment the patient drinks a solution containing the isotope and the body sends the iodine to the thyroid gland. Here it decays and the radiation emitted destroys cancer cells.

Gamma rays are more commonly used as tracers, to detect cancers, tumours or blood flow in various parts of the body. The isotope used is an unstable form of technetium-99. The isotope emits gamma radiation only and has a half-life of 6 hours. This is a particularly suitable half-life for a tracer, as it gives time for the isotope to reach its target while the activity is still high and it is also short enough so that the patient is not exposed to unnecessary radiation. By using technetium-99 in conjunction with other chemicals, it is possible to concentrate the radiation in a particular body organ.

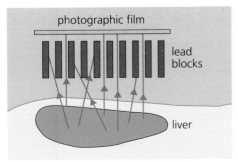

Fig 5 shows how a gamma camera is used to take a photograph of liver containing blood that has been made radioactive with technetium-99. The lead blocks absorb any gamma rays that are not parallel to them. This ensures that the image on the film corresponds to the part of the liver directly below it.

Fig 5 *Using gamma rays*

> **Q2** The technetium-99 used as a tracer only emits gamma radiation. Explain why it is important that tracers do not also emit alpha or beta radiation (see Unit 157).

142 **Earth waves**

In this unit you will learn the answers to these questions:
- ■ How are waves transmitted through the Earth?
- ■ What evidence do wave records provide for the Earth's structure?

In previous units you have studied how waves are reflected and refracted and the difference between longitudinal and transverse waves. In this unit you will study how these properties of waves passing through the Earth provide evidence of the Earth's structure.

Fig 1 Lava from a volcano

Below the surface

Evidence for the Earth's structure comes from various sources. Hot, molten lava flows out of volcanoes and also from cracks in the thin crust under the oceans. This lava comes from the mantle, the layer just below the crust.

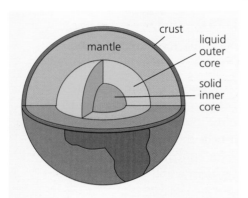

Fig 2 The layered structure of the Earth

If you could travel from the Earth's surface to its centre, you would first need to burrow through the crust. The best place to dig is under the ocean, where the crust can be as thin as 10 km. The thickest crust is 65 km deep and is found under mountains. Descending through the crust, you would notice a rapid rise in temperature. The Earth is still cooling down, five thousand million years after its formation, and it gets hotter as you approach the centre of the Earth. Heat is also being released from the decay of radioactive substances in the crust.

Having travelled through the crust, the next stage is the mantle, 3000 km of it! At first it is partially fluid, but you will soon hit solid rock that is denser than the crust. The end of the mantle marks the half-way stage of the journey; now you are ready to tackle the core. Don't forget that as well as the increase in temperature as you approach the centre of the Earth, the pressure from the weight of rock above you is also increasing. The core is very dense, and is probably liquid iron on the outside and solid iron in the middle. The fact that the iron is solid does not mean that it is cold. The temperature of the inner core is about 7000°C. Extremely high pressure at the centre of the Earth keeps the iron in a solid state. Fig 2 shows the layered structure of the Earth.

> **Q1** The crust and mantle are rich in the oxides of silicon, magnesium and aluminium. The core is mainly iron with some nickel. Describe and explain how the density of the Earth changes between the crust and the core.

The evidence

Large earthquakes hit the news headlines. Fortunately those that cause a lot of damage and loss of life are few and far between, but several minor earthquakes occur each day as layers of rock slip past each other. These cause shock waves to pass through the

Earth. All over the world, geologists are continually monitoring the shock waves from earthquakes using seismometers. A seismometer records movement of the Earth's surface as a trace on a revolving drum.

Seismometers can detect three types of wave that travel from the centre of an earthquake. Surface waves (called L waves because they are long wavelength) travel around the Earth's crust in both directions. Travelling in the least dense

Fig 3 A seismometer

part of the Earth, they are the slowest moving of the waves from an earthquake. The L waves from an earthquake cause damage to buildings as they make the ground move.

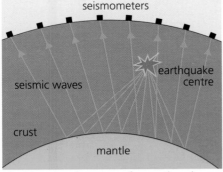

Fig 4 Locating the centre of an earthquake

Two types of wave travel through the body of the Earth, being partially reflected at boundaries between layers of material, and refracted as changes in density cause changes in speed. P (primary) waves are longitudinal waves. They are the fastest moving of the waves from earthquakes and they can travel through all parts of the Earth. S (secondary) waves are transverse. Slower travelling than the P waves, they are detected after them.

Transverse waves are not transmitted through the body of a liquid, and this causes a 'shadow', a region where S waves are not detected because they do not travel through the liquid outer core. This shadow provides the evidence that the outer core is liquid and enables its size to be measured.

Fig 4 shows how partial reflections of S and P waves at the boundary between the crust and the mantle enable the centre of an earthquake to be determined.

Some of the energy from the S and P waves is reflected at each boundary layer. The rest is refracted as it travels through the Earth, causing the waves to

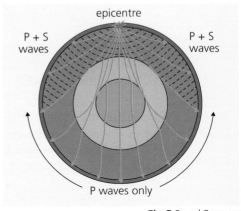

Fig 5 S and P waves

travel in curves. Fig 5 shows how S and P waves travel through the body of the Earth. A typical seismometer record of an earthquake is shown in Fig 6. This shows the P wave arriving first, followed by the S wave and last of all the L wave. By studying such records from different parts of the Earth, geologists can calculate the speed of the waves and work out what materials the waves have travelled through.

Q2 Whereabouts on the Earth's surface could the seismometer record shown in Fig 6 have been recorded?

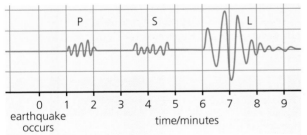

Fig 6 A seismometer record

143 **Plate tectonics**

In this unit you will learn the answers to these questions:
- ■ What are tectonic plates?
- ■ What happens at constructive and destructive plate margins?
- ■ How are rocks recycled?

The outer 100 km of the solid part of the earth is called the **lithosphere**; it consists of the crust and the upper part of the mantle. It is made up of a number of sections called **tectonic plates**, which are moving relative to each other at slow speeds, just a few centimetres a year. The movements of the plates is driven by the convection currents that flow in the mantle. These convection currents result from the energy generated by radioactive decay within the Earth.

Fig 1 shows the plates that cover the surface of the Earth.

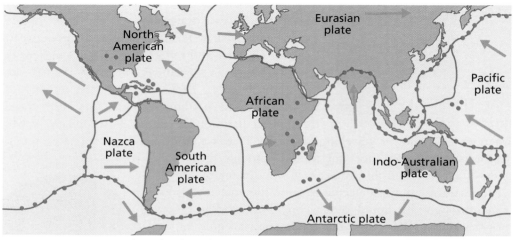

Fig 1 *The plates that cover the Earth's surface (earthquake sites shown by ● ● ● ●)*

Evidence for the existence and movement of the plates comes from the fact that the shapes of the major continents fit together like the pieces of a jigsaw puzzle, and that there are similar rock structures and common fossils found in the different continents. This suggests that they were once joined as shown in Fig 2.

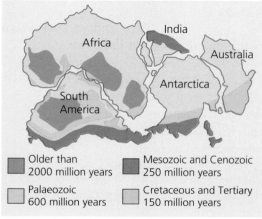

Older than 2000 million years
Palaeozoic 600 million years
Mesozoic and Cenozoic 250 million years
Cretaceous and Tertiary 150 million years

Fig 2 *The continents fitting together. Note the continuity of rocks across continents*

Ideas and evidence   Alfred Wegener

The theory of plate tectonics was first put forward by the German scientist Alfred Wegener in 1912. Prior to that it had been thought that changes in the Earth's crust were caused by contraction as the Earth cooled down. Wegener proposed that all the continents were once joined in a supercontinent in the southern hemisphere, which he called the Pangaea. Wegener's theory was at first rejected by many geologists, but is now widely accepted as more evidence has emerged to support it.

 ICT Extra!

Use simulation software to show the effects of the movement of tectonic plates.

Earthquakes

If you look back to Fig 1 you will notice that most earthquake sites exist on or near to the boundaries of plates. As plates attempt to move relative to each other, stresses and strains build up in the Earth's crust. When the stress and strain is sufficient to overcome the resistive forces and cause movement the result is an earthquake. The ground breaks as the Earth moves. These breaks in the ground are called faults. One famous fault is the San Andreas Fault in California.

Q1 Engineers sometimes try to prevent an earthquake by pumping large amounts of water into the Earth. Why do they do this?

Constructive plate margins

When two plates are moving apart, hot molten rock from the magma comes to the surface of the earth and forms new rocks. This is called a **constructive plate margin**. An important example of this is the submerged ocean ridge along the boundary of plates down the centre of the Atlantic Ocean. Fig 3 shows this constructive plate margin and the changes in magnetic field which accompany it.

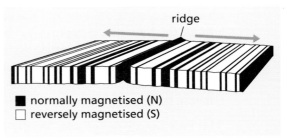

■ normally magnetised (N)
□ reversely magnetised (S)

Fig 3 A constructive plate margin

The magnetic field of the Earth is constantly changing. In the past 3.6 million years it has changed at least nine times. There are alternating bands of normal and reversed magnetism in the ocean floor. The pattern of magnetism is the same on both sides of the plate margin. When molten rock escapes from the magma and solidifies as rock, the internal magnetism of the rock lines up with the Earth's magnetic field and is fixed.

Q2 Why is the pattern of magnetism at a constructive plate boundary the same on both sides of the plate margin?

Destructive plate margins

When two plates collide the rocks are squeezed together. Fig 4 shows two plates moving together. One plate is a continental crust plate with an average density of 2.7 g/cm^3, the other plate is a thinner ocean floor plate which has a density of about 3.3 g/cm^3. The ocean floor plate is forced under the continental plate in a process known as **subducting** and melts back into the magma. This results in an ocean trench where the subducting occurs, and a parallel mountain chain due to the folding of layers of rock on the continental crust plate. When volcanoes in these mountains erupt they release magma melted in the subduction process.

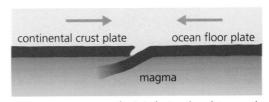

continental crust plate   ocean floor plate

magma

Fig 4 A destructive plate margin

Q3 Explain why the ocean floor plate moves under the continental crust plate.

Magma released from a volcano forms fine-grained rocks as it cools quickly. Cooling of magma deep below the surface results in coarse-grained rocks (see Unit 77). Metamorphic rocks are also formed at subduction zones, due to recrystallisation of rocks at regions of high temperature and pressure.

144 The Earth and the Universe

In this unit you will learn the answer to this question:
■ How are the planets and the Sun arranged in the Solar System?

The Earth is not an object of any great significance in the Universe. It is a small planet orbiting a small star on one of the spiral arms of the Milky Way galaxy, one of an uncountable number of galaxies that make up the Universe. This unit is about the planets in the Solar System.

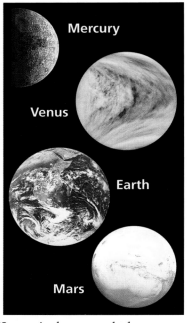

Fig 1 The inner planets

The inner planets

From a viewpoint way above the north pole of the Earth motion in the Solar System is mainly anticlockwise. Th nine known planets move in anticlockwise elliptical orbits around the Sun and, except for Venus, Uranus and probably Pluto, each planet spins anticlockwise about its own axis. Venus has a very slow clockwise spin. Uranus spins on its side, with one pole facing the Sun. Pluto and its moon, Charon, both spin around a common axis.

The four innermost planets are the dense planets. Looking out from the brilliant white **Sun**, the first planet to be seen is **Mercury**. Mercury has the greatest speed of all the planets and the shortest distance to travel to complete an orbit, so it races around the Sun. The further a planet is from the Sun, the slower it moves and the further it has to move to complete an orbit. Consequently, planetary years increase in length with increasing distance from the Sun.

Fig 2

The orange planet **Venus** is the second planet out. Then comes the blue planet **Earth** with its satellite, our Moon. The Earth's moon is similar in size to Mercury, and both have surfaces covered in craters. **Mars**, the red planet, is similar to Earth in some ways. They have similar length days and white clouds and, because of their tilt, they both have seasons.

Asteroids, fragments of rock ranging in size up to 100 km in diameter, orbit the Sun in a belt between the four inner planets and the five known outer ones. The asteroids are the 'left-overs' from the formation of the Solar System, five thousand million years ago. Some of them are large enough to have their own satellites in orbit around them.

> **Q1** Craters are the result of impacts with lumps of rock called meteors. Several meteors reach the Earth each day, but few of them reach the surface as they burn up in the atmosphere. Most of those that do reach the surface hit water rather than land. Neither Mercury nor the Earth's moon have an atmosphere. Explain why both are covered in impact craters and why many of these craters have been undisturbed for millions of years.

The outer planets

The five known outer planets lie beyond the asteroid belt. Our knowledge of **Jupiter** and **Saturn** is much greater now than 20 years ago because of pictures sent back to Earth from the Voyager space probes. Pluto is the only known planet that has not yet been visited by a space probe and so little is known about it.

Jupiter and Saturn are the largest planets in the Solar System, with Jupiter being more massive because of its greater density. Jupiter is more than three hundred times the mass of the Earth and it has sixteen moons. One remarkable feature of its atmosphere is the Great Red Spot, visible in the photo in Fig 3. Its moon Io has many active volcanoes, probably caused by the heating effect of the gravitational forces that act on it.

While the inner planets are dense and rocky, the outer, cooler planets are composed largely of gases and ice. Saturn, the sixth planet out from the Sun, has thousands of small rings made up of ice, dust and small pieces of rock. The yellow appearance of Saturn is due to its ammonia-rich atmosphere.

Uranus and **Neptune** are very similar in size and mass. Both have several moons in orbit around them. They are thought to have a rocky core surrounded by a liquid mantle and an outer atmosphere composed of hydrogen, helium and methane.

Little is known about **Pluto**, the ninth known planet. It has not yet been visited by a space probe and so there are no close-up pictures. Pluto is a tiny planet with a relatively large moon, Charon. Together they act as a double planet, turning around a common axis and always keeping the same face towards each other.

Ideas and evidence

The Starry Messenger

After building one of the world's first telescopes, in 1609, Galileo Galilei observed that there are mountains on the Moon. He later trained his telescope on Jupiter and discovered moons in orbit around the planet. This confirmed his belief in Copernicus' model of the 'World' (as it was then known), which pictured the Sun at the centre with the known planets in orbit around it. For fear of falling out with the teaching of the Catholic Church, Copernicus did not publish his ideas until he knew that he was about to die. Galileo, however, was far more bold. He published his observations and deductions in a book called *The Starry Messenger*, which was well received throughout Europe. This, and other publications, brought him into conflict with the Catholic Church, which taught that 'everything revolves around the Earth'. Galileo was subsequently imprisoned and later allowed to live under house arrest until he died. The Catholic Church finally admitted its mistake – in 1992!

Fig 3 *Four of the five known outer planets*

Q2 Taking the average distance from the Earth to the Sun as 1, the average distances for the other planets are: 5.2, 1.5, 0.4, 30, 39, 9.5, 19, 0.7.
  a) Match each of the distances to the correct planet.
  b) Construct a scale diagram showing the average distance from each planet to the Sun.

145 Gravitational forces

In this unit you will learn the answer to this question:
■ How do gravitational forces affect the motion of planets and comets?

In the last unit you studied the nature of the planets and their positions in the Solar System. This unit deals with the forces keeping the Solar System together and how these affect the motion of planets and comets.

Planetary orbits

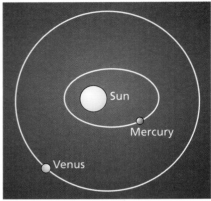

Moons orbit planets and planets orbit the Sun following paths that have the shape of an **ellipse**, or a squashed circle. For most planets and their satellites, the ellipses are very close to being circles. The exceptions are the innermost and outermost planets, Mercury and Pluto. Motion in a circle requires a constant pull or push towards the centre. In the case of planets and their satellites the force pulling the object towards the centre of the circle is the gravitational force. Gravitational forces are always attractive, they can only pull. They act between all objects, but they only have noticeable effects when one of the objects is very massive.

Fig 1 The path of Mercury is an ellipse but Venus follows an almost perfect circle

The size of the Sun's gravitational pull on a planet depends on the distance of the planet from the Sun and the mass of the planet. Jupiter is approximately five times as far from the Sun as the Earth is. Because of the way in which gravitational forces decrease with distance, the force pulling each kilogramme of the Earth towards the Sun is twenty-five times as big as the force pulling each kilogramme of Jupiter to the Sun. However, Jupiter is more than three hundred times as massive as the Earth so although the force on each kilogramme of Jupiter is smaller, the total force pulling Jupiter is bigger than that pulling the Earth.

The seven planets whose orbits are almost circular maintain an almost constant speed in their journeys around the Sun. The speed of a planet in its orbit depends only on its distance from the Sun. Venus has an average speed of 35 km/s, but that of Neptune is only 5.4 km/s. Mercury, being nearest the Sun, has the greatest average speed of all at 48 km/s but its speed varies considerably due to the shape of its orbit.

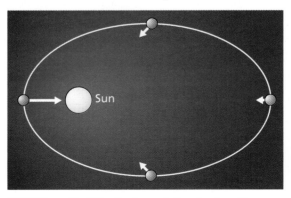

Fig 2 The Sun's gravitational pull on Mercury

Fig 2 shows how the Sun's gravitational pull on Mercury changes in size and direction as Mercury orbits our star. The changing gravitational force on Mercury causes it to speed up as it approaches the Sun and slow down again as its distance from the Sun increases.

Q1 Draw a diagram to show the Earth's gravitational force on the Moon as it orbits the Earth in a circular path.

Comets

Like the planets, comets orbit the Sun in elliptical paths but the ellipses are more elongated than that of any planet. The nucleus of a comet can be anything between 100 m and 10 km in size, and probably consists of frozen water and gases. Comets become visible when they are close enough to the Sun for the water and gases to be vaporised, forming a glowing head and a tail. Fig 3 shows the spectacular appearance of a comet as it passes close to the Sun.

Fig 3 *Comet West*

Although some comets have very short orbit times of a few Earth years and remain closer to the Sun than some planets in the Solar System, many comets have orbit times in excess of 200 years and spend most of their orbit travelling very slowly at great distances from the Sun. As a comet approaches the Sun the increasing gravitational pull causes it to speed up and it passes round the Sun very quickly, slowing down again as it moves further away. So fast is their passage close to the Sun that comets are usually only visible for a few weeks.

Unlike the planets, which all orbit the Sun in one plane, comets can orbit in any plane and any direction. A comet orbit is shown in Fig 4. Comets can sometimes be thrown off course by the gravitational pull of the planets as they pass close by. Most short-period comets are believed to have been long-period comets that were captured by Jupiter and now have orbits that only extend as far as Jupiter's orbit.

As comets pass within the realms of the Solar System, they leave behind them dust, gas and debris. The 'shooting stars' that can be seen in Britain on clear August nights are cometary debris burning up as they move through the Earth's atmosphere, being pulled towards the Earth by the effect of its gravitational field.

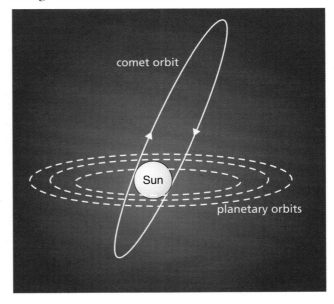

Fig 4 *Orbits of the planets and a comet*

Q2 Use a diagram to describe how the Sun's gravitational force on a comet changes during one orbit. Explain how the changing gravitational force affects the speed of a comet.

146 The life of a star

In this unit you will learn the answer to this question:
■ What are the main stages in the life cycle of a star?

The previous two units have been about the bodies orbiting the star of our Solar System, our Sun. In this unit you will study how stars are formed and the stages in the life cycle of a star.

The birth of a star

Our Sun is believed to be a relatively young star, a mere five thousand million years old. If you look into the sky on a clear night you will see the light from some very young stars that are only a few million years old. New stars are being formed all the time and old ones are coming to the end of their glowing days. Recent pictures from the Hubble telescope have increased our knowledge of how stars form.

Fig 1 The Horsehead Nebula is a large cloud of gas and dust in the constellation of Orion

Stars are born in enormous clouds of dust and hydrogen gas when the attractive gravitational forces between the particles in the cloud cause it to collapse. The contraction of the dust cloud causes heating and it develops a hot dense core. It also causes an increase in the rate at which the cloud spins, just as an ice-skater spins faster when she pulls her arms in. The core becomes hotter and may separate from the spinning cloud which then forms a disc in orbit around the core. It is likely that the planets in our Solar System were formed from such a spinning disc.

Nuclear reactions turn the core of the cloud into a star. The temperature becomes great enough for fast-moving hydrogen nuclei to **fuse** together, creating the nuclei of helium and releasing energy. The star is now in its **main sequence**. Very massive main sequence stars are so hot they appear blue.

Fig 2 The birth of a star and the formation of a planetary system

Death and rebirth

A very massive star may only stay in its main sequence for as little as ten million years before all the hydrogen in the core has fused to helium. The star starts to cool and expand and as it cools it changes colour to red. It is now a **red supergiant** and consists of a core of helium surrounded by a layer of hydrogen still fusing to form more helium, but at a lower temperature than before. As the core contracts under gravitational forces, it becomes hot enough for the helium nuclei to fuse together to form carbon and oxygen. Depending on the size of the star it may become a **white dwarf** or a **blue supergiant**.

In the case of a blue supergiant, after the helium has fused the star once more cools, becoming red and forming elements such as neon, magnesium, silicon and sulphur. Now layered like an onion, the star has the nuclei of heavy elements in the centre and those of lighter elements on the outside. Gravitational forces again cause the star to collapse. The resulting heating makes the star glow exceptionally brightly; it is now a **supernova**. When astronomers notice a sudden increase in the brightness of a star they know that the end is in sight. Intense heat generated as the star collapses causes an explosion. Some of the material made by the nuclear reactions is flung out to form a new **nebula** or dust cloud while the remaining material contracts to form a very dense **neutron star**.

Our Sun is a **second generation** star. It is believed to have formed from the nebula of a cloud of heavy elements, dust and hydrogen from the explosion of a supernova. When the cloud started to spin and separate into a core and a disc, the heavier elements formed the inner, dense planets and the lighter elements in the disc formed the outer planets. Because our Sun is a small star, it is not as hot as a blue supergiant and it is spending a long time in its main sequence. It is too small to ever become a blue supergiant. The likelihood is that after becoming a red giant it will contract, becoming first a white dwarf and finally a black dwarf as it cools and stops emitting light. Fig 3 shows the stages in the life cycle of a large, massive star.

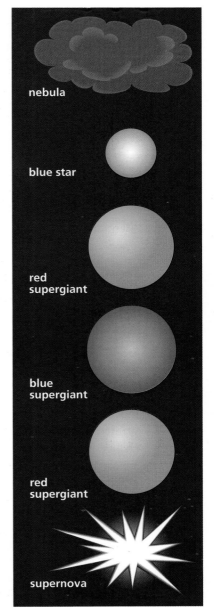

nebula

blue star

red supergiant

blue supergiant

red supergiant

supernova

Fig 3 *The life cycle of a star*

Q1 Suppose that you were watching the formation of our Sun and Solar System from the explosion of a supernova. Write a description of what you might have seen.

Q2 Explain why our Sun is called a second generation star.

147 Our galaxy and the Universe

In this unit you will learn the answer to this question:
- How does the 'big bang' model explain the state of the Universe?

So far in Units 144–146 you have studied the Solar System and the life cycle of stars. Astronomers are interested in what happened at the beginning of time and what will happen to the Universe in the rest of its lifetime. This unit looks out beyond the Solar System at the evidence for the past and the future.

Collections of stars

Just as the Solar System is a collection of objects held together by gravitational forces, stars exist in collections called **galaxies**. Our Sun is in the **Milky Way** galaxy, a vast collection of millions

Fig 1 The Milky Way galaxy, seen edge on

of stars and clouds of dust in the shape of a spiral that is whirling round. We are on one of the arms of the spiral, about two-thirds of the way out from the centre. Light from the centre of the Milky Way galaxy takes 26 000 years to reach us.

Fig 2 A spiral galaxy

Galaxies also exist in groups or clusters. Our galaxy is in a small group that also includes Andromeda and the Large and Small Magellanic Clouds. Large clusters can contain a thousand galaxies each, so the Universe must contain a lot of galaxies.

Astronomical evidence

You may have noticed that when a siren or aircraft is approaching you, the pitch of the note is higher than when it is going away. The frequency of the waves emitted becomes higher or lower because of the object's movement. This is known as the **Doppler effect**. One common use of the Doppler effect is in police radar 'speed traps' where the speed of a vehicle is measured by the change in frequency of radio waves reflected from it.

In a similar way, the frequency of the light we detect from a star is affected by the movement of the star. When stars are moving away from us the frequency of the light that we detect is lower than that emitted. The effect is called '**red shift**' because, although the change in frequency is not enough to make the light appear red, it moves the light towards the red end of the visible spectrum.

Measurements of the amount of red shift enable astronomers to work out the speed at which stars and galaxies are moving away from the Earth. 70 years ago Edwin Hubble, by measuring the red shift of light from distant galaxies, noticed that all the galaxies are moving away from each other, and the most distant galaxies are moving at the greatest speed.

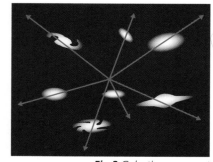

Fig 3 Galactic movement

The beginning of time

Hubble's observations of the movement of galaxies support the '**big bang**' theory of the origin of the Universe. According to this model, the Universe began in an enormous explosion, creating the matter that has since formed into stars, planets and clouds of dust and hydrogen. Since the explosion, the Universe has been expanding and cooling. When the movement of galaxies is traced back, they seem to have all originated in the same place (see Fig 3). Other evidence for the 'big bang' theory is provided by the microwave energy that fills space. This is believed to be radiation left over from the explosion.

Fig 4 The Sombrero galaxy. Measurements of the movement of galaxies give clues to the age of the Universe

Since Hubble's discovery, astronomers have been making measurements of the '**Hubble constant**', the number that measures the expansion rate of the Universe. Accurate knowledge of this number would enable astronomers to calculate the age of the Universe, thought to be between 12 and 18 billion years.

Knowledge of the Hubble constant and the density of the Universe, or the amount of mass it contains, would also enable astronomers to predict the future of the Universe. The amount of known mass in the Universe is not enough for the gravitational forces to stop the expansion and one theory is that it will keep on expanding and cooling. Other possibilities depend on there being more mass in the Universe than we

know about. Given enough mass the gravitational forces could stop the expansion and the Universe could attain a constant, steady size. If the mass of the Universe is much greater than this then it could not only halt the expansion, but the Universe could start to contract again. This would cause tremendous heating and could lead to another explosion as all the matter in the Universe collides.

Fig 5 The Andromeda galaxy is moving towards the Milky Way

Q1 The Andromeda galaxy is the only galaxy known to be moving towards us.
   a) How does the light detected from Andromeda differ from that detected from other galaxies?
   b) Stars within Andromeda are whirling around the centre. Explain how this could affect the light we detect from Andromeda.
Q2 Write a summary of the evidence that supports the 'big bang' theory.

148 Using convection currents

In this unit you will learn the answers to these questions:
- What happens in convection currents?
- How do we make use of convection currents?

Everything is continually transferring energy to its surroundings and receiving some back. When hot drinks cool they lose energy faster than they gain it. Cold drinks taken out of a fridge take in energy faster than they give it out. There is not just one simple way in which cold things warm up and hot things cool down. The four different ways in which energy is transferred are called **conduction**, **convection**, **evaporation** and **radiation**. A hot cup of tea is losing energy in all four ways at once, as is a human body!

This unit examines how energy is transferred by convection currents.

Moving fluids

You can feel the effect of a **convection current** when you open the door of an upright freezer. The cold air inside the freezer is denser than the warmer air in the room, so it sinks underneath the warm air, making your feet feel cold. The cold air is denser because the slower-moving molecules are, on average, closer together than those in the warmer air.

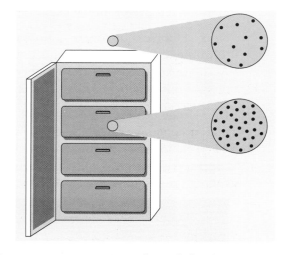

You can also feel the warm air rising from a central heating radiator. When the air is warmed the molecules become faster moving, making the air expand and become less dense.

Fig 1 The cold air in a freezer is denser than the warm air in the room

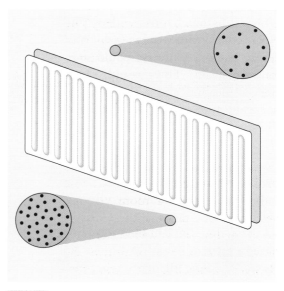

Convection currents are examples of floating and sinking. When part of a liquid or gas is made warmer than its surroundings it expands and rises because it is less dense. The air next to the ice box in a fridge is cooled and so it contracts. The cold air sinks becasue it is denser than the warmer air below it. This movement of air is called a convection current. A dye in the form of a crystal or an ice cube can be used to see convection currents in water.

Convection involves the movement of molecules and so it can only occur in **fluids** (liquids and gases), where the molecules can move within the body of the fluid.

Fig 2 The molecules in the warm air are more widely spaced than those in the cold air, making it less dense

Q1 Explain the movement of the water shown in Fig 3.

Q2 A saucepan of water can be boiled by heating it from the bottom.

    a) Describe how all the water in the saucepan becomes heated.

    b) When soup is heated in a saucepan, it has to be stirred. Explain why this is necessary.

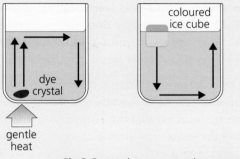

Fig 3 *Convection currents when water is heated and cooled*

Convection and the fridge

When a fridge is working, energy is being removed from the inside of the fridge and transferred to the room. Convection currents are needed to do both jobs. Fig 4 shows the inside of a fridge. Air is cooled at the top of the fridge and downwards-driven convection currents keep the food cool.

Q3 Explain why plastic-coated wire shelves, rather than solid shelves, are used in a fridge.

Q4 **a)** Describe the movement of air inside a fridge.

    b) Explain why the fridge does not work efficiently when it is packed tightly with food.

    c) Suggest why the salad box is covered with a solid shelf.

Fig 4 *Inside a fridge*

Convection currents are also important in removing energy at the back of the fridge. Fridges work by pumping a fluid through pipes both inside and outside. Inside the fridge, the fluid is made to evaporate and this causes cooling (see Unit 151). Outside the fridge, a compressor turns the vapour back into a liquid, which causes heating. The excess heat has to be lost before the fluid can be pumped back inside the fridge. Most of this heat is lost through convection currents. The air that has been warmed by being in contact with the pipes rises and is replaced by colder air. This upwards-driven convection current forces a continuous flow of cooling air over the warm pipes.

Q5 Explain why a fridge should not be positioned too close to a wall.

The convector heater

Convection is important in heating our homes and workplaces. Central heating radiators heat the air around them which is then forced to circulate by convection currents. Some gas heaters also rely on convection to distribute the heat around a room. Electric convector heaters have the advantage of being portable. It is important that these heaters are designed and positioned to allow cold air to enter at the bottom as well as warm air to leave at the top. An electric convector heater relies on the movement of air over the heating element to stop it from getting too hot and causing a fire. It is not a good idea to dry wet clothes by putting them on top of an electric convector heater!

149 Thermal conduction

In this unit you will learn the answers to these questions:
- How does energy flow through solids?
- Why are gases poor conductors of thermal energy?
- Why are metals good conductors of thermal energy?

The convection currents described in Unit 148 allow heating and cooling to occur by the movement of liquids and gases. This unit is about another way in which energy can be transferred. Like convection, it relies on the movement of atoms and molecules. It is the main way in which energy transfers take place in solids, but it also applies to liquids and gases.

What makes conduction work?

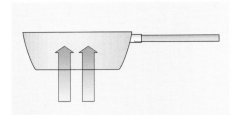

Thermal energy passes easily through some materials and not so easily through others. A saucepan uses a combination of a good conductor and a poor conductor so that the food gets hot but your hands don't burn when you pick the saucepan up.

Fig 1 Energy passes easily through the base of the pan ... but not so easily through the handle

Good conductors are needed to transfer the energy of the hot water in a radiator to the air outside and the energy from the heating element of a kettle into the water. Bricks and building blocks for houses need to be made from poor conductors, as do our clothes and containers that keep food hot.

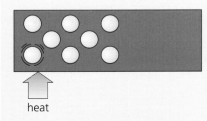

heat

Conduction in a solid. Energy is transferred from molecule to molecule

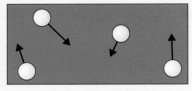

The molecules of a gas are more widely spaced so conduction is a much slower process than in a solid

Fig 2

When one part of a material is hotter than another, the molecules in the hotter part have more energy than the surrounding ones. Heating a substance causes increased motion of the atoms and molecules. In a gas this means that the average speed of the atoms and molecules increases, but in a solid or a liquid it leads to increased vibration. Atoms and molecules do not exist in isolation, and they are continually interacting and swapping energy with their neighbours. The transfer of energy from energetic molecules to those with less energy is responsible for **conduction**.

Gases are poor at transferring energy in this way because the molecules are relatively far apart, compared to a solid or liquid. The more energetic molecules in part of a gas that has been heated travel large distances, in molecular terms, between collisions and so it takes them longer to transfer energy to other molecules.

> **Q1** Some gases are better conductors of thermal energy than others. What other factor, apart from the average spacing of the molecules, affects the conduction of energy in a gas?

Comparing conductors

Fig 3 shows how to compare the rate at which energy flows along solid materials. The results of this comparison show that metals are very good conductors, the heat-sensitive paper changing colour within a few minutes. Non-metals such as glass are very poor conductors in comparison.

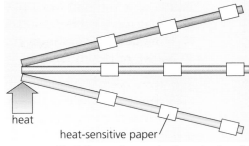

heat

heat-sensitive paper

Fig 3 *Comparing conduction rates in solids*

Metals are such good conductors because, unlike non-metals, even solid metals contain particles that can move. These particles are the **free electrons** that are responsible for the conduction of electricity. They move at high speeds and, because they travel relatively large distances between collisions with the metal atoms, they can transfer energy very quickly.

Copper is a much better conductor of thermal energy than iron, with aluminium being somewhere between the two. A brick made out of copper would conduct energy at five hundred times the rate of a normal house brick! The table lists some common materials in order of their conductivity, the best being at the top of each list. Foam is at the bottom of the list of poor conductors because it contains a very poor conductor – air! The insulation properties of air are discussed in Unit 151.

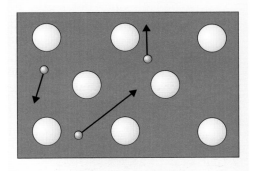

Fig 4 *The high speed of the tiny free electrons enables them to transfer the energy very rapidly*

Good conductors	Poor conductors	Very poor conductors
silver	concrete	hydrogen
copper	glass	helium
aluminium	brick	oxygen
brass	wood	air
iron and steel	foam	carbon dioxide

Q2 a) Most saucepans are made of aluminium, but some cooks prefer to use saucepans with copper bases. Why do some cooks prefer copper saucepans?
   b) Suggest why silver saucepans are not very common.

Q3 In hard water areas, scale forms over the element of an electric kettle. Explain why this can cause a kettle element to overheat.

Choosing a conductor

Irons, sandwich toasters, coffee makers and central heating radiators are just some everyday items that rely on conduction to transfer energy. When choosing a suitable material, manufacturers have to consider other factors apart from which is the best conductor. Cost rules out silver for most applications. Central heating radiators are made out of steel because it is cheap, resilient to knocks and can be easily shaped into panels using hydraulic presses.

Q4 The metal plate of an iron is made from aluminium. Suggest three reasons why aluminium is preferred to copper or steel.

150 Radiant energy

In this unit you will learn the answers to these questions:
- What sort of things radiate energy?
- How does the emission and absorption of radiant energy depend on the nature of the surface?

The two mechanisms of energy transfer studied so far, convection and conduction, both depend on the movement of atoms and molecules. Energy transfer by **radiation** is most efficient when there are no atoms or molecules present, i.e. in a vacuum. This unit describes the properties of radiant energy as well as discussing some everyday uses.

What is radiant energy?

Radio waves, X-rays, gamma rays, ultraviolet and microwaves, light and infrared – these are all parts of the **electromagnetic spectrum** (see Unit 139) and they all transfer energy. The Sun radiates the whole spectrum, but not all of it travels through the Earth's atmosphere. Although all these waves are of the same type, the only differences between them being the wavelength and frequency, they have very different effects on objects that absorb them. Infrared radiation has a heating effect on our skin and other surfaces that absorb it. Grills and toasters give off most of their energy in the form of infrared radiation that heats the food when it is absorbed.

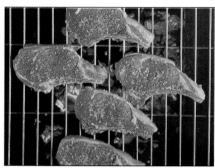
Fig 1 The coals of the barbecue radiate energy to the food being cooked

Infrared describes the part of the electromagnetic spectrum with a wavelength longer than light but shorter than microwaves. Everything radiates energy in the form of infrared radiation and the hotter something is, the more energy it radiates.

Fig 2 Even this ice cream radiates energy, but it receives more than it gives out

Giving and receiving

The properties of electromagnetic waves depend on their wavelength. Infrared radiation is close to light in the spectrum and it behaves in a similar way. Fig 3 shows a demonstration that, like light, infrared radiation is reflected by shiny surfaces and absorbed by dark ones.

You can use a similar arrangement, using two blackened probes, to compare the energy radiated by different surfaces at the same temperature. The results of these experiments show that dark, dull surfaces emit and absorb more radiant energy than light, shiny ones.

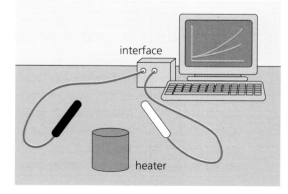

Fig 3 A blackened temperature probe absorbs more energy from the heater than a shiny one does

interface

heater

Q1 Explain why the cooling pipes at the back of a fridge are painted black.

Q2 Kitchen foil is very effective at keeping hot things hot and cold things cold.
   a) Explain how foil containers help to keep take-away food hot while it is transported home.
   b) Explain how wrapping ice cream in foil can help to stop it from melting.

Using radiant energy

The photograph (Fig 4) shows a common sight in many countries in southern Europe. Energy from the Sun is used to heat water as it passes through pipes in a panel. The hot water is then stored in the tank above the panel. There are two important design features of the panel that maximise the energy absorbed; the panel is painted black and it has a glass cover.

Fig 4 Solar-heated water panel

The glass cover is important because black is not only the best absorber of radiant energy, it is also the best emitter and so the hot water pipes give off a lot of radiant energy. We know that glass is transparent to light because we can see through it. It is also transparent to the infrared that is closest to light in the spectrum, the shortest wavelength infrared radiation, but it

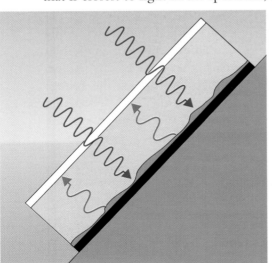

does not allow long-wavelength infrared radiation to pass through it. The Sun, being very hot, gives off radiation of all wavelengths but the blackened panel, being relatively cool, only emits long-wavelength infrared radiation, which does not escape through the glass. This is how greenhouses stay warm.

Q3 Explain why the hot water tank shown in the photograph is shiny on the outside.

Fig 5 Short-wavelength radiation from the Sun passes through the glass and heats the water. The longer wavelength radiation cannot escape

Thermograms are photographs taken using the infrared radiation emitted by an object. They are used in medicine (see Unit 139) and by meteorologists. Weather satellites have sensors that detect infrared radiation as well as sensors that detect light. The signals that are sent back to Earth give a temperature map. By studying how these maps change meteorologists can make predictions about changes in the weather that are likely to take place in the near future.

151 Evaporation and insulation

In this unit you will learn the answers to these questions:
- Why does evaporation cause cooling?
- How can energy losses be minimised?
- How does insulation work?

So far energy transfers by three different methods have been considered. This unit starts with a study of the fourth method, **evaporation**, and then looks at some aspects of **insulation** in a domestic context.

Keep cool

Evaporation is the process by which particles from a liquid form a vapour. Perfumes are designed to evaporate over a time period of several hours. The appetising smell of cooking food is due to evaporation.

As a way of cooling down, evaporation is important to us when we are in a hot climate. This is because liquids need energy to evaporate, and they take this energy from their surroundings. You can feel the cooling effect if you put a drop of a liquid that evaporates easily, such as surgical spirit, on your hand. The liquid quickly evaporates, leaving a cold patch on your hand. Water is slower to evaporate. It takes a lot of energy to turn water into water vapour, which is why the evaporation of sweat removes a lot of energy from the body, helping to keep it cool.

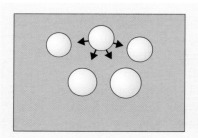

The attractive forces from neighbouring molecules make it hard for a molecule to evaporate

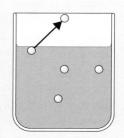

This molecule is near the surface and has enough energy to evaporate

Fig 1

To leave a liquid, molecules need energy to move against the attractive forces from the other liquid molecules. Only the most energetic molecules near the surface can escape. When this happens the average energy of the remaining molecules is reduced, so the liquid cools.

Evaporation only applies to liquids or objects that contain a large proportion of liquid, such as human beings and other animals. When a hot drink cools, the main energy loss is through evaporation. Keeping a lid on it is an effective way of reducing this energy loss.

Q1 Explain why hot liquids evaporate at a greater rate than cold ones.

Q2 A hot drink can be cooled down by blowing across the surface. Explain how this increases the energy loss from the liquid.

Using evaporation

Fridges, freezers and air-conditioners use the evaporation of a liquid to cause cooling. When a liquid evaporates it takes in energy from its surroundings, causing them to cool. In a fridge the fluid is pumped round and forced to evaporate by being squirted through a jet into a wide tube in the freezer compartment. The vaporising liquid cools rapidly, and absorbs energy as it passes through the freezer compartment.

Keeping food hot

Hot food can lose energy in all four of the ways described so far. The most effective insulator for food is the vacuum flask. This minimises energy transfer by conduction, convection, evaporation and radiation so it can keep food hot for several hours. Fig 3 shows the important parts of a vacuum flask. Vacuum flasks are not only used for keeping things hot – they are equally good at keeping things cold. Chiropodists use liquid nitrogen at a temperature of −200°C to kill verrucas. By keeping the nitrogen in a vacuum flask, they can keep it cold for weeks before it all evaporates and a fresh supply has to be bought.

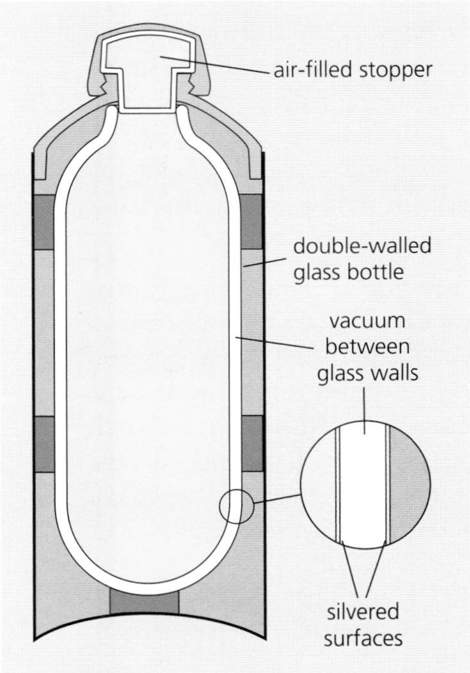

freezer compartment

liquid evaporates removing heat

expansion valve

motor

liquid refrigerant

the compressor changes the vapour back into a liquid

heat lost to surroundings

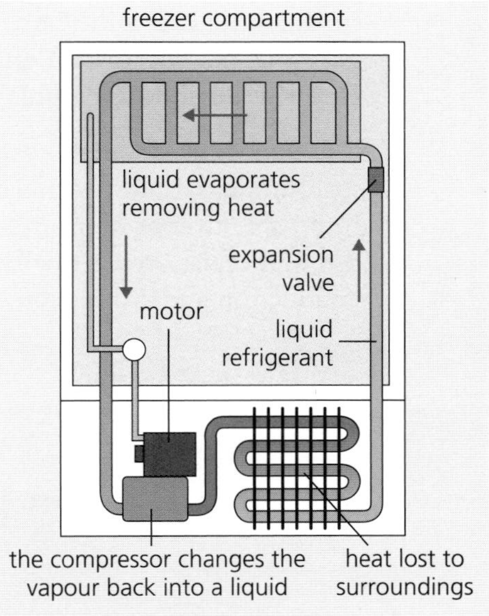

Fig 2 Evaporation and condensation in a fridge

Q3 The important features of a vacuum flask are the stopper, the vacuum between the walls and the silvering on the walls. Explain how these features together reduce energy transfer by convection, conduction, radiation and evaporation.

air-filled stopper

double-walled glass bottle

vacuum between glass walls

silvered surfaces

Fig 3 A vacuum flask

Trapping air

Gases are very poor conductors of thermal energy but they are very good at transferring energy by convection currents. To use the insulating properties of a gas it has to be prevented from moving. Fast-food packaging is often made from expanded polystyrene – this is a plastic material that contains trapped bubbles of gas. The gas helps to minimise the energy transfer through the packaging, so keeping the food hot.

Air is an important material for keeping ourselves warm in a cold environment. Clothing traps a layer of air next to our bodies that acts as an insulator. The more layers of clothing we wear, the more layers of air are trapped, making us even better insulated.

Fig 4 The expanded polystyrene contains trapped air to keep the food hot

152 Insulating a house

In this unit you will learn the answers to these questions:
- How can the loss of energy from houses be reduced?
- How does house insulation work?

Of the four different ways in which warm things can lose energy to their surroundings, only two need to be considered when insulating a house. Houses need to be able to lose moisture, otherwise they would be very damp places. Energy losses through radiation are small, so effective house insulation reduces energy losses due to conduction and convection.

Why insulate?

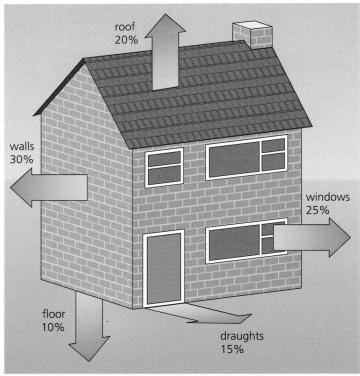

Fig 1 The energy flow out of an uninsulated house

No matter how much energy you put into heating a house, it all leaves through the floor, walls, windows, doors and roof. When a warm house has reached a steady temperature, energy flows out of it at the same rate as it flows in. The diagram (Fig 1) shows the ways in which energy flows out of an uninsulated house.

Insulating a house means that less energy flows out of it, and so less energy needs to be supplied to maintain a comfortable temperature. Reduced fuel bills are not only beneficial for the householder, they also conserve the nation's fuel resources!

> **Q1** Draw a bar chart to illustrate the information in Fig 1.

Where to insulate

The first place to start with the house shown in Fig 1 would be to eliminate the draughts! However, it is important to remember that human beings and gas-burning appliances need a constant supply of oxygen. If a gas fire or central heating boiler does not have enough oxygen the partial combustion of the fuel results in carbon monoxide being released into the air. This can have fatal results. There should always be an air intake into any room where gas is burned.

Once unnecessary draughts have been eliminated, the three common ways of reducing energy losses are loft insulation, cavity wall insulation and double glazing. All these methods rely on using the insulating properties of air.

Loft insulation is the most cost-effective form of domestic insulation. The cost for an average-sized house is less than £100 and that money is easily saved with reduced heating bills. In an uninsulated loft, energy conducted through the ceiling is transferred to the roof by convection currents. Fibreglass insulation traps pockets of air. The trapped air cannot form convection currents so energy can only be transferred through the fibreglass by conduction, and air is a very poor conductor.

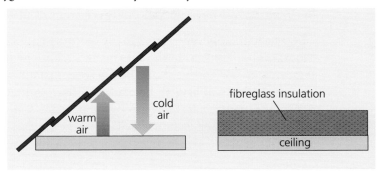

Fig 2 An uninsulated loft and an insulated loft

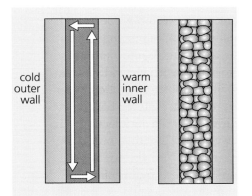

Fig 3 The convection currents in a cavity wall are stopped by insulating foam

Cavity wall insulation involves insulating the walls of a house. Houses are double-walled. In older houses both walls are brick. In modern houses building blocks, which are better insulators than brick, are used for the inside walls. The gap between the walls is called a cavity. If there is only air in this cavity then convection currents transfer energy from the inside wall to the outside wall. Filling the cavity with mineral wool or foam stops the convection currents. This halves the rate at which energy is transferred through the walls. For an average house cavity wall insulation costs a few hundred pounds.

Double glazing an average house is likely to cost several thousand pounds. It is not a cost-effective way of insulating a house but it does bring other benefits. The energy flow through a single-glazed window is about ten times that through the same area of uninsulated cavity wall. This is because windows are much thinner than walls. Double glazing uses twice the thickness of glass, because there are two panes, and also traps air. If the air gap between the inner and outer panes is thin then convection currents cannot flow over the surfaces of the glass, so a thin air gap is a better insulator than a wide one.

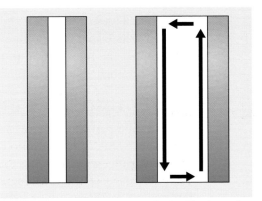

Fig 4 Convection currents make a wide air gap less effective than a narrow one in double glazing

Q2 Despite the cost, a lot of houses now have double-glazed windows. What benefits do these bring to a householder?

Q3 Some householders put a layer of kitchen foil on the walls behind central heating radiators. Explain whether you think this is a good idea or not.

153 Using energy resources efficiently

In this unit you will learn the answers to these questions:
- What does efficiency mean when applied to energy transfer?
- Why do we need to use energy resources efficiently?

The United Kingdom relies heavily on non-renewable fuels for its energy resources. Non-renewable fuels are those that cannot be replenished in the lifetime of the Earth. Reserves of oil and coal are being used up and cannot be replaced. Replacement energy sources will have to be exploited during the twenty-first century. Hydroelectric power and wind generators are two renewable sources that currently supply less than one per cent of our daily needs. This unit examines how we use our energy resources and looks at alternative sources of energy for the twenty-first century.

Where our energy comes from

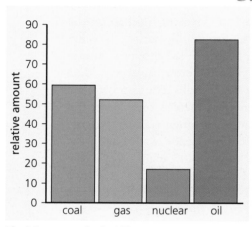

Fig 1 *Energy use in the UK*

As consumers of energy resources, we use some directly and others indirectly. Petroleum products such as petrol, diesel and paraffin are burned in engines that power road, sea and air transport. As the number of vehicles on the roads goes up each year and we take more foreign holidays, the amount of fuel used for transport also rises. Gas, oil and coal are burned to heat buildings that we live and work in. Electricity is an energy source that we use for lighting, producing movement using electric motors and also for heating. Most of our electricity is produced by burning fuels. Fig 1 compares the amounts of each energy source that we use each year. Wind and hydroelectric power are not shown because the quantities are very small.

Q1 a) Which of the fuels shown is not a fossil fuel?
b) Which fuel is only used to generate electricity?
c) Use the information in the bar chart to draw a pie chart showing the proportions of each fuel used.

Using resources efficiently

If you boil a pan of water on a gas ring, not all of the energy from the gas goes into the water. Some of it goes into the air in the room. Boiling water in a kettle is a more **efficient** process because less energy is wasted. The **efficiency** of an energy transfer is the percentage of the available energy that is transferred to where you want it. Fig 2 illustrates the efficiencies of some common energy transfers.

A car engine transfers 20% of the energy in the fuel to the drive mechanism

A filament lamp transfers 5% of the energy from the electricity into light

A microwave cooker transfers 55% of the energy from the electricity to the food

Fig 2

Q2 a) Describe what happens to the 80% of the energy from fuel that is not transferred to a car's drive mechanism.

  b) A 60 W lamp takes in energy from electricity at the rate of 60 J per second. How much of this energy is transferred to light?

Electricity is generated from a variety of fuels, the main ones being coal, gas, nuclear and oil. Energy is lost as heat at all stages in the process, the major loss occurring when steam from the turbines is condensed back into water. Fig 3 shows the energy flow through a coal-burning power station.

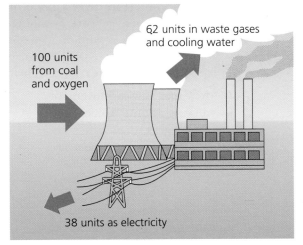

100 units from coal and oxygen

62 units in waste gases and cooling water

38 units as electricity

Fig 3 Energy flow through a power station

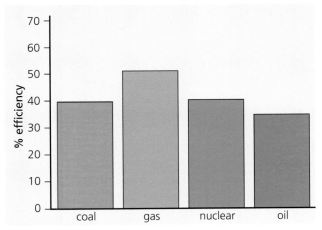

Fig 4 Power station efficiency

Fig 4 shows the maximum possible efficiency of power stations generating electricity from these fuels.

Q3 Coal could be used more efficiently if some of the energy wasted in a power station were used in the local community. Suggest some possible uses for this energy.

Q4 a) Explain why gas is becoming an increasingly popular fuel for new power stations.
  b) What are the advantages and disadvantages of using gas instead of coal in power stations?

The efficiency of renewable resources

Photovoltaic cells transfer energy from the Sun into electricity with an efficiency of around 17%. This seems low compared to the efficiency of a power station, but power plants of this type are helping to conserve our fuel resources. **Solar panels** at the moment have a high capital cost and a low efficiency. If both these factors were to be improved they could be a major energy resource in the twenty-first century.

Q5 Describe the advantages and disadvantages of using solar panels to provide electricity for a home.

We receive energy each day from the Sun, far more than our total needs. If we can use more of this energy then we can reduce our dependence on fossil fuels. Energy from the Sun can be extracted from moving air and water and can be 'stored' by growing plants. Scientists and engineers are trying to find ways of using this energy more efficiently to provide for our future needs.

154 Forces and work

In this unit you will learn the answers to these questions:
- When are forces working and when are they not working?
- How much work does a working force do?
- What is the link between work and energy transfer?

Everything we do involves a force making something move. Even if we sit perfectly still there are forces at work pumping blood and moving air in and out of our bodies. While all this work is going on, energy is on the move.

Measuring work

A force that causes movement is working. Some forces and the movement they cause are easily recognised – others are less obvious.

Fig 1 *Forces working*

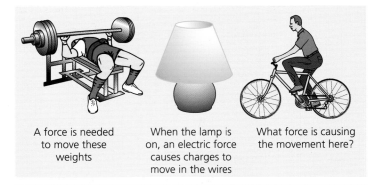

A force is needed to move these weights

When the lamp is on, an electric force causes charges to move in the wires

What force is causing the movement here?

Some forces do not work. The upward force from your chair is a very useful force because it is supporting you, but it is not causing any movement so it is not working.

Q1 Which of the following forces are working and which are not working?
  a) the friction force supporting a shelf on a wall
  b) the force used to push a lawnmower
  c) the Earth's pull on a falling parachutist
  d) the Earth's pull on a floating ship

The amount of work a force does when it causes movement is calculated using the formula:

> **work done = force × distance moved in its own direction   or $W = F \times d$**

Work is measured in **joules** (J).

Example

A 65 N force is used to push a supermarket trolley for 180 m. How much work does the force do?

Answer

$W = F \times d$
$\quad = 65 \, \text{N} \times 180 \, \text{m}$
$\quad = 11\,700 \, \text{J}$

Q2 Calculate the amount of work done by the following.
  a) A crane lifts a 3000 N load through a height of 15 m.
  b) A high-jumper lifts her own weight of 600 N through a height of 1.8 m.
  c) A man uses a 45 N force to push a pram a distance of 1500 m.

Work and energy transfer

Nothing can work unless it has energy. People get their energy from food. Motorised transport obtains energy from the fuel and oxygen supply. A lot of our work is done with energy from electricity. When something or someone is at work, energy is on the move! Fig 2 shows how you can measure the energy that passes through a motor when it lifts a weight or drags it up a slope. You could make the same comparison with your own energy, using a forcemeter and a metre rule.

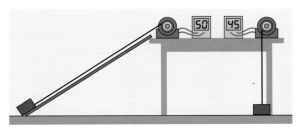

Fig 2 *Comparing the energy transfer when a weight is dragged up a slope or lifted to the same height*

As the weight moves up, it is gaining energy due to its position. The motor is doing the work to lift or drag the motor up, using energy from electricity. All the time the motor is working, it is transferring energy from electricity to the weight. Not all of the energy from the electricity goes to the weight, some of it stays in the motor as heat in the wires.

It takes more energy to drag the weight up the slope than to lift it. It does not matter which way the job is done, the weight gains the same amount of energy because it has been moved through the same vertical height. More energy is needed to drag the weight because of the frictional forces opposing the motion up the slope. Movement against these frictional forces causes a small amount of heating.

Whenever anything works, it is transferring energy. The amount of energy transferred is equal to the work being done. Fig 3 shows the energy transfer from the motor when it is lifting and dragging the weight uphill.

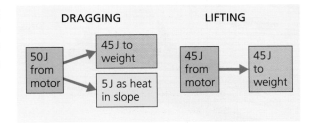

Fig 3 *The motor does more work when it drags the weight up the slope than when it lifts it straight up*

> **Q3 a)** Which process is more efficient, lifting the weight or dragging it? Explain your answer.
>   **b)** Even though it takes more energy, people prefer to drag heavy things up a ramp rather than lift them. Explain why this is.

Cyclist at work

To keep cycling at a steady speed on a level road, a cyclist has to keep working. Resistive forces would slow the cyclist down if she stopped pedalling. As she works energy flows from her, through the cycle mechanism, ending up as heat in the surroundings.

Fig 4 *The cyclist is travelling at terminal velocity, with the resistive force equal to the driving force*

> **Q4** The driving force on the cycle in Fig 4 is 80 N. Calculate the amount of work done when the cycle travels a distance of 120 m.

Cycling up a hill at the same speed needs a bigger force – more work has to be done. The cyclist gains energy due to her position as she moves uphill, so she has to provide a bigger energy input to the cycle.

155 **Power**

In this unit you will learn the answers to these questions:
- ■ What is the scientific meaning of power?
- ■ How is power calculated?

How long does it take a kettle to boil some water? How powerful is a person? How much energy is transferred from the mains supply when a lamp is left on overnight? This unit shows how you can answer these questions if you know the power of the device being used.

What is power?

The diesel engine that drives a train has to be more powerful than that of a car because there is a lot more mass to be accelerated. A 2 kW fan heater provides more heat each second than a 1 kW heater and it costs more to run. A 36 W fluorescent light fitting uses less electricity than a 100 W lamp but it gives out more light each second because it transfers energy more efficiently.

Fig 1 Both of these kettles can boil a pint of water, but the one that does it faster is more powerful

Power describes the rate of working or energy transfer. This is how much work is done or how much energy is transferred each second. The 100 W lamp transfers energy from electricity into light and heat at a rate of 100 joules each second. A 2 kW fan heater transfers energy into heat and movement at a rate of 2000 joules each second.

Fig 2 A jet aircraft needs very powerful engines to accelerate it to take-off speed in only a few seconds

The equation for calculating power is:

$$\text{power} = \frac{\text{work done or energy transfer}}{\text{time taken}} \quad \text{or} \quad P = \frac{W}{t}$$

Power is measured in **watts** (W) when the energy transfer is in joules (J) and the time is in seconds (s).

Example

Calculate the power of a cyclist who transfers 105 000 J of energy to the pedals in 300 s.

Answer

power = energy transfer ÷ time
= 105 000 J ÷ 300 s = 350 W

Q1 Calculate the power of the following.
   a) A kettle that transfers 750 000 J of energy into heat in the 300 s it takes to boil some water.
   b) A weightlifter who does 12 000 J of work to lift some weights in 1.5 s.
   c) A clock that transfers 240 J of energy from the mains supply each minute.

Measuring your own power

Human beings are not the most powerful creatures on Earth. They can work at a low power of a few hundred watts for extended periods of time and, working in short bursts, they can work at high power over short time periods. Footballers and marathon runners need to be able to work at a steady rate for long periods of time but sprinters and cricket fast bowlers work at a higher power for shorter times.

You can measure your own power by getting someone to time you as you do a job such as running up some stairs. The work that you do to run upstairs is equal to your *weight × change in height*. This is the energy that is transferred from your body muscles. You lose the energy from your muscles and gain it in the form of gravitational potential energy (see Unit 156).

The person in Fig 3 weighs 600 N. He climbs the stairs in 4.0 s. To calculate his power you first of all need to calculate how much work he does:

work = weight × change in height
     = 600 N × 1.5 m = 900 J

Next divide by the time to calculate the power:

power = work done ÷ time taken
      = 900 J ÷ 4.0 s
      = 225 W

Fig 3

Q2 In the following examples, first calculate the work done or energy transfer. Then calculate the power by dividing the work or energy transfer by the time.
 a) A boy who stacks shelves in a supermarket lifts 500 N weight of sugar through a height of 0.8 m in 16 s.
 b) A father pushes a pram for a distance of 1500 m with a force of 80 N. The journey takes 20 minutes (1200 s).
 c) A swimmer pushes on the water with an average force of 150 N as she swims 200 m in 75 s.
Q3 Use the power equation to work out the following.
 a) The time it takes for a 800 W vacuum cleaner to transfer 4000 J of energy from the mains supply.
 b) The energy transferred by a 2500 W immersion heater in 10 minutes.
 c) The power of a crane that lifts a 2500 N load through a height of 6 m in 10 s.

In this unit you will learn the answers to these questions:
- What causes a change in gravitational potential energy?
- How much kinetic energy do moving objects have?

A child swinging on a swing has energy. Pulling the swing back lifts her further from the ground, so she gains gravitational potential energy (g.p.e. or just potential energy for short). When the swing is released she speeds up as she loses height. The energy due to the girl's movement is kinetic energy. It comes from the potential energy she gained when the swing was pulled back. As the swing rises up and slows down the kinetic energy is transferred back to potential energy.

Potential energy

Gravitational potential energy, usually referred to as potential energy, is the energy that an object has because of its position. A force that causes movement is needed to lift something up and this involves an energy transfer. A weight being lifted up gains potential energy. It can be made to do useful work, such as driving a clock mechanism, when it falls down again.

Fig 1 *As the child swings, energy is being transferred from kinetic to potential to kinetic to …*

You can calculate the energy transfer when an object changes position using the equation:

change in potential energy = weight × change in height   or $\Delta E_p = mg\Delta h$

This is equivalent to:

energy transfer = force × distance moved when an object moves vertically

Fig 2 shows how the girl moves through a vertical height of 0.3 m when the swing is pulled back. She gains potential energy equal to:

$mg\Delta h = 450\,\text{N} \times 0.3\,\text{m} = 135\,\text{J}$

Q1 Calculate the change in potential energy for each of the following.
a) A sack of potatoes weighing 500 N is lifted 0.8 m into a car boot.
b) A lift and passengers of total mass 650 kg moves through a vertical height of 7.5 m. Take $g = 10\,\text{N/kg}$.
c) In a pumped storage system for generating electricity using the potential energy of water, 1 tonne (10 000 N) of water falls through a height of 215 m.

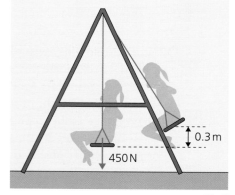

0.3 m

450 N

Fig 2

Kinetic energy

All moving objects have kinetic energy. When a car accelerates, energy is being transferred from the fuel to kinetic energy of the car. The faster it goes, the more kinetic energy the car has. In stopping the car, the brakes transfer the kinetic energy into heat. Fig 3 shows typical braking distances for a car in good driving conditions.

This diagram shows that, when the speed of a car is **doubled**, the braking distance becomes **four times** as great. The same braking force acting over four times the distance does four times as much work and removes four times as much energy. Travelling at 30 m/s (67 mph) a car has four times as much kinetic energy as when it travels at 15 m/s (33.5 mph). The kinetic energy of a moving object depends on its mass and its (speed)².
The formula for kinetic energy is:

$$E_k = \tfrac{1}{2} mv^2$$

A car of mass 800 kg travelling at 20 m/s has kinetic energy $E_k = \tfrac{1}{2} \times 800 \times (20)^2 = 160\,000\,J$.

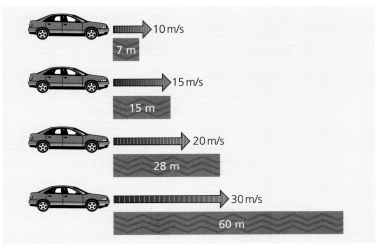

Fig 3

Q2 Calculate the kinetic energy of each of the following.
   a) A 0.5 kg ball travelling at 4 m/s.
   b) A cycle and cyclist of total mass 85 kg travelling at 8 m/s.
   c) A 30 tonne (30 000 kg) lorry travelling at 30 m/s.

Potential to kinetic energy transfer

For centuries energy has been stored as gravitational potential energy. Lift up a mass and it gains energy. Let the mass fall and it can do a useful task such as driving a clock mechanism as it moves down. If the mass is allowed to fall freely it speeds up, transferring the energy from potential to kinetic. A fast-moving mass of water can drive a generator to make electricity. A fast-moving heavy weight can be used as a 'hammer' to drive steel poles into the ground to provide the foundations for large buildings.

Fig 4 This sky diver speeds up as he falls. Energy is being transferred from potential to kinetic

In the absence of resistive forces, a falling object gains kinetic energy at the same rate as it loses potential energy, so that the total energy (kinetic + potential) remains constant. Similarly, when a ball is thrown upwards the loss of kinetic energy as it slows down is balanced by the gain in potential energy.

Q3 A 0.5 kg ball is thrown vertically upwards with a speed of 20 m/s.
   a) Calculate the kinetic energy of the ball moving at 20 m/s.
   b) When it reaches its maximum height, all the kinetic energy has been transferred to potential energy. How high does the ball go?

157 Radioactive emissions

In this unit you will learn the answers to these questions:
- ■ Where do radioactive emissions come from?
- ■ What are the differences between the three main types of radioactive emission?

Many radioactive materials are as old as the Earth. Others are very short-lived. Radioactive materials are used to generate electricity on a small scale in heart pacemakers and on a large scale in nuclear power stations. The first atomic bomb, used more than 50 years ago, and the Chernobyl disaster in 1986 caused long-lasting damage to the Earth. Radioactive materials bring many benefits to humans, but they need to be used with great care. This unit examines the properties of the emissions from radioactive materials.

Why are some materials radioactive?

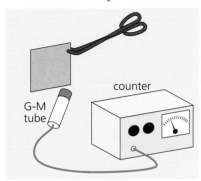

Fig 1 Detecting radioactive decay

A Geiger-Müller tube connected to a counter can be used to detect emissions from radioactive decay. Fig 1 shows how to compare the emissions from different substances. Experiments such as this show that while substances containing elements such as uranium are strongly radioactive, those containing copper and sodium are not.

Substances which are radioactive have nuclei that are not stable. When they change to a more stable state, they give out particles or electromagnetic radiation or both. Unstable substances commonly kept in schools include radium–226, americium–241, strontium–90 and cobalt–60.

Different types of emission

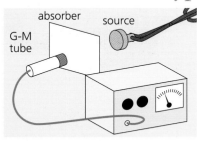

Fig 2 Comparing the penetration of radioactive emissions

Fig 3 Alpha radiation is intensely ionising

Fig 2 shows how a Geiger-Müller tube and counter can be used to compare the penetration of emissions from different sources. Emissions from radioactive materials are classified according to their penetration, which shows that there are three distinct types. These are named alpha (α), beta (β) and gamma (γ) after the first three letters of the Greek alphabet.

Alpha radiation is easily stopped by paper or thin card and it cannot penetrate more than a few centimetres of air. **Beta radiation** is more penetrative but is absorbed by a thin sheet of aluminium or any other metal. **Gamma radiation** is the most penetrative of all. It is partially absorbed by lead but some radiation will always penetrate even a ten centimetre thick lead wall.

Do not be fooled into thinking that alpha radiation is harmless because it is not very penetrative. It is the most intensely ionising radiation, as a spark counter shows (Fig 3). Damage to human tissue is due to ionisation, and alpha radiation can be particularly dangerous to humans if breathed in.

The nature of the emissions

Alpha particles are the largest of the three types of radioactive emission. Because of their size, they undergo frequent collisions when passing through air or other materials, slowing down at each collision until all their energy has been lost. Alpha particles consist of two protons and two neutrons, and they are often referred to as **helium nuclei**. When a nucleus ejects an alpha particle, its atomic number decreases by two, leaving a nucleus of an atom two places lower in the Periodic Table. The equation describes the decay of radium into radon and an alpha particle.

$$^{226}_{88}Ra \implies {}^{222}_{86}Rn + {}^{4}_{2}He$$

Beta particles are **electrons** that have been ejected from the nucleus of an atom when a neutron changes to a proton. Decay by beta emission causes the nucleus to change to that of an atom one place higher in the Periodic Table – the atomic number increases by one. The next equation describes the decay of radioactive carbon, carbon-14, into nitrogen and an electron.

$$^{14}_{6}C \implies {}^{14}_{7}N + {}^{0}_{-1}e$$

If you have previously studied Unit 142, you will already know that gamma radiation is **short-wavelength electromagnetic radiation**, given out when a nucleus loses excess energy. The emission of gamma radiation alone does not cause a change in the atomic mass or atomic number.

The table summarises the properties of alpha, beta and gamma radiation.

Radioactive emission	Nature	Charge	Mass	Penetration	Affected by electric and magnetic fields	Causes ionisation	Detected by
alpha particle	two neutrons and two protons	positive	4x the mass of a proton	absorbed by paper or a few cm of air	yes	intensely	G-M tube photographic film spark counter solid state detector
beta particle	fast-moving electron	negative	1/2000 of the mass of a proton	absorbed by 3 mm of aluminium	yes	weakly	G-M tube photographic film solid state detector
gamma ray	short-wavelength electromagnetic radiation	none	none	reduced by several cm of lead	no	very weakly	G-M tube photographic film solid state detector

Q1 A radioactive source is placed next to a Geiger-Müller tube connected to a counter. When a piece of paper is inserted between the source and the tube the count-rate decreases from 60 counts per second to 40 counts per second. Inserting a sheet of aluminium has the same effect as a sheet of paper.
a) What type or types of radiation is the source emitting?
b) What further test could be done to confirm this? What would the result be?

Q2 Electric fields affect charged particles and magnetic fields affect electric currents. Explain why alpha and beta particles are affected by both types of field but gamma rays are not affected by either.

158 Radioactive decay

In this unit you will learn the answers to these questions:
- **What is 'background radiation'?**
- **What does half-life mean and how is it worked out?**

In the last unit you studied the three main types of emission that are given out when an unstable nucleus undergoes a change to make it more stable. This unit is concerned with the pattern of radioactive decay.

Background radiation

We live in a radioactive world. All living things are radioactive, as are all things that have been alive. Many rocks in the Earth's crust are radioactive, giving particularly high levels of radioactivity in areas built on granite. There is a constant stream of radiation from the Sun and space, although some of it is very difficult to detect. All this radiation is collectively referred to as **'background radiation'**.

If a Geiger-Müller tube and counter is set up away from any radioactive sources, it detects a random pattern of background radiation. It may go for a few seconds without detecting anything, and then there may be several 'pulses' in a short space of time. Counting the number of pulses over a period of 1 or 2 minutes results in an average background radiation of around 1 count per second, depending on where you live. This may seem very low, but a more sensitive detector would record much higher levels of background radiation.

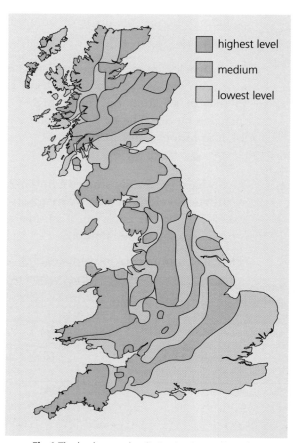

Fig 1 The background radiation in some areas of Britain is higher than in others due to the radioactivity of the rock

The decay pattern

Radioactive decay is a random process. There is no way of predicting when an unstable nucleus will change to a more stable form. However, for a sample of material containing a large number of atoms with an unstable nucleus, the average rate of decay should be proportional to the number of undecayed atoms present. This means that a sample containing two million unstable nuclei of an element should, on average, be expected to decay at twice the rate of a sample containing one million unstable nuclei of the same element. So as the nuclei in a radioactive material decay into a more stable form, the rate of decay should go down. A typical decay curve is shown in Fig 2. The shape of the curve is similar for all substances, but the time scale can vary from a tiny fraction of a second to many millions of years.

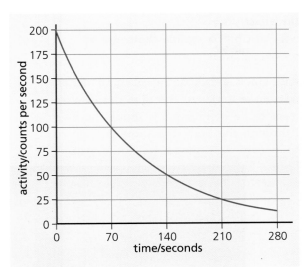

Fig 2 Half-life curve

ICT Extra!

Use computer simulations to show the effects of half-life and to make measurements.

Q1 Use the graph in Fig 2 to work out the time for the activity of the sample to change from:
a) 200 counts/s to 100 counts/s,
b) 150 counts/s to 75 counts/s,
c) 120 counts/s to 60 counts/s.

You should find your answers to each part of **Q1** are all very similar. The average value of your answers is the **half–life** of the radioactive substance. Half-life is a measure of the rate at which radioactive material decays. It is the average time for the number of undecayed nuclei in a sample of material to halve. A substance with a long half–life remains active for much longer than one with a short half-life.

The activity of a sample of radioactive material can be expected to halve after one half-life, halve again after another half-life and so on.

Q2 The form of technetium-99 used as a tracer in medicine is a gamma emitter that decays with a half-life of 6 hours. A fresh sample has an activity of 1200 counts/s.
a) Calculate the expected activity after 6 hours.
b) Calculate the expected activity 24 hours after the sample was made.
c) Explain why measurements of the activity after 6 hours and after 24 hours may differ from the correct answers to **a)** and **b)**.

Measuring activity

Routine tests are carried out on many materials to measure the level of radioactivity. Fig 3 shows a device for measuring the radioactivity of food samples. The detector is placed in the centre of a food container made of thick lead. The lead acts as a shield to absorb any background radiation that would affect the detector.

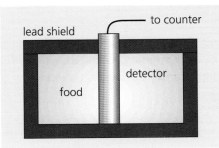

Fig 3 Measuring the radioactivity of food

When measuring the activity of radioactive samples, it is necessary to either shield the detector from background radiation or take it into account by subtracting the average level of background radiation from the measured count rate.

Q3 Explain why it is more important to take background radiation into account when measuring the activity of a sample with a low count rate of 10 counts/s than it is for a more active sample of 1000 counts/s.

159 Radioactive dating

In this unit you will learn the answer to this question:
■ How do measurements of the radioactivity of objects enable their age to be estimated?

In the last unit you learned how the rate at which a radioactive material decays depends on its half-life. When choosing a suitable material to monitor the flow of blood around a person's body, the half-life needs to be considered. It should be long enough to still be active when it has spread through the body, but short enough to limit the amount of the radiation that the person is exposed to. Some natural radioactive substances have very long half-lives, and this makes them suitable for finding the age of objects. This unit is concerned with two ways of using radioactivity to date objects.

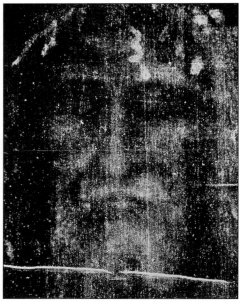

Radioactive carbon

The most common form of carbon is carbon-12, a stable isotope with six protons and six neutrons in the nucleus. Cosmic rays cause the continual formation of the isotope carbon-14 in the atmosphere. It then enters the carbon cycle as carbon dioxide. Living things eat food containing radioactive carbon as well as normal carbon, and the concentration of carbon-14 in the body of a plant or animal stays at a constant level until it dies. After death, the activity of the carbon-14 decreases with a half-life of 5730 years. There would not be much change in activity over a period of a few years, but measurable changes occur over periods of hundreds of years.

Fig 1 *This shroud was believed to have been used for the body of Christ, until radiocarbon dating dated the linen between 1260 and 1390AD*

The simplest way of using radioactive carbon to estimate the date of some old, dead organic material is by comparing its activity with similar material that is still living or has died recently. Using the half-life, the time lapse since death can be calculated. There are two principal reasons why this leads to unreliable results.

1 The samples available from important relics or archaeological sites are often tiny, and the measurable radioactivity can hardly be distinguished from background radioactivity.

2 This method assumes that the level of radioactive carbon present in the carbon cycle has been constant for thousands of years. We know that this is not the case. The level of carbon-14 in the atmosphere is affected by things such as sun-spot activity, variations in the Earth's magnetic field as well as the burning of fossil fuels and the explosion of atomic bombs.

Q1 The activity of the carbon-14 in living material is 15.3 counts per minute for each gram of carbon. Explain why it would be difficult to date a seed from an ancient plant by measuring its radioactivity.

Various techniques have been used to date objects using radioactive carbon, and they do not always give the same results. The most modern technique uses a principle called mass spectrometry to compare the amount of carbon-14 in a sample with the amount of carbon-12. Having used the half-life to estimate the age of the sample assuming a constant level of carbon-14, a more accurate value for the age is then estimated using a calibration curve that takes into account changes in the level of atmospheric carbon-14.

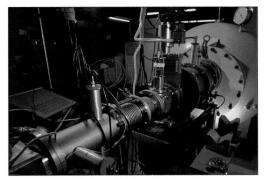

Fig 2 A mass spectrometer similar to that used to date the Turin Shroud

Dating rocks

Using radioactivity levels to date rocks can be done with more precision than radiocarbon dating because there are no other factors that affect the radioactivity of a rock sample. The method depends on measuring the relative amounts of a radioactive material and the substance produced when it decays.

Uranium-238 decays into lead-206 with a half-life of 4500 million years. This is similar to the age of the Earth, which is believed to be 4600 million years. Rocks formed at the same time as the Earth contain the same proportion of lead-206 and uranium-238 atoms, the lead having been formed by the decay of uranium. Rocks formed since then have a higher proportion of uranium-238 to lead-206.

As with radiocarbon dating, mass spectrometers can be used to determine the precise proportions of different atoms contained in rock. Moon rocks have been dated using this technique, giving ages of up to 4400 million years. The evidence from these rocks is that the Moon was not formed at the same time as the Earth.

Fig 3 An astronaut gathering samples of Moon rock for radioactive dating

Q2 Uranium-235 decays to lead-207 with a half-life of 700 million years. Explain why uranium-235 cannot be used to date rock as old as the Earth.

160 **Using radioactivity**

In this unit you will learn the answers to these questions:
- ■ **What are radioactive materials used for?**
- ■ **What factors need to be considered when selecting a source of radiation for a particular purpose?**

In the last unit you studied how naturally occurring radioactive substances can be used to estimate the age of rocks and dead organic material. The use of gamma radiation as a medical tracer and for therapy was described in Unit 142. This unit looks at some other uses of radioactive materials.

Gauging the thickness

Paper, cling film, aluminium foil and other sheet materials need to be produced to a constant thickness. In the manufacturing process, the thickness of the material is continually monitored by measuring the amount of radioactive emission from a source that penetrates the material. Strontium-90, a beta-emitting source with a half-life of 29 years, is used in an arrangement similar to that shown in Fig 1.

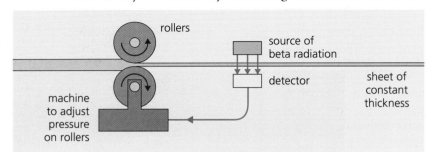

Fig 1 *Controlling the thickness of a sheet material*

> **Q1 a)** Explain why a beta-emitting source is suitable for this purpose, but alpha-emitting or gamma-emitting sources would not be.
>
> **b)** Explain why sources with half-lives of 3 years or 300 years would not be suitable.

Some uses of tracers

Radioactive tracers can be used to monitor the flow of fluid in pipes, and from pipes in the case of a suspected leak. The principle is shown in Fig 2. Factors to be considered when choosing a suitable radioactive material to use as a tracer include how easily it mixes with the fluid, the type or types of radiation emitted and the half-life.

Radioactive tracers are also used by plant biologists to monitor the flow of liquid in the plant and the uptake of minerals from the soil. Phosphates that incorporate a radioactive form of phosphorus, phosphorus-32, are used to make a fertiliser for the soil that the plants are grown in.

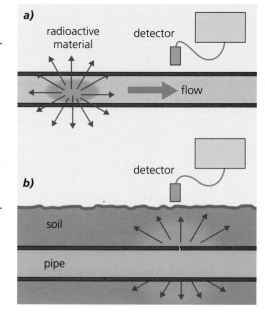

Fig 2 a) *Measurement of flow rate in a pipe*
b) *Detection of a leak in an underground pipe*

Q2 A tracer is to be used to detect a leak in an underground water pipe.
   a) What type of emission could be detected from a liquid leaking from a pipe underground?
   b) What factors should be considered when selecting a material with a suitable half-life?
   c) Name one other important property that the radioactive material used as the tracer should have.

Nuclear power

Unlike the examples of radioactivity studied so far, the fuel in a nuclear power station does not decay spontaneously and randomly. The splitting up of atoms in the process called **nuclear fission** is an example of a controlled **chain reaction**. Uranium-235 is a naturally occurring substance with a very long half-life (see Unit 159). When it captures a neutron, it splits into two roughly equal halves and two or three other neutrons. The fragments of the fission have a large amount of kinetic energy, which is the form of energy released from the fuel in a nuclear reactor. Fig 3 shows the fission of a uranium-235 nucleus.

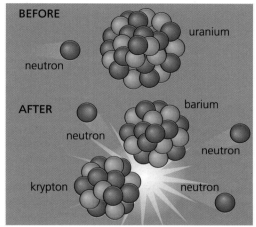

Fig 3 The fission of uranium-235

In a nuclear reactor an average of one neutron released at each fission goes on to cause further fissions, and the other neutrons are absorbed by control rods. In this way the rate of the reaction is maintained at a constant level. The heat generated by the fission process is removed by a coolant. The coolant is then used to generate steam, which drives a turbine as in a coal-fired power station. Fig 4 shows the principle of a nuclear power station.

Fission reactions used in nuclear power stations are different to the nuclear reaction taking place in the Sun and the stars, which is a **fusion reaction**. In a fusion reaction, two light nuclei collide at high speed, releasing energy as they combine. Fusion reactions are only possible at very high temperatures. These have been created on Earth, but have only been able to be sustained for a tiny fraction of a second.

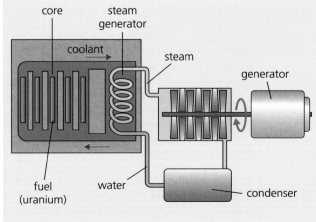

Fig 4 A nuclear power station

Q3 Explain what could happen if the spare neutrons from each fission were not absorbed.

Glossary

A

absolute zero – the minimum possible temperature is $-273°C$ or $0K$.

active transport – energy-requiring process which enables the movement of particles across a membrane often against a concentration gradient.

addition polymer – product formed when many molecules of a monomer react to form one large molecule. No other substances are formed.

addition reaction – reaction in which two molecules react together to form one molecule.

adenosine triphosphate (ATP) – adenosine triphosphate is an 'energy-rich' compound produced during respiration and photosynthesis.

air resistance – the backwards-directed force that acts on all objects moving through the air.

alchemists – a type of science that combined aspects of chemistry with mysticism. It was developed in Egypt and China over 2000 years ago. In Europe the main aim of alchemists was to turn metals such as lead into gold.

algal bloom – excessive growth of algae, e.g. during eutrophication.

alkane – a family of hydrocarbons containing only single carbon to carbon bonds. Alkanes have a general formula C_nH_{2n+2}.

alkene – family of hydrocarbons containing a carbon to carbon double bond. Alkenes have a general formula C_nH_{2n}.

allele – genes may exist in more than one form, each form is known as an allele.

alloy – mixture of two or more metals, e.g. copper and zinc in brass.

alpha radiation – a radioactive emission consisting of two neutrons and two protons.

anaerobic respiration – the release of energy from a food molecule, such as glucose, in the absence of oxygen.

angle of incidence – the angle between the direction of light incident on a surface and the normal line.

angle of reflection – the angle between the direction of light reflected from a surface and the normal line.

angle of refraction – the angle between the direction of light passing into a medium and the normal line.

artery – blood vessel that carries blood away from the heart to organs, tissues and cells.

asteroid – a fragment of rock that orbits the Sun between the inner and outer planets.

atmospheres – measurement of pressure. One atmosphere is approximately 100 000 Pa (100 000 N/m²).

average bond energy – the amount of energy required to break a typical type of covalent bond when more than one is present in a molecule, e.g. the average bond energy of a C–H bond in CH_4 is 413 kJ.

B

background radiation – radiation from the ground, the atmosphere and buildings.

balanced equation – a chemical equation where the number and types of atoms in the products is the same as the number and types of atoms in the reactants.

beta radiation – a radioactive emission that consists of a fast-moving electron.

Big Bang – a theory that the Universe started with an enormous explosion.

biodegradable – substances that can be broken down by such processes as decomposition by bacteria and can therefore be reused by living organisms.

bleach – a solution containing chloride (Cl^-) and chlorate(I) ions (ClO^-) made by dissolving chlorine in sodium hydroxide solution. Bleach will decolourise dyes.

bond energy – the amount of energy required to break a particular type of covalent bond. It is the same as the energy released when that bond forms.

braking distance – the distance a vehicle travels between the brakes being applied and it coming to a halt.

brine – a concentrated solution of sodium chloride in water.

buckminsterfullerene – one form of the element carbon. It exists in the form of molecules, such as C_{60}, which has the same sort of a shape as a geodesic dome.

C

capillary – very small blood vessels with a wall which is only one cell thick.

carbon dating – a method of dating objects made from once-living materials according to the amount of radioactive carbon that they contain.

carcinogenic – substance that causes cancer. Chemical carcinogens include tar and some dyes.

cast iron – iron made by pouring the molten metal from the blast furnace into a mould and letting it cool.

catalyst – a substance which increases the rate of a chemical reaction but is itself unchanged.

catalytic cracking – breaking down of long-chain hydrocarbon molecules by the action of a heated catalyst to produce short molecules useful for making polymers.

cement – substance made by heating powdered limestone with clay. On mixing with water it sets to a hard mass.

CFC's – chlorofluorocarbons are atmospheric pollutants.

chalk – sedimentary rock consisting of very small particles of calcium carbonate.

circuit breaker – a device that cuts off the voltage supply if a fault develops in a circuit.

collide – make violent contact with another object.

combining power – measure of the ability of an ion to combine with others. Magnesium has a combining power of two and chloride one. Two chloride ions join with one magnesium ion.

combustion – combination of a substance with oxygen to release energy.

comet – an object consisting of frozen ices that orbits the Sun in a highly-elliptical orbit.

compensation point – the outcome of photosynthesis reverses the outcome of aerobic respiration. The point where photosynthetic production of glucose exactly balances the glucose used by respiration is called the compensation point.

concentration – the quantity of a solute dissolved in a volume of solvent.

contact metamorphism – a type of metamorphism that occurs when a rock has been altered by the effects of high temperatures. This often occurs when volcanic intrusions pass near bedding plains of rock.

corrode – suffer chemical attack.

corrosive – a corrosive substance may damage your eyes and skin. It is represented by a tube dropping a liquid onto a hand in the Hazchem code.

covalent bond – type of bonding involving the sharing of one or more pairs of electrons. The electrons are provided by the atoms that are combining.

cracking – breaking down of long-chain hydrocarbon molecules by the action of a heated catalyst or by heat alone to produce short molecules useful for making polymers.

cytoplasm – the term used to describe all the components of a cell outside the nucleus.

D

denatured – when the structure of a protein molecule is permanently changed, e.g. by high temperature or extreme pH.

denitrifying bacteria – soil bacteria that break down nitrates and release nitrogen gas into the air.

density – mass per unit of volume of material, measured in kg/m^3 or g/cm^3.

diamond – one form of the element carbon. The carbon atoms are held together by covalent bonds in a strong giant structure.

diatomic – an element which exists naturally as molecules containing two atoms.

diffraction – the spreading out of a wave as it passes through a narrow gap or past an obstacle.

disinfectants – substances which kill bacteria.

dispersion – the splitting of light into its constituent colours.

displayed formula – chemical formula that shows every atom and bond. It is sometimes called a graphical formula or full structural formula.

DNA – deoxyribonucleic acid is found in chromosomes.

dominant – a dominant allele always expresses itself (works) whether it is partnered with another like itself or with a recessive allele.

dot and cross diagrams – a drawing representing the electrons in a molecule. Dots and crosses are used to indicate the atom from which the electron has originated.

double bond – covalent bond in which there are two shared pairs of electrons between atoms, e.g. oxygen and ethene.

double circulation – blood passes through the heart twice on each complete circuit of the mammalian body. It uses the pulmonary circuit and the systemic circuit.

double insulation – applies to an electrical appliance with no exposed metal parts that can become live.

E

electrode – an electrical connection from the power supply to a conductor such as an electrolyte.

electromagnetic induction – a voltage is induced in a conductor when the magnetic field through it changes.

electromagnetism – all electric currents have a magnetic field.

electroplating – covering one metal with a thin layer of another by the process of electrolysis.

electrostatic attraction – attraction between opposite charges. Present in ionic compounds.

endoscope – a device that uses fibre optics for seeing inside the body.

endothermic – a reaction which takes in heat from the surroundings.

energy level diagram – diagram showing the energy content at stages during a reaction.

exothermic – reaction which gives out energy to the surroundings.

extinction – the condition which exists when all the members of a species have died and their genetic material has been lost.

extrusive – igneous rocks that have cooled and solidified as crystals on the surface of the Earth, e.g. basalt.

F

fault – beds of rocks that are distorted with a loss of continuity.

fibre optic – a device used to transmit light round corners using total internal reflection.

fission – the splitting up of an atomic nucleus into fragments.

fold – beds of rock that are distorted without loss of continuity.

frequency – the number of oscillations or vibrations per second.

G

galaxy – a group of stars held together by gravitational forces.

gamma radiation – a radioactive emission consisting of short-wavelength electromagnetic radiation.

gaseous exchange – involves the exchange of gases needed for biological processes.

gauze – a mesh of fine wire.

genotype – genetic make-up of an organism (symbols are used to represent the alleles present for a particular gene).

glass – supercooled liquid which forms a hard, brittle substance which is usually transparent. Common glass is made by limestone with sodium carbonate and sand.

global warming – rise in the average temperature of the Earth's surface. It is thought to be caused by the greenhouse effect.

graphite – one form of the element carbon. The carbon atoms are present in layers. These layers are only weakly held to each other.

gravitational field – the region around an object where it exerts forces on masses.

greenhouse gases – gases such as carbon dioxide and methane that contribute to the greenhouse effect.

H

half-life – the time it takes for the number of undecayed nuclei in a sample of a radioactive isotope to halve.

halide – a compound containing the ions of a halogen (element in Group 7).

harmful – harmful substance is poisonous but less so than a toxic substance. It is represented by a cross in the Hazchem code.

Hazchem code – set of simple representations used to warn about the dangers from chemicals.

heterozygous – condition where an organism has two different alleles for a particular gene.

highly flammable – substance that catches fire easily. It is represented by a flame in the Hazchem code.

homozygous – condition where an organism has two of the same alleles for a particular gene.

hydrocarbon – compounds made up from the elements carbon and hydrogen only.

I

infra-red radiation – electromagnetic radiation with a wavelength longer than that of light.

intensive farming – techniques to enable more food to be produced from less land.

intrusive rocks – igneous rocks that have cooled and solidified as crystals inside the Earth, e.g. granite.

ionic compound – compound formed by the electrostatic attraction between positive ions and negative ions.

ionic equation – concise method of writing down the important changes to ions in a chemical reaction. Ions that take no part in the reaction are not usually included.

K

khemeia – the root of the word chemistry. Its origin was from ancient Egypt and described the secret processes that were used for embalming the dead.

L

laser – an instrument used to produce an intense beam of light of a single wavelength.

lava – molten rock that escapes from a volcano.

limekiln – building in which limestone is roasted and turned into quicklime.

limestone – common name for calcium carbonate, $CaCO_3$.

limiting factor – factor that holds back a process e.g. low light intensity can limit photosynthesis.

liquefy – turn from solid or gas into liquid.

loudspeaker – a device that transfers energy from electricity into movement of the air as sound.

M

magnetic field – a region around a permanent magnet or electric current where forces are exerted on magnetic materials.

manure – fertiliser made from animal faeces.

metabolism – Metabolism = Anabolism ('synthetic reactions') + Catabolism ('break-down reactions').

micro-organism – plant or animal which can only be seen by the use of a microscope.

micropropagation – technique that can be used to produce a large clone from a small piece of parent tissue.

microwave – a short-wavelength radio wave used in telecommunications and cooking.

minerals – compounds contained within rocks.

mitochondrion – cell organelle that contains the enzymes needed for aerobic respiration.

moment – the effect a force has in causing rotation.

monatomic – used to describe an element which exists naturally as individual atoms.

N

Natural Selection – hypothesis that Darwin used to explain evolution.

neurone – nerve cell.

neutralising – cancelling out acidity or alkalinity to make the solution neutral.

nitrifying bacteria – group of soil bacteria which convert ammonia to nitrates.

nitrogenous – containing the element nitrogen.

non-metal – an element which is not a metal.

O

open-cast mining – a technique that collects an ore from the surface of the Earth's crust.

optimum pH – the pH of maximum reaction; used to describe the action of an enzyme.

orbit – the path of a planet around the Sun or the Moon around a planet.

oxidise – to bring about an oxidation process.

P

periodic table – classification of the elements in order of their atomic numbers. Elements with similar properties appear in columns known as groups.

peristalsis – movements caused by alternate, antagonistic contractions of circular and longitudinal muscles in the walls of tubes.

phenotype – describes the way the physical and physiological features of the characteristic are shown.

pig iron – impure iron produced by the blast furnace. It contains a high percentage of carbon.

plate tectonics – slow movements of parts of the Earth's crust known as plates. The driving force for this movement is thought to be convection currents in the mantle.

pressure – the force acting per unit area.

products – the substances which remain after a chemical reaction has taken place. They appear to the right of the arrow in the equation.

properties – what a chemical substance is like or what reactions it will undergo.

proteins – large molecules which are polymers of amino acids.

Q

quicklime – common name for calcium oxide, CaO.

R

radio wave – the longest-wavelength electromagnetic waves, used for communications.

radioactivity – the breakdown of an unstable nucleus, leading to the emission of particles or electromagnetic radiation.

rate of reaction – the speed with which products are formed and reactants disappear during a chemical reaction.

reactivity – how vigorously a substance reacts with other substances.

recessive – a recessive allele works only when it is partnered by another like itself except for an X-linked recessive. These are single – there is no functional allele on the Y-chromosome.

recycled – used again.

red shift – the shift in wavelength of light towards the red end of a spectrum when an object moves away from an observer.

relative atomic mass – the mass of an atom measured on a scale where one atom of the isotope carbon-12 is exactly 12 units.

relative formula mass – mass in grams obtained by adding together the masses in grams of all of the atoms shown in the formula of a compound.

relay – an electromagnetic switch.

repeat unit – that part of the structure of a polymer that repeats itself along the polymer chain.

retina – the tissue lining the back of the eye that includes two types of light-sensitive cells, rods and cones.

rock salt – impure salt (sodium chloride) which is present as deposits in the ground.

S

satellite – an object that orbits another object.

seismometer – an instrument that detects earthquakes.

selectively permeable membrane – allows some particles to pass through it and not others.

shells – locations of electrons around the nucleus of an atom.

slaked lime – common name for calcium hydroxide, $Ca(OH)_2$.

specific temperature – a precise temperature.

stable – not likely to take part in a chemical reaction.

star – a large mass that gives out light due to the energy generated in fusion reactions.

state symbols – symbols used in a chemical equation to indicate whether each substance is a solid (s), liquid (l), gas (g) or in solution in water (aq).

steel – an alloy of iron with a small percentage (under 4%) of carbon.

sterilise – kill bacteria.

stopping distance – the distance travelled by a vehicle between the times when the driver notices a hazard and the vehicle stops.

succession–layers of rock one above the other. Older rocks are usually at the bottom of the succession.

surface area – the area of the surface of a solid object, usually measured in cm^2.

survival of the fittest – Variation exists in sexually produced offspring and some variants have an advantage over others so they survive.

symbol equation – summary of a chemical reaction using the chemical symbols and formulae of the reactants and products.

symbol – one or two letters used to represent a chemical element. The first letter is always a capital.

synapse – microscopic gap between two consecutive, communicating neurones.

T

thermal cracking – breaking down of long-chain hydrocarbon molecules by the action of a heat alone to produce short molecules useful for making polymers.

thermal decomposition – breaking down of compounds by the action of heat.

thinking distance – the distance travelled by a vehicle during the driver's reaction time.

toxic – poisonous substance It is represented by a skull and crossbones in the Hazchem code. It is important not to swallow them, touch them or get them on your skin.

transgenic organism – contains one or more artificially inserted genes.

U

ultrasound – compression waves with a frequency above that of the range of human hearing.

ultraviolet radiation – electromagnetic radiation with a wavelength shorter than that of light.

unsaturated – compound which contains at least one double bond, e.g. ethene C_2H_4.

W

water potential – a measure of the tendency for water to move away from a particular place with pure water having the maximum water potential – adding solutes lowers the water potential.

weight – the size of the Earth's gravitational pull on a mass.

word equation – summary of a chemical reaction using the chemical names of the reactants and products.

X

X-ray – short-wavelength electromagnetic radiation used for producing images of inside the body.

Y

yield – the percentage of the maximum possible amount of a product which is actually produced in a chemical reaction.

INDEX